# MODERN
## Elementary

Holt, Rinehart and Winston of Canada, Limited
Toronto

EUGENE D. NICHOLS

WAGNER G. COLLINS
edited by
ERIC D. MacPHERSON

# LGEBRA

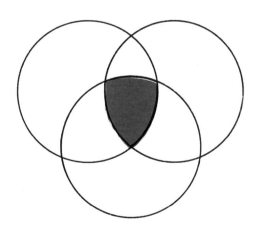

About the authors»

**Dr. Eugene D. Nichols** is Professor of Mathematics Education and Lecturer in Mathematics

**Wagner G. Collins** is Mathematics Consultant

**Eric D. MacPherson** is Assistant Professor of Education and Mathematics, University of British Columbia, Vancouver, British Columbia.

# PREFACE

Many groups, composed of teachers of mathematics, mathematical educators, and professional mathematicians, are engaged in vigorous activities aimed at the improvement of the teaching of high school mathematics. In harmony with their efforts, this book is intended to help the teacher to present algebra to the student as an ever unfolding structure; to guide the student to the discovery of mathematical principles; and to give him ample opportunities to use these principles in the solution of problems. The book contains a large amount of exercise material designed to strengthen what has been learned.

The development of mathematical concepts cannot be haphazard. It must be logical. Ideas must flow. At the same time, the level of sophistication must be suited to the student's mathematical maturity. The latter was assured for this textbook through its preliminary use with the 8th and 9th grade students. The authors are indebted to administration for providing an opportunity for the preliminary version of this textbook to be tested. Many changes and refinements followed and several revisions of these materials culminated in this edition of MODERN ELEMENTARY ALGEBRA.

The students with whom this text was used in its preliminary form found the study of algebra an exciting adventure, and it is hoped that other students will also experience the thrill that comes with discovery of new truths.

A few of the important features of the textbook should be mentioned:

1. Students are introduced to the basic concepts of sets in the first chapter. These concepts are used throughout the book, because they serve well to clarify other algebraic concepts and to unify the subject of algebra. The language of sets provides an elegant way of expressing many mathematical relations.

2. Throughout, there is emphasis on reasoning, discovery, and justification of algebraic processes through basic principles. The *why* and *how* of mathematical processes are given serious attention.

3. At the end of each chapter, there is a summary of vocabulary, chapter review exercises, and a chapter test. Beginning with Chapter 2, there are also included cumulative review exercises. These provide the necessary practice materials to keep alive all of the important concepts developed up to that point. In addition, chapter tests and cumulative tests are available in a supplementary booklet.

4. The exposition of new topics is complete and clear. It is important that the student read the textbook carefully, so that he will truly be led to discover truths for himself. Each new concept is developed clearly and thoroughly, and is reinforced through ample exercise materials.

5. The familiar concepts of arithmetic or the previously introduced algebraic concepts are consistently used as a springboard for introduction of new concepts.

6. An ingenious approach to the solution of word problems, tried and proved successful, is introduced. The student makes up word problems to fit given equations, followed by a reversal of the process. This device has resulted in much greater proficiency of students in solving word problems.

# CONTENTS

vii

# Sets

## 1 · Introduction

In everyday conversation we often speak of collections of things or objects. For example, you might need to refer to a collection of books in the library of your school, or of the pencils in your desk, or of the students in your school, or of the boys and girls in Canada less than 17 years of age. Each of these groups of objects is a **set.** We will agree to think of a **set** as a collection of objects. A description will be given enabling us to tell whether or not an object belongs to a given set.

Consider the following:
   *A*. The set consisting of the numbers 1, 5, 10, 20.
   *B*. The set consisting of the students in this class.
   *C*. The set of all desks in this room.

Now consider three other sets:
   *D*. The set consisting of all counting numbers; that is, 1, 2, 3, 4, 5, · · ·
   *E*. The set consisting of all even counting numbers; that is, 2, 4, 6, 8, · · ·
   *F*. The set consisting of all odd counting numbers; that is, 1, 3, 5, 7, · · ·

The three dots in each case above indicate that the sequences of numbers continue in the same pattern. It should be easy for you to see the pattern in each case and to decide how to continue. For example, in the case *D*, the number following 5 would be 6, then 7, and so on. In the case *E*, 10 would follow 8, then 12, and so on. Name the four numbers following 12. Name the four numbers following 7 in *F*.

1

We shall refer to a member of a set as an element. For example, the number 5 is an *element* or *member* of the set described in *A;* however, the number 3 is not an element of this set. If there is a girl by the name of Mary in your class, then Mary is an **element** of the set described in *B.* We can express the same thought by saying that Mary **belongs** to the set described in *B.* The Greek letter $\epsilon$ is used to indicate that an object belongs to a particular set.

For example, if *G* is the set of all girls in this room and Mary is one of the girls in the group, then Mary $\epsilon$ *G* is read, "Mary is a member of *G.*"

· If *N* is the set of all counting numbers, then 107 $\epsilon$ *N* means, 107 is a member of the set of all counting numbers.

We may desire to indicate that Jane is *not* an element of set *G.* We do so by drawing a diagonal line through the symbol $\epsilon$ as follows: Jane $\notin$ *G.*

The number 5 belongs to or is a member of the set described in *D.* The number 2,035,717 is also an element of this set. Explain. Is the number 2,035,717 a member of the set described in *E?* In *F?* How many elements are there in the set described in *A? B? C? D? E? F?*

From your answers to the preceding question you will see a difference between the sets *A, B, C,* and the sets *D, E, F.* Can you describe this difference?

Sets such as *A, B,* and *C* are called "finite sets," and *D, E,* and *F* are called "infinite sets." Can you explain the reason for choosing the words finite and infinite to describe these sets?

It is awkward to write: "the set of numbers 1, 2, 3" every time we want to indicate that we are speaking of the *set of these numbers,* rather than the *numbers themselves.* To simplify writing, we shall use braces within which we shall list the members of the set. Thus, {1, 2, 3} means the set consisting of the numbers 1, 2, 3.

Similarly, {Johnny, Susie} means the set consisting of Johnny and Susie.

Since it is impractical to list all members of large sets, we list several members of the set and then write three dots. The dots indicate that the pattern established by the first few elements of the set continues indefinitely. It is important, however, to list enough members so that the reader will get the pattern and know how to continue in case he wants to list more members. For example, to describe a set as {1, · · ·} is not enough to show what set is intended; but the description of the set {1, 3, 5, 7, 9, · · ·} is sufficient to indicate that the set of all odd counting numbers is intended.

There is one set which we have not yet mentioned. It is the one which contains no members, and is called the *empty* or *null* set. We use the symbol "$\phi$" to refer to the **empty set.**

# EXERCISES

1. Give three examples of finite sets.
2. Give three examples of infinite sets.
3. Would you be able to count, given sufficient time and patience, the elements of any finite set? Explain your answer.
4. Would you be able to count, given sufficient time and patience, the elements of any infinite set? Explain your answer.
5. List the first five members of the set of all counting numbers divisible by:
   **a.** 3     **b.** 5     **c.** 10     **d.** 12     **e.** 13     **f.** 15
6. List the first ten members of the set of all prime numbers. (A **prime number** is a number divisible only by itself and by 1; 1 is not a prime number.)
7. List the elements of the sets described as follows:
   **a.** The counting numbers less than six.
   **b.** The three largest cities in your province.
   **c.** The cities in Canada of over 1 million population.
   **d.** The cities in your province with over 100,000 population.
   **e.** The provinces bordering the Great Lakes.
   **f.** The provinces whose boundaries touch oceans.
   **g.** The football teams in the Canadian Football League.
   **h.** The months of the year.
   **i.** Your teachers this year.
   **j.** The names of months starting with the letter D.
   **k.** The counting numbers less than 9 and greater than 6.
   **l.** The fish you caught last summer.
8. What objects would belong to the sets described below?
   **a.** The books on your desk.
   **b.** The odd counting numbers less than twenty.
   **c.** The planets of the solar system.
   **d.** The seasons of the year.
   **e.** The pets in your house.
   **f.** The odd counting numbers less than twenty which are divisible by five.
9. What do the sets described below have in common? List their elements:
   **a.** The counting numbers less than seven which are also greater than five.
   **b.** The odd counting numbers less than twenty which are also divisible by seven.
   **c.** The provinces of Canada entirely surrounded by water.

**10.** Each of the following two phrases describes the *null set:*

The set of all polar bears in your classroom.

The set of all girls on your school's rugby team.

Give three or more sentences each describing the null set.

**11.** Let $P$ be the set of prime counting numbers less than 11. Label the following statements as true or false:

**a.** $6 \in P$

**b.** $9 \notin P$

**c.** $3 \in P$

**d.** $7 \in P$

**e.** $5 \notin P$

**12.** Let $T$ be the set of counting numbers divisible by three. Label the following statements as true or false:

**a.** $39 \in T$

**b.** $17 \notin T$

**c.** $117 \notin T$

**d.** $237 \in T$

**e.** $112 \in T$

## 2 · Matching Sets

Consider the following two sets:

$$\{1, 2, 3\}; \quad \{100, 101, 102\}$$

The elements of the first set are the numbers 1, 2, 3, and the elements of the second set are the numbers 100, 101, 102. We can attempt to pair up the elements of one set with the elements of the other in this way:

$$
\begin{array}{cccc}
1 \longleftrightarrow 100 & 1 \longleftrightarrow 100 & 2 \longleftrightarrow 100 \\
3 \longleftrightarrow 101 \quad \text{or} & 2 \longleftrightarrow 101 \quad \text{or} & 1 \longleftrightarrow 101 \\
2 \longleftrightarrow 102 & 3 \longleftrightarrow 102 & 3 \longleftrightarrow 102
\end{array}
$$

and so on. In how many different ways can the elements of these two sets be matched?

Note that each time you pair or match the elements of the two sets above, no elements are left over in either set. For each element in the first set there is a corresponding element in the second set, and for each element in the second set there is a corresponding element in the first set. When the elements of two sets can be matched in this way, the relationship is called a **one-to-one correspondence** between the two sets. When a one-to-one correspondence exists between two sets, they are called **matching sets.**

Is it possible to establish a one-to-one correspondence between the two following sets? Why?

$$\{1, 2, 3, 4\}; \quad \{17, 19, 21, 23, 25\}$$

You probably found that it is only necessary to be able to count in order to tell whether or not two finite sets are matching sets. What about infinite sets?

Let $A$ be the set of *all* counting numbers and $B$ the set of all *even* counting numbers. We display in writing only parts of infinite sets and then indicate by three dots that not all of the set is described:

$$A = \{1, 2, 3, 4, 5, 6, 7, 8, \cdots\}$$
$$B = \{2, 4, 6, 8, 10, 12, 14, 16, \cdots\}$$

Is it possible to establish a one-to-one correspondence between sets $A$ and $B$? Let us try.

$$A: \{1, \; 2, \; 3, \; 4, \; 5, \; \; 6, \; \; 7, \; \; 8, \; \cdots\}$$
$$\updownarrow \; \updownarrow \; \updownarrow \; \updownarrow \; \updownarrow \; \; \updownarrow \; \; \updownarrow \; \; \updownarrow$$
$$B: \{2, \; 4, \; 6, \; 8, \; 10, \; 12, \; 14, \; 16, \; \cdots\}$$

The double arrows above show which element of set $A$ is paired with an element of set $B$ and vice versa. Now, you should observe that it is possible to know how to continue this process of pairing as far as you please. In this pairing, what is true of the element of $B$ which is paired with an element of $A$? What element of $B$ would be matched with the element 201 of $A$? With 1024 of $A$? 3000001 of $A$?

We can therefore conclude that the set of *all* counting numbers and the set of *even* counting numbers are matching sets.

Let us consider another pair of infinite sets:

$$X = \{1, 2, 3, 4, 5, 6, 7, 8, \cdots\}$$
$$Y = \{100, 101, 102, 103, 104, 105, 106, 107, \cdots\}$$

The set $X$ is the set of all counting numbers and the set $Y$ is the set of counting numbers which are greater than 99. Both sets are infinite sets. Why? Are $X$ and $Y$ matching sets?

To answer this question, we display one way of establishing a one-to-one correspondence between these two sets:

$$X: \{ \; 1, \quad 2, \quad 3, \quad 4, \quad 5, \quad 6, \quad 7, \quad 8, \quad \cdots\}$$
$$\updownarrow \quad \updownarrow \quad \updownarrow \quad \updownarrow \quad \updownarrow \quad \updownarrow \quad \updownarrow \quad \updownarrow$$
$$Y: \{100, \; 101, \; 102, \; 103, \; 104, \; 105, \; 106, \; 107, \; \cdots\}$$

Thus, the number 1 in the set $X$ is paired with the number 100 in the set $Y$;

2 with 101; and so on. What number in $Y$ would be paired with 20 in $X$? With 100 in $X$? With 106 in $X$? With 1007 in $X$? What number in $X$ would be matched with 107 in $Y$? With 200 in $Y$? With 1075 in $Y$?

Let us compare two finite sets:

$$A = \{a, b, f, h, m\}$$
$$B = \{g, k, r, n, t\}$$

We may match the elements of $A$ and $B$ as follows:

A: { a,  b,  f,  h,  m}          A: { h,  a,  b,  m,  f }
   ↕  ↕  ↕  ↕  ↕      or            ↕  ↕  ↕  ↕  ↕
B: { g,  r,  t,  n,  k }          B: { t,  k,  g,  n,  r }

In either case we have established that $A$ and $B$ are matching sets by showing the one-to-one correspondence between the members of the two sets.

## EXERCISES

1. Are the following pairs of sets matching sets?
   **a.** $S = \{b, 3, j, 4, 6\}$
   $T = \{\text{Mike, Bob, Hal, Leroy, Ed, Bill}\}$
   **b.** $C = \{\text{Vancouver, Edmonton, Ontario}\}$
   $D = \{\text{Victoria, Calgary, Prince Albert, Quebec}\}$
   **c.** $G = \{1, 3, 5, 7, 9, \cdots\}$
   $H = \{2, 4, 6, 8, 10, \cdots\}$

2. Give examples of three pairs of finite sets such that the two sets in each pair are matching sets.
3. Give examples of three pairs of finite sets such that no two sets in a pair are matching sets.
4. Give examples of three pairs of infinite sets such that the two sets in each pair are matching sets.

## 3 · Subsets

We have discussed the individual elements belonging to a given set. It is also possible to form sets whose elements are totally contained in the original given set. The set from which we choose members to form a new set is called the **universe** or **universal set.** Sets formed from elements of the universe are called **subsets** of the universe. For example, you may want to consider your mathematics class to be the universal set under discussion. Next, you might want to refer to the set of boys and the set of girls in this class. Each of these sets is a part, or subset, of the entire class.

Let $C$ stand for the set of all students in this class, $G$ for the set of all girls in this class and $B$ for the set of all boys in this class. We will agree that **$G$ is a subset of $C$** (written $G \subseteq C$) **means that every element of $G$ is also an element of $C$.** Similarly $B \subseteq C$ means that the set of boys in the class is a subset of all the students in the class. How would you interpret the abbreviation $C \subseteq C$?

The last statement says that the set of all students in this class is a subset of the set of all students in this class. We will agree that *every set is a subset of itself*. This fits our definition since each element of $C$ is also an element of $C$. We will also agree that the null or empty set is a subset of every set. If a set $M$ is *not* a subset of set $N$, that is, there is at least one element in $M$ which is not in $N$, we write $M \not\subseteq N$, which is read "$M$ is not a subset of $N$."

We frequently restrict the choice of our elements to some inclusive set called the universe or universal set, usually designated by $U$. The elements from the universe may be combined in various ways to form a set which is a subset of the universal set. In our illustration above many other subsets of the universal set could have been formed. We could have the subset $E$ which would contain those students in the class wearing glasses. Another subset of the universe $C$ might be $F$, the set of all basketball players in this mathematics class.

If we let our universal set be the set of the provinces of Canada, some interesting subsets could be formed. We might call the universal set $C$, while set $P$ could be those provinces of Canada touching the Pacific Ocean. Do you observe a relationship between $C$ and $P$? Since all of the elements of $P$ are also elements of $C$, we could say that $P$ is a subset of $C$; that is $P \subset C$. Set $S$ might be the set of provinces touching the border of the United States. Again, the elements of $S$ must be chosen from the universe $C$. (Yukon touches Alaska, but is not in $C$.) $S$ would be a subset of $C$ but not a subset of $P$, although $S$ and $P$ would have an element in common. Can you name it?

We could form another subset of $C$, called $L$, which would be the provinces directly adjoining the St. Lawrence River. $L$ and $P$ would have no elements in common. Another subset of $C$ might be $R$, the provinces east of the Rocky Mountains and we would agree that $L \subseteq R$.

Letting our universe be the set of all counting numbers, we shall form two subsets of the universe. Given two different sets, two possibilities exist. Either they have no elements in common or they may have one or more elements in common.

Consider, for example, the following two subsets of the counting numbers $C$.

$A$ = the set of all counting numbers between 25 and 37 not including 25 and 37.

$B$ = the set of all counting numbers less than 32.

Sets $A$ and $B$ have some elements in common. For example: $30 \in A$ and $30 \in B$.

Answer the following questions concerning sets $A$ and $B$:

How many elements are there in set $A$?
How many elements are there in set $B$?
How many elements are common to sets $A$ and $B$?
Name several elements common to sets $A$ and $B$.
Name several elements which belong to $A$ but not to $B$.
Name several elements which belong to $B$ but not to $A$.

The relationship between sets $A$ and $B$ described above may be portrayed in the following manner:

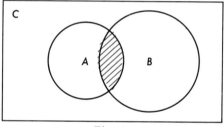

Fig. 1

In *Figure 1*, we will designate the set of points within circle $A$ to be the elements of set $A$. The set of points within circle $B$ will represent the elements of set $B$. The elements of both $A$ and $B$ are contained in set $C$ (the set of all counting numbers) which is represented by the rectangle $C$. The shaded part represents the elements which belong to both $A$ and $B$.

Pictorial representations of a set and its subsets are called **Venn diagrams.**

## VENN DIAGRAMS

The eighteenth-century Swiss mathematician Euler introduced the idea of using circles in this way. Venn, a British logician of the nineteenth-century, introduced further refinements to the idea. Therefore, these diagrams are referred to as Euler circles or Venn diagrams.

Now consider the following two sets:

    $G$ = the set of all counting numbers less than 20.

    $D$ = the set of all counting numbers between 10 and 17, not including 10 and 17.

What can you say about every element of $D$ as far as its membership in the set $G$ is concerned? *Figure 2* represents the relationship between the sets $G$ and $D$.

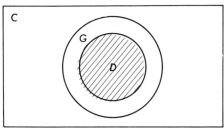
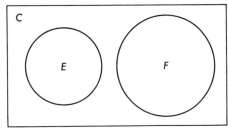

        *Fig. 2*                               *Fig. 3*

Consider another pair of sets:

    $E$ = the set of all counting numbers less than 12.

    $F$ = the set of all counting numbers between 50 and 100.

Is *Figure 3* a correct representation of the relationship between these two sets?

Two sets which have no common elements are called **disjoint sets.** Thus, sets $E$ and $F$ described above are disjoint sets. What about sets $G$ and $D$? $A$ and $B$?

# EXERCISES

1. In this exercise, the universal set $U$ is the set of all counting numbers and zero. $A$ and $B$ are subsets of $U$. In each instance, tell whether or not the set $A$ is a subset of $B$.

    **a.** $A = \{1, 2, 3\}$; $B = \{1, 2, 3, 4, 5\}$

    **b.** $A = \{0, 1\}$; $B = \{0\}$   [Hint: the set consisting of the number 0 is *not* the null set, because it has one element in it, namely the number 0.]

    **c.** $A = \{1, 4, 6\}$; $B = \{1, 6, 7\}$

    **d.** $A$ is the set of all counting numbers divisible by 10.
        $B$ is the set of all counting numbers.

    **e.** $A$ is the set of all counting numbers less than 100.
        $B$ is the set of all counting numbers greater than 55.

**f.** $A = \{1, 2\}$; $B = \{1, 2\}$      **h.** $A = \phi$; $B = \{0\}$

**g.** $A = \{0\}$; $B = \{0\}$      **i.** $A = \phi$; $B = \phi$

2. Make a pictorial representation (draw a Venn diagram) of the relationship between each pair of sets in Exercise 1, **a-h.**
3. In each exercise, let $U$ be the universal set, and, state the relationship which exists between the given subsets of $U$.

**EXAMPLE**
$U = \{4, 6, 8, 10, 12\}$
$A = \{4\}$
$B = \{4, 6\}$

**SOLUTION**
$A \subseteq B$

**a.** $U = \{0, 1, 2, 3, 4, 5\}$
$A = \{1, 3, 4, 5\}$
$B = \{1, 4, 5\}$

**b.** $U = \{a, b, c, f, g\}$
$A = \{a, b\}$
$B = \{b, c, f, g\}$

**c.** $U = \{g, h, j, k, l\}$
$A = \{g, h, l\}$
$B = \{j, k\}$

**d.** $U = \{$Alberta, Saskatchewan, British Columbia, Ontario$\}$
$A = \{$Alberta, Saskatchewan$\}$
$B = \{$Ontario, Saskatchewan, Alberta$\}$

**e.** $U = \{$Toronto, Vancouver, Montreal, Prince George$\}$
$A = \{$Vancouver, Montreal$\}$
$B = \{$Montreal$\}$

**f.** $U = \{1, 2, 3, 4, 5, 6, 7, 8, 9\}$
$A = \{1, 3, 7, 9\}$
$B = \{3, 7, 8, 9\}$

**g.** $U = $ the set of all counting numbers less than 20.
$A = $ the set of counting numbers less than 9.
$B = $ the set of counting numbers greater than 5 and less than 8.

**h.** $U = $ the set of all counting numbers.
$A = $ the set of all even counting numbers.
$B = $ the set of all odd counting numbers.

4. Tell which of the pairs of subsets $A$ and $B$ in Exercise 3 are disjoint sets.
5. Sketch Venn diagrams illustrating the relationship of the sets in each part of Exercise 3.
6. **a.** Give examples of two sets $A$ and $B$ such that $A$ is a subset of $B$ and $B$ is not a subset of $A$.
   **b.** Give examples of two sets $C$ and $D$ such that $C$ is not a subset of $D$ and $D$ is not a subset of $C$.
   **c.** Give examples of two sets $E$ and $F$ such that $E$ is a subset of $F$ and $F$ is a subset of $E$. (Do you end up with two different sets $E$ and $F$?)
7. List the members of your household as a set $H$. Form three different subsets of $H$.
8. Given the following sets:

$$E = \{1, 3, 4, 6\}; \ G = \{1, 6\}; \ H = \{1, 3, 4, 6, 8, 9\}$$

Label each statement as true or false:

| | | | |
|---|---|---|---|
| **a.** $E \subseteq G$ | **d.** $H \subseteq G$ | **g.** $\phi \subseteq E$ | **j.** $E \nsubseteq G$ |
| **b.** $H \subseteq E$ | **e.** $E \subseteq H$ | **h.** $\phi \subseteq G$ | **k.** $H \nsubseteq H$ |
| **c.** $G \subseteq H$ | **f.** $H \subseteq H$ | **i.** $\phi \subseteq H$ | **l.** $G \nsubseteq H$ |

9. **a.** Suppose you know that $5 \in X$ and $5 \in Y$, where $X$ and $Y$ are some sets. Are you justified in concluding that $X \subseteq Y$? $Y \subseteq X$? $X$ and $Y$ are not disjoint?
   **b.** Suppose you know that sets $M$ and $P$ have 3 common elements. Give one conclusion you are justified in drawing from this fact.

# 4 · Operations with Sets

You are already familiar with at least four operations with numbers: addition, subtraction, multiplication, and division. Each of these is called a **binary** operation because each requires a pair of numbers. Examine the meaning of the word "binary" in your dictionary.

To show, for example, that addition does require a pair of numbers, all you need to do is to take the following simple example:

add 3 and 5

which can be written as $3 + 5$.

It is obvious that if you said "add 3" it would not be clear what is to be done. You must name a second number before addition can be performed. The same is true for subtraction, multiplication, and division.

Each of these operations requires a pair of numbers before it can be carried out. Now we will learn to perform operations with sets.

Consider the following two sets:

$$A = \{1, 5, 7, 16\}$$
$$B = \{7, 16, 21\}$$

We shall obtain a third set, $C$, by combining the elements of the set $A$ with the elements of the set $B$, without repeating the elements belonging to both $A$ and $B$: $C = \{1, 5, 7, 16, 21\}$.

The set $C$ is called **the union** of sets $A$ and $B$. We will use the following notation for the operation of union: $A \cup B = C$, or $\{1, 5, 7, 16\} \cup \{7, 16, 21\} = \{1, 5, 7, 16, 21\}$. $A \cup B$ is read '$A$ union $B$'.

Another example is worked out for you below. Study it carefully:

$$X = \{5, 10, 15\}$$
$$Y = \{7, 9, 11, 13\}$$
$$\{5, 10, 15\} \cup \{7, 9, 11, 13\} = \{5, 7, 9, 10, 11, 13, 15\}$$

Note one interesting difference between the pairs of sets $A$ and $B$, and $X$ and $Y$. Sets $A$ and $B$ have elements which are common to both of them, whereas the sets $X$ and $Y$ have no common elements. That is, sets $X$ and $Y$ are disjoint sets, whereas sets $A$ and $B$ are not disjoint sets.

Note that the set $X = \{5, 10, 15\}$ has three elements. The set, $Y = \{7, 9, 11, 13\}$ has four elements. The union of the two sets, $X \cup Y = \{5, 7, 9, 10, 11, 13, 15\}$ has seven elements. What is the relationship between the numbers 3, 4, and 7?

Now, observe the set $A = \{1, 5, 7, 16\}$. It has four elements. The set $B = \{7, 16, 21\}$ has three elements. The union, $A \cup B = \{1, 5, 7, 16, 21\}$ has five elements.

The examples above show that the union of any pair of sets $X$ and $Y$ is a set consisting of all the elements which belong to $X$ or $Y$. The word "or" is being used here in a sense which may be different from the sense to which you are accustomed.

The phrase: "$a$ is a member of $X$ **or** $Y$" may imply any one or all three of the following:

1. $a$ is a member of $X$
2. $a$ is a member of $Y$
3. $a$ is a member of both $X$ and $Y$

Assigning such meaning to the word "or" is referred to as being "inclusive or" rather than "exclusive or." That is, the sentence "$a$ is a member of $X$ or $Y$" is true if $a$ belongs to either one, or both $X$ and $Y$.

Are you able to draw a conclusion concerning the number of the elements in the union of two disjoint sets? In the union of two sets which are not disjoint sets?

Let us now obtain a third set from the sets $A$ and $B$ above in a different way. We will take this third set to be the set of only those elements which are in *both* $A$ and $B$.

Thus, $A = \{1, 5, 7, 16\}$
$B = \{7, 16, 21\}$

The only elements which are in both $A$ and $B$ are 7 and 16. The set $D$, then, consisting of elements belonging to both $A$ and $B$ is: $D = \{7, 16\}$. We shall call this set the **intersection** of $A$ and $B$. The notation for the operation of intersection we will use is $A \cap B = D$, or $\{1, 5, 7, 16\} \cap \{7, 16, 21\} = \{7, 16\}$. $A \cap B$ is read '$A$ intersect $B$'.

The intersection of two sets, then, is a set consisting of only those elements which are common to both sets.

Now sets $X$ and $Y$ do not have any common elements. Therefore, their intersection is the empty set. Thus: $\{5, 10, 15\} \cap \{7, 9, 11, 13\} = \phi$.

Observe that it takes a pair of sets to perform the operations of union and intersection. Therefore, **union and intersection are binary operations.**

Given any pair of sets, there is a set which is their union. Also, given any pair of sets, there is a set which is their intersection.

## EXERCISES

1. Name the set which is the intersection of each pair of sets below.
   a. Set I: All natural numbers; that is, all counting numbers 1, 2, 3, 4, 5, 6, 7, · · · ·
      Set II: All odd natural numbers.
   b. Set I: All natural numbers.
      Set II: All even natural numbers.
   c. Set I: All odd natural numbers.
      Set II: All even natural numbers.
   d. Set I: All natural numbers.
      Set II: All prime natural numbers.
   e. Set I: All students in your school.
      Set II: All students in your school enrolled in mathematics courses.
   f. Set I: All students in your school over 15 years of age.
      Set II: All students in your school under 15 years of age.

2. Name the set which is the union of each pair of sets in Exercise 1.
3. Give an example of a pair of finite disjoint sets.
4. Give an example of a pair of infinite disjoint sets.
5. Give an example of a pair of finite sets which are not disjoint.
6. Give an example of a pair of infinite sets which are not disjoint.
7. Find the intersection of each pair of sets in Exercise 3-6.
8. Find the union of each pair of sets in Exercises 3-6.
9. Explain why the intersection of the null set with any set is the null set. This may be stated as follows:

$$\text{For every set } A, \; A \cap \phi = \phi$$
$$\text{thus,} \qquad \phi \cap \phi = \phi$$

10. Explain why the union of the null set with any set is that set. This may be stated as follows:

$$\text{For every set } A, \; A \cup \phi = A$$
$$\text{thus,} \qquad \phi \cup \phi = \phi$$

11. Let $A = \{1, 3, 5\}$, $B = \{3, 5, 7, 9\}$, and $C = \{4, 6, 8, 10\}$.

Find:

a. $A \cup B$       c. $A \cup C$       e. $B \cup C$
b. $A \cap B$       d. $A \cap C$       f. $B \cap C$

g. $(A \cup B) \cup C$   [Hint: Parentheses here mean that you first find the set $A \cup B$; then you find the union of the resulting set with $C$.]

h. $A \cup (B \cup C)$       j. $A \cap (B \cap C)$       l. $(A \cup B) \cap (A \cup C)$
i. $(A \cap B) \cap C$       k. $A \cup (B \cap C)$       m. $A \cap (B \cup C)$

12. Given any set $A$, tell what each of the following is:

a. $A \cup A$       c. $(A \cup A) \cup A$       e. $(A \cup A) \cap A$       g. $A \cup \phi$
b. $A \cap A$       d. $(A \cap A) \cap A$       f. $(A \cap A) \cup A$       h. $A \cap \phi$

........................................................................................

# THE THEORY OF SETS

The ideas of sets were developed toward the end of the nineteenth-century. George Boole (1815–1864) and Georg Cantor (1845–1918) are two mathematicians credited with the development of these ideas. You may have heard people speak of "Boolean Algebra," that is the algebra of sets. It is so called in honor of Boole, who was the first to introduce these ideas. Cantor is considered to be the founder of set theory.

## 5 · Subsets of a Finite Set

When studying various sets, it is good practice to specify the collection of objects from which the elements of sets are selected. For example, we may agree that, for the purposes of our study for this particular moment, we shall select the elements of our sets from the set of natural numbers: $\{1, 2, 3, 4, \cdots\}$. In this case we refer to the set of natural numbers as being the *universal set* or the *universe*. Thus,

$$U = \{1, 2, 3, 4, \cdots\}$$

Of course, there is no limit to the number of subsets we can get from this universe.

For example, the set $A = \{1\}$ is a subset of $U$. So is $B = \{3, 7, 10\}$. Both $A$ and $B$ are subsets of $U$. Why? Thus, $A \subseteq U$ and $B \subseteq U$. Sometimes, instead of writing $A \subseteq U$ we shall write $U \supseteq A$ which is read: the set $U$ contains the set $A$ or simply $U$ contains $A$.

Name a few more subsets of $U$, where $U$ is the set of all natural numbers.

Now consider the universe $L$, where $L = \{1, 2\}$; that is, the only members in the universe are the numbers 1 and 2. Let us form all possible subsets of $L$. In doing this, we must remember that the null set is a subset of every set. Furthermore, we must remember that every set is a subset of itself. Now, we are ready to list all subsets of $L = \{1, 2\}$.

$$\phi \qquad \{1\} \qquad \{1, 2\}$$
$$\{2\}$$

Thus, the set $L = \{1, 2\}$ has two elements and four subsets.

Now, take the universe $K = \{1, 2, 3\}$. Form all possible subsets of $K$.

$$\phi \qquad \{1\} \qquad \{1, 2\} \qquad \{1, 2, 3\}$$
$$\{2\} \qquad \{1, 3\}$$
$$\{3\} \qquad \{2, 3\}$$

Thus, the set $K$ has three elements and eight subsets.

Now, take the universe $T = \{1, 2, 3, 4\}$. Form all possible subsets of $T$.

$$\phi \quad \{1\} \quad \{1, 2\} \quad \{1, 2, 3\} \quad \{1, 2, 3, 4\}$$
$$\{2\} \quad \{1, 3\} \quad \{1, 2, 4\}$$
$$\{3\} \quad \{1, 4\} \quad \{1, 3, 4\}$$
$$\{4\} \quad \{2, 3\} \quad \{2, 3, 4\}$$
$$\{2, 4\}$$
$$\{3, 4\}$$

Thus, the set $T$ has four elements and sixteen subsets.

Let us tabulate our results:

| Number of elements in a set | Number of all possible subsets |
|:---:|:---:|
| 2 | $4 = 2 \cdot 2$ |
| 3 | $8 = 2 \cdot 2 \cdot 2$ |
| 4 | $16 = 2 \cdot 2 \cdot 2 \cdot 2$ |

If you examine carefully the table above, you should see a pattern. This pattern tells you the relationship between the number of elements in the universal set and the number of all possible subsets. According to this pattern, there should be $2 \cdot 2 \cdot 2 \cdot 2 \cdot 2$ or 32 subsets that can be formed from a universal set with five elements. Work it out, listing all the subsets, and see whether or not you obtain 32 subsets. According to this pattern, how many subsets does a set with 6 elements have? A set with 7 elements? What about a set with one element? To fit into the pattern, a set with one element would have to have 2 subsets. Let us check.

Let $A = \{5\}$. The subsets of $A$ are $\phi$ and $\{5\}$. Thus, $A = \{5\}$ has two subsets.

# EXERCISES

In Exercises 1-6, $A = \{\frac{1}{2}, \frac{1}{3}, \frac{1}{4}, \frac{1}{5}\}$ and $B = \{\frac{1}{4}, \frac{1}{5}, \frac{1}{6}, \frac{1}{7}, \frac{1}{8}\}$.

1. Form all subsets of $A$. How many subsets are there?
2. How many subsets are there in set $B$?
3. Determine $A \cup B$.
4. How many subsets may be formed from $A \cup B$?
5. Determine $A \cap B$.
6. Form all subsets of $A \cap B$. How many are there?

## ★6 · Subsets of Infinite Sets

You have learned how to predict the number of subsets we can obtain from a given finite set. What about subsets of infinite sets? First of all, since there is no end to the number of elements in an infinite set, there is no end to the number of subsets one can obtain. This is easily seen by considering only those subsets which have one element. For example, take the set of all counting numbers $\{1, 2, 3, 4, 5, 6, \cdots\}$. Some subsets are:

$$\{1\}, \{2\}, \{3\}, \{4\}, \{5\}, \{6\}, \text{ and so on.}$$

Each of these subsets has only one element and there is no end to the number of these subsets.

There is at least one interesting thing about subsets of infinite sets which you already might have observed in the discussion of matching sets in Section 2. We saw that given any finite set, say $A = \{5, 7, 10\}$, and deleting at least one element of it, say, 5, we obtain a subset $B = \{7, 10\}$ which cannot be matched with the original set $A$. This is simply because the set $A$ has more elements than the set $B$.

Let us now see whether the same is true for infinite sets. In the set of all natural numbers $N = \{1, 2, 3, 4, 5, \cdots\}$, let us delete the number 1. We obtain the set $K = \{2, 3, 4, 5, 6, \cdots\}$ such that $K \subseteq N$, because every member of $K$ is also a member of $N$. Now the question we want to ask is whether it is possible to establish a one-to-one correspondence between the set $N$ and its subset $K$. The answer, of course, is "yes." Here it is:

$$N: \{ \ 1, \ 2, \ 3, \ 4, \ 5, \ 6, \ \cdots \ \}$$
$$\updownarrow \ \updownarrow \ \updownarrow \ \updownarrow \ \updownarrow \ \updownarrow$$
$$K: \{ \ 2, \ 3, \ 4, \ 5, \ 6, \ 7, \ \cdots \ \}$$

That is, to every number which is a member of the set $N$ we assign a number, 1 larger, which is a member of $K$. Do you see that *every* member of $N$ has a "mate" in $K$? That every member of $K$ has a "mate" in $N$? Thus, here is one way of establishing a one-to-one correspondence between the set of all natural numbers and its subset, all natural numbers except 1.

We shall call set $S$ a **proper subset** of $T$, if every element of $S$ is also in $T$ and if there is at least one element of $T$ which is *not* in $S$. We designate this by $S \subset T$. $S \subset T$ is read, '$S$ is a proper subset of $T$'.

For example, if $A = \{5, 7, 10\}$ then $\{5, 7, 10\}$ is a subset of $A$, but it is *not* a proper subset. On the other hand $B = \{7, 10\}$ *is* a proper subset of $A$, because $B \subseteq A$ and $B \neq A$. Similarly, for the sets $N$ and $K$ above, $K$ is a proper subset of $N$, because $K \subseteq N$ and $K \neq N$.

Now we should be ready to state some conclusions. They will be contained in the answers to the following questions, which you should be able to answer:

If $X$ is a finite set and $Y$ is a proper subset of $X$, can $X$ and $Y$ be matching sets?

If $W$ is an infinite set and $Z$ is a proper subset of $W$, can $W$ and $Z$ be matching sets?

## EXERCISES

1. Let the universal set be the set of all natural numbers, $U = \{1, 2, 3, 4, 5, 6, \cdots\}$.

   a. Show one way of establishing a one-to-one correspondence between $U$ and the set of all natural numbers greater than 100.

   b. Is it possible to establish a one-to-one correspondence between $U$ and the set of all even numbers? If your answer is yes, show one way of doing it. If your answer is no, explain.

   c. Is it possible to establish a one-to-one correspondence between $U$ and the set of all counting numbers less than 1001? If your answer is yes, show one way of doing it. If your answer is no, explain.

2. Let $U_1 = \{1, 2, 3, 4, 5, \cdots\}$
   $U_2 = \{1, 3, 5, 7, 9, \cdots\}$
   $U_3 = \{100, 101, 102, 103, 104, 105, \cdots\}$

   Find:

   a. $U_1 \cup U_2$     d. $U_1 \cap U_2$     g. $(U_1 \cup U_2) \cup U_3$

   b. $U_1 \cup U_3$     e. $U_1 \cap U_3$     h. $(U_1 \cap U_2) \cap U_3$

   c. $U_2 \cup U_3$     f. $U_2 \cap U_3$     i. $(U_1 \cup U_2) \cap U_3$

3. Using the sets $A$ and $B$ given in the Exercises on page 16, tell whether the set $A$ is a *proper* subset of $B$.

★ 7 · Complement of a Set

Take the universe to be the set $U = \{1, 2, 3, 4, 5, 6, 7, 8, 9, 10\}$; that is, the natural numbers from 1 through 10. Now take a subset of $U$, say $A = \{5, 6, 7\}$. We will consider the set of elements remaining in $U$ after the set $A$ has been formed. This set is $B = \{1, 2, 3, 4, 8, 9, 10\}$. You will note two things about $A$ and $B$. First, they are disjoint; that is, $A \cap B = \phi$. Second, the union of $A$ and $B$ gives us the universe; that is, $A \cup B = U = \{1, 2, 3, 4, 5, 6, 7, 8, 9, 10\}$.

The set $B$ is called the complement of the set $A$ and we will use the symbol $\bar{A}$ to mean the **complement** of $A$. (The symbol $A'$ is also widely used.) Thus, we have

$$A \cap \bar{A} = \phi$$
and
$$A \cup \bar{A} = U$$

Using our previous way of representing relationships between sets pictorially, we show this in the following Venn diagram:

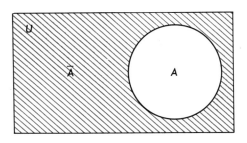

*Fig. 4*

If the rectangle represents the universe and the circle the set $A$, then $\bar{A}$, the complement of $A$, is represented by the shaded area. The Venn diagram makes it easy to see that a set and its complement are always disjoint sets and that the union of a set and its complement is the universe.

## EXERCISES

**EXAMPLE**    Determine $\bar{A}$ if $U = \{1, 2, 3, 4, 5, 6, 7, 8\}$ and $A = \{1, 2, 6\}$

**SOLUTION**    $\bar{A}$ is the set of elements in $U$ other than the elements of $A$. Therefore, $\bar{A} = \{3, 4, 5, 7, 8\}$

1. **a.** $U = \{1, 2, 3, 4, 5, 6, 7, 8\}$, $A = \{2, 4, 6, 8\}$. Determine $\bar{A}$.
   **b.** $U =$ the same as in **a**, $A = \{1, 3, 5, 7\}$. Determine $\bar{A}$.
   **c.** $U =$ the same as in **a**, $A = \{1, 8\}$. Determine $\bar{A}$.

2. Let $U = \{1, 2, 3, 4, 5, 6, 7\}$, $A = \{1, 2\}$, $B = \{2, 4, 5\}$.
   Determine the following sets, and draw a Venn diagram for each case:
   **a.** $\bar{A}$  **d.** $\overline{A \cap B}$  **g.** $\bar{A} \cup \bar{B}$  **j.** $\bar{A} \cap B$
   **b.** $\bar{B}$  **e.** $\bar{A} \cap \bar{B}$  **h.** $\bar{A} \cap A$  **k.** $A \cap \bar{B}$
   **c.** $A \cap B$  **f.** $\overline{A \cup B}$  **i.** $\bar{B} \cap B$  **l.** $\bar{A} \cup B$

3. Let $U = \{a, b, c, d, f, g, h, k\}$, $A = \{d, f, g\}$, $B = \{a, h, k, d\}$, and $G = \{b, c\}$.
   Determine the following sets:
   **a.** $\bar{A}$  **d.** $\bar{A} \cap \bar{G}$  **g.** $(\bar{A} \cup \bar{B}) \cap G$
   **b.** $\bar{G}$  **e.** $A \cup G$  **h.** $G \cap (\bar{A} \cap \bar{B})$
   **c.** $\bar{B}$  **f.** $\overline{A \cup G}$  **i.** Using Venn diagrams depict **d** and **f**

4.  $U = \{1, 3, 5, 7, 9, 11\}$, $A = \{1, 5\}$, $B = \{7, 9, 11\}$, $C = \{3, 7, 9, 11\}$, $D = \{1, 11\}$.

Determine the following sets:

|   |   |   |   |   |   |
|---|---|---|---|---|---|
| **a.** $\bar{B}$ | **f.** $A \cap U$ | **k.** $\bar{B} \cap \phi$ |
| **b.** $\bar{C}$ | **g.** $\overline{A \cap U}$ | **l.** $\overline{U \cap A}$ |
| **c.** $\bar{D}$ | **h.** $C \cap \bar{D}$ | **m.** $\overline{D \cup B}$ |
| **d.** $\bar{A}$ | **i.** $U \cap \bar{C}$ | **n.** $\bar{D} \cap \bar{B}$ |
| **e.** $A \cup U$ | **j.** $D \cap \phi$ | **o.** Using Venn diagrams depict **h** and **n**. |

5.  Let $U = $ the set of all natural numbers. Describe in words the complement of each of the following sets:

a.  $A = \{1, 2, 3\}$
b.  $B = \{100, 101, 102, 103, \cdot \cdot \cdot\}$
c.  $C = \{10, 20, 30, 40, \cdot \cdot \cdot, 210\}$
d.  $D = \{1000, 900, 800, \cdot \cdot \cdot, 100\}$
e.  $E = \{17, 18, 19, 20, \cdot \cdot \cdot, 58, 59, 60\}$
f.  $F = \{2, 4, 6, 8, 10 \cdot \cdot \cdot\}$
g.  $G = \{1, 3, 5, 7, 9, 11, \cdot \cdot \cdot\}$
h.  $H = \{1, 4, 7, 10, 13, 16, \cdot \cdot \cdot\}$
i.  $I = \{2, 3, 5, 7, 11, 13, 17, 19, 23, 29, \cdot \cdot \cdot\}$
j.  $J = \{7, 14, 21, 28, 35, 42, \cdot \cdot \cdot\}$

**EXAMPLE**   Given a universal set $U$ containing six elements and two subsets $A$ and $B$. $A$ contains three elements, and $B$ contains four elements. $B \cap A$ contains two elements. How many elements are there in each of the following sets?

|   |   |   |
|---|---|---|
| **a.** $\bar{A}$ | **c.** $\bar{A} \cup B$ | **e.** $\overline{A \cup B}$ |
| **b.** $\bar{B}$ | **d.** $\bar{B} \cap \bar{A}$ |

**SOLUTION**   For the purpose of making a pictorial representation the six elements of $U$ will be called $a, b, c, d, e,$ and $f$; or, $U = \{a, b, c, d, e, f\}$. (Any six objects could be chosen.)

$B \cap A$ contains two elements. We draw $A$ and $B$ so that they have two elements in common. $B \cap A = \{b, c\}$ so $B \cap A$ contains two elements.

$\bar{A}$ would be all the elements in $U$ not in $A$. Therefore, $\bar{A} = \{e, d, f\}$, or $\bar{A}$ contains three elements.

$\bar{B}$ would be all the elements in $U$ that are not in $B$. Therefore, $\bar{B} = \{a, f\}$, or $\bar{B}$ contains two elements.

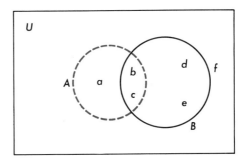

$\bar{A}$ contains three elements and $B$ contains four elements, but $\bar{A} \cup B$ does not necessarily contain seven elements. Remember $\bar{A} = \{e, d, f\}$, $B = \{b, c, e, d\}$. Since $e$ and $d$ are common to both $\bar{A}$ and $B$, $\bar{A} \cup B = \{b, c, d, e, f\}$, or $\bar{A} \cup B$ contains five elements.

$\bar{B} = \{a, f\}$, $\bar{A} = \{d, e, f\}$; so $\bar{B} \cap \bar{A}$ contains only the elements common to both $\bar{A}$ and $\bar{B}$. Thus, $\bar{B} \cap \bar{A} = \{f\}$ or $\bar{B} \cap \bar{A}$ contains one element.

$A = \{a, b, c\}$, $B = \{b, c, d, e\}$, $A \cup B = \{a, b, c, d, e\}$. The elements in $\overline{A \cup B}$ are all of the elements in $U$ that are not in $A \cup B$. Therefore, $\overline{A \cup B} = \{f\}$, or $\overline{A \cup B}$ contains one element.

6. Given a universal set $U$ containing thirteen elements and two subsets $C$ and $D$; $C$ contains four elements and $D$ contains seven elements; $C \cap D$ contains two elements.

   Indicate how many elements there are in the following sets: (Venn diagrams will prove helpful.)

   **a.** $C \cup D$      **d.** $\bar{C} \cup D$      **g.** $\overline{C \cap D}$

   **b.** $\bar{C}$      **e.** $\bar{D} \cup C$      **h.** $\bar{C} \cup \bar{D}$

   **c.** $\bar{D}$      **f.** $C \cap \bar{D}$      **i.** $\bar{C} \cap \bar{D}$

7. Given a universal set $U$ containing nine elements, and three subsets $G$, $F$, and $K$; $G$ contains four elements, $F$ contains six elements, $K$ contains two elements, $G \cup F$ contains seven elements, $K \cap F$ contains one element and $G \cap K$ contains two elements.

   How many elements are there in each of the following sets?

   **a.** $G \cap F$           **f.** $K \cup F$

   **b.** $\bar{G} \cap F$          **g.** $G \cup K$

   **c.** $\bar{F} \cap G$          **h.** $\bar{K}$

   **d.** $\bar{F} \cup \bar{G}$         **i.** $\bar{K} \cap \bar{G}$

   **e.** $\overline{F \cap G}$         **j.** $\overline{K \cup G}$

# VOCABULARY

| | |
|---|---|
| binary (11) | member (2) |
| Boolean Algebra (14) | natural number (13) |
| complement (18) | null set (2) |
| disjoint sets (9) | one-to-one correspondence (4) |
| element (2) | prime number (3) |
| empty set (2) | proper subset (17) |
| Euler circles (8) | set (1) |
| finite set (2) | subset (6) |
| infinite set (2) | union (12) |
| intersection (13) | universe (6) |
| matching sets (5) | Venn diagram (8) |

·····················································

# REVIEW EXERCISES

1. Let $P$ be the set of prime numbers less than 100. Label each statement as either true or false.

   **a.** 2 is the only even number such that $2 \in P$.

   **b.** $P \subset T$, where $T$ is the set of all prime numbers less than 200.

   **c.** $101 \in P$      **e.** $\{2, 11, 21\} \subset P$      **g.** $81 \notin P$

   **d.** $169 \in P$      **f.** $\{37, 41, 43\} \not\subset P$      **h.** $13 \notin P$

2. Is each of the following statements true or false?

   **a.** The set of even natural numbers and the set of prime numbers are disjoint sets.

   **b.** The set of even natural numbers and the set of odd natural numbers are matching sets.

   **c.** If $U$ = the set of natural numbers, and $A = U$, then $\bar{A} = \phi$.

   **d.** A set with four elements has 16 subsets.

   **e.** $\{1, 3, \frac{1}{2}\} \cap \{\frac{1}{4}, \frac{1}{2}\} = \{1\}$.

   **f.** For every set $X$, $X \cap X = \phi$.

   **g.** For every set $Y$, $Y \cap \phi = Y$.

   **h.** For every set $M$, $M \cup \phi = M$.

   **i.** If $A = \{0, \frac{1}{2}, \frac{1}{4}\}$ and $B = \{0, \frac{1}{3}, \frac{1}{9}\}$, then $A \cap B = \phi$.

   **j.** $\{\frac{1}{2}, \frac{1}{3}, \frac{1}{4}\} \subset \{\frac{1}{2}, \frac{1}{4}, \frac{1}{8}, \frac{1}{16}\}$.

3. **a.** How many subsets of $\{10, 15, 20, 25\}$ have exactly one element? Two elements? Three elements? Four elements? Five elements?

**b.** List the elements of the set described by "all natural numbers less than 17 and greater than 11."

**c.** Which of the following sentences describe the empty set?

    (1) The set of all natural numbers greater than 15 and less than 16.

    (2) The set of all fractions greater than $\frac{1}{2}$ and less than $\frac{1}{3}$.

    (3) The set of all prime numbers less than 3.

    (4) The set of all odd natural numbers greater than 21 and less than 23.

    (5) The set of all voters in Canada less than 19 years of age.

**4.** Draw Venn diagrams to verify the truth of each of the following statements for any two sets $A$ and $B$, that are subsets of the universe $U$.

    **a.** $U \cap A = A$           ★ **d.** $\overline{A \cup B} = \bar{A} \cap \bar{B}$

 ★ **b.** $A \cup \bar{A} = U$        ★ **e.** $\overline{A \cap B} = \bar{A} \cup \bar{B}$

 ★ **c.** $A \cap \bar{A} = \phi$        ★ **f.** $\bar{\bar{A}} = A$

**5.** If the sets $A$, $B$, and $C$ are as pictured in *Figure 5*, name the elements of each of the following:

    **a.** $C \cap B$                ★ **h.** $\bar{B}$

    **b.** $A \cap B$               ★ **i.** $\bar{C}$

    **c.** $B \cap C$               ★ **j.** $\overline{(A \cup B) \cup C}$

    **d.** $A \cup B$               ★ **k.** $(A \cap B) \cap C$

    **e.** $(A \cup B) \cup C$       ★ **l.** $\overline{(A \cap B) \cap C}$

    **f.** $A \cup (B \cup C)$       ★ **m.** $A \cap (B \cap C)$

 ★ **g.** $\bar{A}$                ★ **n.** $\overline{(A \cup B)} \cap C$

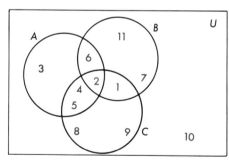

*Fig. 5*

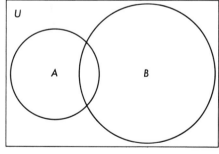

*Fig. 6*

**6.** Which of the following describes correctly what is pictured in the Venn diagram in *Figure 6*?

    (a) $A \subset B$,    (b) $A \cap B = \phi$,    (c) $(A \cup B) \subset A$,    (d) $(A \cap B) \subset A$,

    (e) $A \cup B = A$.

## CHAPTER TEST

1. Define:
   **a.** Matching sets
   **b.** $A$ is a subset of $B$
   **c.** Intersection of $X$ and $Y$
   **d.** Union of $A$ and $B$
   **e.** Disjoint sets
   ★ **f.** Complement of a set

2. **a.** $A = \{1, 7, 13, 41, 67\}$
      $B = \{a, c, d, f, g, k\}$
      Are $A$ and $B$ matching sets? Explain.
   **b.** Give an example of one pair of infinite sets which are matching sets.

3. For each of the following pairs of sets tell whether the set $A$ is a subset of $B$:
   **a.** $A = \{0, 1, 2\}$; $B = \{0, 1, 2, 3, 4, 5\}$
   **b.** $A = \{5, 6, 7\}$; $B = \{6, 7\}$
   **c.** $A = \{2, 4, 6, \cdot \cdot \cdot\}$; $B = \{1, 2, 3\}$
   **d.** $A = \{1, 3, 5, \cdot \cdot \cdot\}$; $B = \{1, 2, 3, \cdot \cdot \cdot\}$
   **e.** $A = \{$all prime numbers$\}$; $B = \{1, 2, 3, \cdot \cdot \cdot\}$

4. Find *both* the intersection and union of each of the following pairs of sets:
   **a.** $A = \{5, 6, 7, 8, 9\}$; $B = \{7, 8, 9, 10\}$
   **b.** $C = \{1, 3, 5, \cdot \cdot \cdot\}$; $D = \{2, 4, 6, \cdot \cdot \cdot\}$
   **c.** $E = $ All students in your school over 16 years of age.
      $F = $ All students in your school under 16 years of age.
   **d.** Which parts of this Exercise (4) describe *disjoint* sets?

5. Determine whether or not each of the following statements is true for every set $A$, and explain:
   **a.** $A \cap \phi = \phi$
   **b.** $A \cup \phi = \phi$

★ 6. If the universal set is the set of natural numbers, determine the complement of each of the following sets:
   **a.** $A = \{1, 2, 3, 4, 5\}$
   **b.** $B = \{1, 3, 5, \cdot \cdot \cdot\}$
   **c.** $C = \{5, 10, 15, \cdot \cdot \cdot\}$

7. List the elements of the following sets:
   **a.** The counting numbers less than eleven and greater than seven.
   **b.** The even counting numbers less than thirteen.
   **c.** The prime counting numbers less than twelve.

8. Suppose $A = \{a, b, c\}$. List all the possible subsets of $A$.

9. Given the universal set $U$ and subsets $C$, $F$, and $G$:

$$U = \{a, b, c, d, e, f, g, k\}$$
$$C = \{b, f, g, k\} \qquad F = \{a, b, d, f\} \qquad G = \{a, b, c, e, k\}$$

List the elements of each of the following sets:

   **a.** $C \cap F$      **d.** $(C \cup F) \cap G$      **g.** $U \cup C$
   **b.** $F \cup G$      ★**e.** $\overline{G \cap F}$      ★**h.** $C \cup \bar{C}$
   ★**c.** $\bar{C}$      **f.** $U \cap F$      ★**i.** $F \cap \bar{G}$

......................................................................................

# BIBLIOGRAPHY

Bakst, A., *Mathematics, Its Magic and Mastery*, Van Nostrand, Toronto.

Bakst, A., *Mathematical Puzzles and Pastimes*, Van Nostrand, Toronto, 1954.

Glenn, W. H., and Johnson, D. A., *Fun With Mathematics*, Webster Publishing Company, St. Louis, Missouri, 1960.

Glenn, W. H., and Johnson, D. A., *Sets, Sentences, and Operations*, Webster Publishing Company, St. Louis, Missouri, 1960, pages 1–34.

School Mathematics Study Group, *Mathematics for High School (Revised Edition): First Course in Algebra*, School Mathematics Study Group, New Haven, Connecticut, 1960, pages 1–18.

School Mathematics Study Group, *Mathematics for Junior High School: Supplementary Units*, School Mathematics Study Group, New Haven, Connecticut, 1959, pages 1–27.

The National Council of Teachers of Mathematics, *The Mathematics Student Journal*, Washington, D.C.

Woodward, E. J., and McClennan, R., *Elementary Concepts of Sets*, Holt, Rinehart and Winston, of Canada, Limited, Toronto.

# 2

# Operations

# On Numbers of Arithmetic

## 1 · Symbols for Grouping

In the English language, as in other languages, we use punctuation marks such as the comma and period in order to make clear what we want to say. Punctuation marks are very important. The following example illustrates this point.

A story is told about an employee who was out traveling for his employer. His task was to investigate the merit of buying certain stock on a stock market. He found the price rather high; therefore, he decided to wire his boss before deciding whether or not to buy the stock. The return wire from his boss read as follows:

### NO PRICE TOO HIGH

He went ahead and bought the stock not knowing, of course, that his boss intended to say

### NO, PRICE TOO HIGH

The punctuation symbol **9** was of crucial importance in that case.

In mathematics, there are similar situations in which it is necessary to use mathematical punctuation symbols such as ( ) parentheses, [ ] brackets, and { } braces. These symbols are often necessary in order to make clear what is to be done in mathematics problems. Consider, for example, the following arithmetic problem: Write $2 + 3 \times 7$ in as simple form as possible.

There are basically two possible ways of doing this simplification:

$$(1) \quad 2 + 3 \times 7 = 5 \times 7 = 35$$
$$\text{or} \quad (2) \quad 2 + 3 \times 7 = 2 + 21 = 23$$

Obviously, both ways cannot be intended, because 35 is not 23. The expression $2 + 3 \times 7$ *must* have only one meaning, otherwise we will be in difficulty. It is customary to use parentheses, or mathematical punctuation marks, to make the meaning of this phrase clear.

We shall agree that one should perform the operation inside the parentheses first. Thus, we use parentheses to indicate that certain groups of numbers are to be operated on first.

$$(2 + 3) \times 7 = 5 \times 7 = 35$$
$$2 + (3 \times 7) = 2 + 21 = 23$$

You will find that, for convenience and brevity, parentheses are frequently omitted in expressions like the one above. In this case, it is necessary for us to reach some kind of an agreement on the unique meaning of $2 + 3 \times 7$. We shall agree that, whenever addition, subtraction, multiplication, and division are involved in a problem and there are no parentheses to guide us, we shall perform the multiplication and division first, then the addition and subtraction. *IN ORDER FROM LEFT TO RIGHT.*

According to this agreement,

$$2 + 3 \times 7 = 2 + 21 = 23$$

Similarly,

$$2 + 6 \div 3 = 2 + 2 = 4$$
$$\tfrac{1}{2} \times 7 - 16 \div 8 = 3\tfrac{1}{2} - 2 = 1\tfrac{1}{2}$$
$$3 \times 5 - 2 \times 3 + 7 \times 11 = 15 - 6 + 77 = 9 + 77 = 86$$

Whenever a series of divisions and multiplications are indicated, the operations are performed in the order of their occurrence, from left to right.

**EXAMPLE 1**
$$
\begin{aligned}
3 \times 4 \div 2 \times 6 \div 4 \div 2 &= 12 \div 2 \times 6 \div 4 \div 2 \\
&= 6 \times 6 \div 4 \div 2 \\
&= 36 \div 4 \div 2 \\
&= 9 \div 2 \\
&= 4\tfrac{1}{2}
\end{aligned}
$$

The same is true when addition and subtraction appear consecutively.

**EXAMPLE 2**
$$
\begin{aligned}
10 - 8 + 4 + 6 - 3 + 5 &= 2 + 4 + 6 - 3 + 5 \\
&= 6 + 6 - 3 + 5 \\
&= 12 - 3 + 5 \\
&= 9 + 5 \\
&= 14
\end{aligned}
$$

We will use various ways of expressing the product of, say, 3 and 4. Instead of writing $3 \times 4$, we will also indicate this product by $3 \cdot 4$, $(3)4$, $3(4)$, and $(3)(4)$.

## EXERCISES

Work each of the following until it appears in the simplest form possible:

**EXAMPLE 1**    $7 \cdot (\frac{1}{2} - \frac{1}{3})$

**SOLUTION**    $7 \cdot (\frac{1}{2} - \frac{1}{3}) = 7 \cdot (\frac{3}{6} - \frac{2}{6})$
$$= 7 \cdot \tfrac{1}{6}$$
$$= \tfrac{7}{6}$$
$$= 1\tfrac{1}{6}$$

**EXAMPLE 2**    $\frac{1}{2} \times [\frac{1}{3} \times (.7 - \frac{1}{2})]$

**SOLUTION**    $\frac{1}{2} \times [\frac{1}{3} \times (.7 - \frac{1}{2})]$
$$= \tfrac{1}{2} \times [\tfrac{1}{3} \times (.7 - .5)]$$
$$= \tfrac{1}{2} \times [\tfrac{1}{3} \times .2]$$
$$= \tfrac{1}{2} \times [\tfrac{1}{3} \times \tfrac{2}{10}]$$
$$= \tfrac{1}{2} \times [\tfrac{2}{30}]$$
$$= \tfrac{2}{60}$$
$$= \tfrac{1}{30}$$

**EXAMPLE 3**    $\{[7 + (6 \cdot 3)] \cdot 2\} \cdot 5$

**SOLUTION**    $\{[7 + (6 \cdot 3)] \cdot 2\} \cdot 5$
$$= \{[7 + 18] \cdot 2\} \cdot 5$$
$$= \{25 \cdot 2\} \cdot 5$$
$$= 50 \cdot 5$$
$$= 250$$

1. $5 \cdot (\frac{2}{5} - \frac{1}{5})$
2. $2 \cdot (\frac{5}{7} - \frac{2}{7})$
3. $\frac{1}{2} \cdot (\frac{2}{3} - \frac{1}{2})$
4. $.5 \times (.3 - .1)$
5. $50 \times (.2 - .1)$
6. $(17 - 13) \times (20 + 5)$
7. $(\frac{3}{5} - .2) \times (.6 - \frac{1}{2})$
8. $3 \cdot [4 \cdot (7 - 5)]$
9. $5 \cdot [3 \cdot (2 + 7)]$
10. $5 \cdot (7 + 2 - 8) + 3 \cdot \frac{1}{2}$
11. $1737 + 14.75 + 13.6$
12. $14.75 + 1737 + 13.6$
13. $1737 + 13.6 + 14.75$
14. $.675 \times 1.3$
15. $1.3 \times .675$
16. $(15.7 + 198.5) + 3.6$
17. $15.7 + (198.5 + 3.6)$
18. $(6.2 \times 3.7) \times 1.2$
19. $6.2 \times (3.7 \times 1.2)$
20. $(3.7 \times 6.2) \times 1.2$
21. $5 \cdot (6 + 7)$
22. $5 \cdot 6 + 5 \cdot 7$
23. $(11 + 12) \cdot 10$
24. $11 \cdot 10 + 12 \cdot 10$
25. $3 \times [(4 \cdot 6) + (7 \cdot 9)]$
26. $\{[4(3) + 14] \div 13\} + 4 \cdot 7$

## 2 · Basic Principles of Addition and Multiplication

Each set of examples below is intended to illustrate an important principle governing the operations with numbers. Study each set, then give two more examples which will fit into the particular pattern.

**SET 1**
$2 + 7 = 9$ and $7 + 2 = 9$, therefore

**$2 + 7 = 7 + 2$**

$\frac{1}{2} + 3 = 3\frac{1}{2}$ and $3 + \frac{1}{2} = 3\frac{1}{2}$, therefore

**$\frac{1}{2} + 3 = 3 + \frac{1}{2}$**

$.7 + 1.2 = 1.9$ and $1.2 + .7 = 1.9$, therefore

**$.7 + 1.2 = 1.2 + .7$**

$\frac{3}{2} + \frac{7}{2} = 5$ and $\frac{7}{2} + \frac{3}{2} = 5$, therefore

**$\frac{3}{2} + \frac{7}{2} = \frac{7}{2} + \frac{3}{2}$**

Give three more examples of your own that fit into this pattern. What pattern or principle is suggested by the examples above? This pattern is called

### THE COMMUTATIVE PRINCIPLE OF ADDITION

What does the word "commutative" suggest to you? Look it up in a dictionary.

**SET 2**
$3 \cdot 24 = 72$ and $24 \cdot 3 = 72$, therefore

**$3 \cdot 24 = 24 \cdot 3$**

$\frac{1}{2} \cdot 17 = 8\frac{1}{2}$ and $17 \cdot \frac{1}{2} = 8\frac{1}{2}$, therefore

**$\frac{1}{2} \cdot 17 = 17 \cdot \frac{1}{2}$**

$.36 \times 1.6 = .576$ and $1.6 \times .36 = .576$, therefore

**$.36 \times 1.6 = 1.6 \times .36$**

$\frac{2}{3} \times \frac{4}{5} = \frac{8}{15}$ and $\frac{4}{5} \times \frac{2}{3} = \frac{8}{15}$, therefore

**$\frac{2}{3} \times \frac{4}{5} = \frac{4}{5} \times \frac{2}{3}$**

Is this pattern clear to you? Give three more examples of your own that fit into this pattern. What principle is suggested by the examples above? You probably have already guessed that this principle is called

### THE COMMUTATIVE PRINCIPLE OF MULTIPLICATION

From the two principles above, you will notice that commutativity is a property of operations on numbers. The operations of addition and multiplication have this property. What about subtraction? Is $5 - 2 = 2 - 5$ true? Of course not. Explain.

And what about division. Is $4 \div 8 = 8 \div 4$ true? The answer is "no," since $4 \div 8$ is $\frac{1}{2}$ and $8 \div 4$ is 2 and $\frac{1}{2} \neq 2$ (read "$\frac{1}{2}$ is not equal to 2").

We therefore say that multiplication and addition are *commutative operations*. On the other hand, division and subtraction are *non-commutative* operations.

**SET 3**

$(3 + 16) + 34 = 19 + 34 = 53$, and

$3 + (16 + 34) = 3 + 50 = 53$; therefore

$$(3 + 16) + 34 = 3 + (16 + 34)$$

$(.3 + .8) + 34.5 = 1.1 + 34.5 = 35.6$, and

$.3 + (.8 + 34.5) = .3 + 35.3 = 35.6$; therefore

$$(.3 + .8) + 34.5 = .3 + (.8 + 34.5)$$

$(.13 + .3) + 1.9 = .43 + 1.9 = 2.33$, and

$.13 + (.3 + 1.9) = .13 + 2.2 = 2.33$; therefore

$$(.13 + .3) + 1.9 = .13 + (.3 + 1.9)$$

Give three more examples of your own, to show that you understand this pattern. What principle is suggested by the examples above? This principle is called

## THE ASSOCIATIVE PRINCIPLE OF ADDITION

The choice of the word associative is quite sensible here. This can be seen by observing what is involved in this principle. Examine, for example, $(3 + 16) + 34 = 3 + (16 + 34)$. On the left side of the equality sign, 16 is grouped or associated with 3. On the right side of the equality sign, 16 is grouped with 34. Thus, the Associative Principle of Addition tells us that 16 can be grouped with either 3 or 34 and the answer will be the same. We shall agree that if parentheses are omitted, as in $3 + 5 + 7$, it will mean $(3 + 5) + 7$.

**SET 4**

$(13 \cdot 8) \cdot 4 = 104 \cdot 4 = 416$, and

$13 \cdot (8 \cdot 4) = 13 \cdot 32 = 416$; therefore

$$(13 \cdot 8) \cdot 4 = 13 \cdot (8 \cdot 4)$$

$(\frac{1}{7} \cdot \frac{2}{3}) \cdot \frac{1}{2} = \frac{2}{21} \cdot \frac{1}{2} = \frac{1}{21}$, and

$\frac{1}{7} \cdot (\frac{2}{3} \cdot \frac{1}{2}) = \frac{1}{7} \cdot \frac{1}{3} = \frac{1}{21}$; therefore

$(\frac{1}{7} \cdot \frac{2}{3}) \cdot \frac{1}{2} = \frac{1}{7} \cdot (\frac{2}{3} \cdot \frac{1}{2})$

$(1.13 \times 4) \times 1.5 = 4.52 \times 1.5 = 6.78$, and

$1.13 \times (4 \times 1.5) = 1.13 \times 6 = 6.78$; therefore

**$(1.13 \times 4) \times 1.5 = 1.13 \times (4 \times 1.5)$**

Give three more examples of your own that follow this same pattern.

What principle is suggested by the examples above? Do you see a similarity between this principle and the Associative Principle of Addition? You should not have any difficulty guessing that the name for this principle is

## THE ASSOCIATIVE PRINCIPLE OF MULTIPLICATION

As in the case of commutativity, associativity is a property of an operation on numbers and $2 \cdot 3 \cdot 4$ will mean $(2 \cdot 3) \cdot 4$. You have seen that the operations of addition and multiplication are associative.

To check subtraction and division for associativity, let us take an example for each operation. Is $(10 - 5) - 4 = 10 - (5 - 4)$ a true statement? To decide on the answer, we work out each side separately as shown below.

$$(10 - 5) - 4 = 5 - 4 = 1$$
$$10 - (5 - 4) = 10 - 1 = 9$$
$$\text{and } 1 \neq 9$$
$$\text{Thus, } (10 - 5) - 4 \neq 10 - (5 - 4)$$

Is one example sufficient to prove that the operation of subtraction is not associative?

Now for the operation of division. Is $(12 \div 6) \div 3 = 12 \div (6 \div 3)$ true?

**EXAMPLE**      $(12 \div 6) \div 3$

**SOLUTION**     $(12 \div 6) \div 3 = 2 \div 3 = \frac{2}{3}$
$$12 \div (6 \div 3) = 12 \div 2 = 6$$
$$\text{and } \frac{2}{3} \neq 6$$
$$\text{Thus, } (12 \div 6) \div 3 \neq 12 \div (6 \div 3)$$

We can therefore conclude that neither subtraction nor division is an associative operation.

# EXERCISES

In each exercise below, some principle is illustrated. Name the principle.

**EXAMPLE 1**     $3 + 4 = 4 + 3$

**SOLUTION**     The principle illustrated is the Commutative Principle of Addition.

**EXAMPLE 2**     $7 \times (6 \times 2) = (7 \times 6) \times 2$

**SOLUTION**     The Associative Principle of Multiplication is illustrated.

1. $19 + 35 = 35 + 19$
2. $\frac{1}{2} + 30 = 30 + \frac{1}{2}$
3. $(6 + 7) + 9 = 6 + (7 + 9)$
4. $3 \times \frac{1}{3} = \frac{1}{3} \times 3$

5. $6 \times 998 = 998 \times 6$
6. $(1 \cdot 3) \cdot 5 = 1 \cdot (3 \cdot 5)$
7. $(0 \cdot 2) \cdot 13 = 0 \cdot (2 \cdot 13)$
8. $(1 \cdot 2) + 3 = (2 \cdot 1) + 3$

9. $(3 + 5) \times (4 \times 10) = (5 + 3) \times (4 \times 10)$
10. $(1 \times 17) \times (6 + 11) = (17 \times 1) \times (6 + 11)$

The Commutative and Associative Principles of Addition and Multiplication can be used to good advantage in simplifying arithmetical operations. Study the examples below, then find a way of grouping numbers to simplify the computations as much as possible in each exercise that follows.

**EXAMPLE 1**     $(12 + 19) + 1$

**SOLUTION**
$$(12 + 19) + 1 = 12 + (19 + 1)$$
$$= 12 + 20$$
$$= 32$$

**EXAMPLE 2**     $(3.1 + 4.7) + .9$

**SOLUTION**
$$(3.1 + 4.7) + .9 = (4.7 + 3.1) + .9$$
$$= 4.7 + (3.1 + .9)$$
$$= 4.7 + 4.0$$
$$= 8.7$$

11. $(56 + 97) + 3$
12. $(178 + 987) + 13$
13. $(159 + 1999) + 1$
14. $(998 + 376) + 2$
15. $(901 + 455) + 99$

16. $(870 + 869) + 130$
17. $(3.2 + 9.9) + .1$
18. $(\frac{1}{4} + \frac{3}{2}) + \frac{1}{2}$
19. $(\frac{3}{7} + \frac{1}{3}) + \frac{4}{7}$
20. $(\frac{1}{9} + \frac{1}{2}) + \frac{8}{9}$

## 3 · Closure

Let us for the moment consider the set of natural numbers as our universal set. You have no difficulty in seeing that if you add any pair of natural numbers, there is always a natural number which is their sum. For example, $1 + 21 = 22$, $179 + 382 = 561$, $5 + 5 = 10$, and so on. You would face an impossible task if you should decide to search for a pair of natural numbers whose sum is not a natural number. There is a name for this property. It is called **closure.** Thus, the set of natural numbers is said to be *closed* under the operation of *addition*.

What about the operation of multiplication? Given a pair of natural numbers, is there always a natural number which is the product of the pair? Perhaps you already answered "yes," and you are right. Again you would have an impossible task to find an example where this is not true.

Therefore, the set of natural numbers is said to be *closed* under the operation of *multiplication*.

Let us now examine the operation of subtraction. For example, $7 - 3 = 4$; but $3 - 7 = ?$ has no answer among the natural numbers. One example of failure for an answer to exist is sufficient to conclude that the set of natural numbers is *not closed* under the operation of *subtraction*.

You will see very soon that we can obtain a more adequate system of numbers in which subtraction always "works." In that system you will be able to subtract a number from a smaller number.

In division for example, $10 \div 5 = 2$; but $5 \div 10 = ?$ has no answer among natural numbers. Thus, the set of natural numbers is *not closed* under the operation of *division*.

You see then that the set of natural numbers is closed under addition and multiplication. It is *not* closed under subtraction and division.

## EXERCISES

For each exercise determine whether the given set of numbers is closed under the given operations.

**EXAMPLE**     Set: odd natural numbers.
          Operations: addition and multiplication.

**SOLUTION**    *Addition.* Is the sum of a pair of odd natural numbers an odd natural number? Let us try:

$$3 + 5 = 8$$

Answer: No, the set of odd natural numbers is not closed under addition.

*Multiplication.* The question here is: Is the product of a pair of odd natural numbers an odd natural number? Let's try a few:

$$5 \times 5 = 25, 7 \times 11 = 77, 9 \times 7 = 63$$

Answer: There seems to be no reason to suspect that the product of a pair of odd numbers is not an odd number (later you will be able to prove it). Therefore we can say that the set of odd natural numbers seems to be closed under multiplication.

For each exercise determine whether or not the given set of numbers is closed under the given operations.

1. Set: even natural numbers
   Operations: addition and multiplication
2. Set: natural numbers divisible by 3
   Operations: addition and multiplication
3. Set: natural numbers divisible by 4
   Operations: addition and multiplication
4. Set: even natural numbers
   Operation: take half of the sum of two numbers
5. Set: natural numbers divisible by 5
   Operation: multiplication
6. Set: natural numbers divisible by 3
   Operation: take half of the product of two numbers
7. Set: natural numbers divisible by 9
   Operation: take one-third of the sum of two numbers
8. Set: all natural numbers and all fractions
   Operations: multiplication and division
9. Set: $\{1, 2\}$
   Operations: multiplication and addition
10. Set: $\{\frac{1}{2}, 1, 2\}$
    Operations: multiplication and division
11. Set: $\{\frac{1}{2}, \frac{1}{4}, \frac{1}{8}, \frac{1}{16}, \frac{1}{32}, \cdots\}$
    Operations: addition and multiplication
12. Set: $\{\frac{1}{3}, \frac{1}{9}, \frac{1}{27}, \frac{1}{81}, \cdots\}$
    Operation: multiply by $\frac{1}{3}$
13. Set: $\{0, 1\}$
    Operations: addition, multiplication and subtraction
14. Set: $\{1, \frac{1}{5}, \frac{1}{25}, \frac{1}{125}, \cdots\}$
    Operation: multiply by $\frac{1}{5}$
15. Set: $\{1, 4, 9, 16, 25, 36, 49, 64, \cdots\}$
    Operation: multiply by itself

## 4 · More About Addition and Multiplication

Suppose a man is selling tickets for a benefit at $3 each. If he sells seventeen tickets the first day and four tickets the next, what are the total receipts?
We could arrange our computation in the following manner:

$$3 \times (17 + 4) = 3 \times 21 = 63$$

That is, knowing the total number of tickets sold (21) and the price of each ticket ($3), we find the total receipts to be $63.
But he could also write it as follows:

$$(3 \times 17) + (3 \times 4) = 51 + 12 = 63$$

The product of three and seventeen indicates the receipts for the first day, and the product of three and four indicates the receipts for the second day. Their sum is the total intake.
We see, then, that $3 \times (17 + 4) = 3(17) + 3(4)$.

## EXERCISES

1. Work each of the following in the two ways shown above, and determine whether or not the result is the same:

**EXAMPLE**     $4 \times (3 + 5)$

**SOLUTION**     $4 \times (3 + 5) = 4(8) = 32$
            $4 \times (3 + 5) = 4(3) + 4(5) = 12 + 20 = 32$

**a.** $6 \times (7 + 4)$    **e.** $\frac{3}{5} \times (\frac{1}{2} + \frac{1}{3})$    **i.** $1 \times (17 + 99)$
**b.** $8 \times (5 + 7)$    **f.** $31 \times (11 + 12)$    **j.** $3.3 \times (.5 + .4)$
**c.** $\frac{2}{3} \times (6 + 9)$    **g.** $\frac{4}{7} \times (\frac{1}{3} + \frac{1}{2})$    **k.** $.05 \times (100 + 200)$
**d.** $\frac{1}{3} \times (.6 + 9)$    **h.** $1.5 \times (1.5 + 1.5)$    **l.** $.005 \times (1000 + 2000)$

2. If the symbols $\triangle$, $\square$, and $\bigcirc$ hold places for number symbols, give a replacement for each which will result in a true statement. (In some cases there is more than one replacement.)
   **a.** $5 \times (6 + 9) = \square \times (6) + \square \times (9)$
   **b.** $3 \times (\triangle + 6) = 3(5) + 3(6)$
   **c.** $\square \times (4 + 11) = 5(4) + 5(11)$
   **d.** $6 \times (\triangle + \square) = 6(5) + 6(13)$
   **e.** $\triangle \times (3 + \square) = 6(3) + 6(5)$
   **f.** $\triangle \times (\bigcirc + \square) = (5 \times 7) + (5 \times 11)$

## 5 · The Distributive Principle

In the exercises of the last section you learned to make use of "frames" to stand in place of number symbols. These frames are very useful in stating some general principles which are true for all numbers. For example, $\square + \triangle = \triangle + \square$ states the Commutative Principle of Addition. You can replace $\square$ by, say, 3 and $\triangle$ by, say, 7 and obtain this true statement:

$$3 + 7 = 7 + 3$$

The statement $3 + 7 = 7 + 3$ is a specific instance of a general principle which you already know to have the name The Commutative Principle of Addition.

We will agree on the basis of Exercise 1 on page 35 that statements of the form

$$\square \times (\triangle + \bigcirc) = (\square \times \triangle) + (\square \times \bigcirc)$$

where $\square$, $\triangle$, and $\bigcirc$ can be replaced by number symbols, are true. We will refer to this general principle as

### THE DISTRIBUTIVE PRINCIPLE

This principle tells us that multiplication is distributive with respect to addition. For example, in this principle 17 may replace $\square$, 5 may replace $\triangle$, and 6 may replace $\bigcirc$, to yield

$$17 \cdot (5 + 6) = (17 \cdot 5) + (17 \cdot 6)$$

Work this example both ways and see whether you get the same answer each time.

We can now summarize the properties of operations on numbers which we have observed thus far.

1. Addition is commutative and associative.
2. Multiplication is commutative and associative.
3. Multiplication is distributive with respect to addition.

It is appropriate to ask whether or not some other operation is distributive with respect to addition or with respect to any other operation. Let us try some combinations of operations with which you are familiar.

First, let us introduce another symbol to be used in a way similar to the way we used the symbols $\square$, $\triangle$, and $\bigcirc$.

We agreed that we could replace each of these symbols by symbols for numbers. For example, $\square + \triangle + \bigcirc$ becomes $6 + \frac{4}{5} + .76$ when $\square$ is replaced by 6, $\triangle$ is replaced by $\frac{4}{5}$, and $\bigcirc$ is replaced by .76.

The new symbols, let us say $\oplus$ and $\odot$, will be used with an intent of having them replaced by symbols for operations $+$, $-$, $\div$, $\times$.

Now we are in a position to write the sentence

$$\square \oplus (\triangle \odot \bigcirc) = (\square \oplus \triangle) \odot (\square \oplus \bigcirc)$$

where the symbols $\square$, $\triangle$ and $\bigcirc$ are replaceable by symbols for numbers, and the symbols $\oplus$ and $\odot$ are replaceable by symbols for operations.

We already know that replacing $\oplus$ by $\times$, and $\odot$ by $+$ will always give us true statements no matter what symbols for numbers go in place of $\square$, $\triangle$ and $\bigcirc$. Let us now try another replacement. Put $+$ in place of $\oplus$ and $+$ in place of $\odot$. Does the pattern

$$\square + (\triangle + \bigcirc) = (\square + \triangle) + (\square + \bigcirc)$$

yield true statements no matter what symbols for numbers are put in place of $\square$, $\triangle$ and $\bigcirc$? Let us test this.

Is $2 + (5 + 7) = (2 + 5) + (2 + 7)$ a true statement?

$$2 + (5 + 7) = 2 + 12 = 14$$

and
$$(2 + 5) + (2 + 7) = 7 + 9 = 16$$

Since $14 \neq 16$, the statement is false, and we conclude that the operation of addition is not distributive with respect to itself. Is one example sufficient to prove this?

The answer to the preceding question is, of course, "yes." It is sufficient to show one exception in order to prove that a statement is false. This is known as a "counter-example." Can you think of an operation which is distributive with respect to itself?

## EXERCISES

Work each of the following in two ways:

**EXAMPLE**     $3 \cdot (5 + 7)$

**SOLUTION**     (a) $3 \cdot (5 + 7) = 3 \cdot 12$
$$= 36$$
(b) $3 \cdot (5 + 7) = (3 \cdot 5) + (3 \cdot 7)$
$$= 15 + 21$$
$$= 36$$

Work each of the following two ways:

1. $16 \cdot (3 + 5)$
2. $\frac{1}{3} \cdot (7 + 3)$
3. $.5 \times (.6 + 5)$
4. $\frac{1}{2} \cdot (\frac{1}{3} + \frac{1}{4})$
5. $.08 \times (\frac{1}{2} + .3)$

6. $33 \cdot (\frac{1}{3} + \frac{1}{11})$
7. $42 \cdot (\frac{1}{2} + \frac{1}{7})$
8. $.1 \times (.7 + .5)$
9. $.02 \times (.02 + .03)$
10. $5(7) + 5(13)$

11. $11(12) + 11(16)$
12. $(\frac{3}{4})(\frac{5}{6}) + (\frac{3}{4})(\frac{7}{6})$
13. $7(20) + 13(7)$
14. $37(46) + 37(4)$
15. $25(48) + 2(25)$

Work out two examples for each case to check whether or not each of the following statements is true.

**EXAMPLE**   Multiplication is distributive with respect to multiplication.

**SOLUTION 1**   $3 \times (4 \times 5) = (3 \times 4) \times (3 \times 5)$

$$3 \times (4 \times 5) = 3 \times 20 = 60$$
$$(3 \times 4) \times (3 \times 5) = 12 \times 15$$
$$= 180$$
$$60 \neq 180$$

**SOLUTION 2**   $\frac{1}{2} \times (\frac{2}{3} \times \frac{4}{7}) = (\frac{1}{2} \times \frac{2}{3}) \times (\frac{1}{2} \times \frac{4}{7})$

$$\frac{1}{2} \times (\frac{2}{3} \times \frac{4}{7}) = \frac{1}{2} \times \frac{8}{21}$$
$$= \frac{8}{42} = \frac{4}{21}$$
$$(\frac{1}{2} \times \frac{2}{3}) \times (\frac{1}{2} \times \frac{4}{7}) = \frac{2}{6} \times \frac{4}{14}$$
$$= \frac{1}{3} \times \frac{2}{7}$$
$$= \frac{2}{21}$$
$$\frac{2}{21} \neq \frac{4}{21}$$

The statement is false.

16. Division is distributive with respect to multiplication.
17. Division is distributive with respect to subtraction.
18. Division is distributive with respect to division.
19. Subtraction is distributive with respect to subtraction.
20. Multiplication is distributive with respect to subtraction.
21. Multiplication is distributive with respect to division.
22. Addition is distributive with respect to multiplication.
23. Addition is distributive with respect to division.
24. Addition is distributive with respect to subtraction.
25. Subtraction is distributive with respect to multiplication.
26. Subtraction is distributive with respect to addition.
27. Subtraction is distributive with respect to division.

## 6 · More Principles

In the four sets of examples below, each set is intended to portray a certain pattern or principle. Try to discover these principles. Supply two more examples which fit each pattern. After you have discovered the pattern for each case, see the names of these principles given at the top of the next page.

**SET 1**

$$165 \cdot 1 = 165$$
$$0 \cdot 1 = 0$$
$$\tfrac{4}{7} \cdot 1 = \tfrac{4}{7}$$
$$1.67 \times 1 = 1.67$$

$$\cdot$$
$$\cdot$$
$$\cdot$$

**SET 2**

$$39 \div 1 = 39$$
$$0 \div 1 = 0$$
$$\tfrac{13}{17} \div 1 = \tfrac{13}{17}$$
$$3.5 \div 1 = 3.5$$

$$\cdot$$
$$\cdot$$
$$\cdot$$

**SET 3**

$$79 + 0 = 79$$
$$0 + 0 = 0$$
$$\tfrac{12}{19} + 0 = \tfrac{12}{19}$$
$$17.6 + 0 = 17.6$$

$$\cdot$$
$$\cdot$$
$$\cdot$$

**SET 4**

$$135 \cdot 0 = 0$$
$$0 \cdot 0 = 0$$
$$\tfrac{2}{7} \cdot 0 = 0$$
$$6.75 \times 0 = 0$$

$$\cdot$$
$$\cdot$$
$$\cdot$$

Before you turn the page, try to express these principles in your own words.

1. The Principle of Multiplication by One.
2. The Principle of Division by One.
3. The Principle of Addition of Zero.
4. The Principle of Multiplication by Zero.

Can you suggest some other patterns that might be familiar from your previous study of arithmetic?

## EXERCISES

In each example below, name the principle involved in going from one statement to another.

**EXAMPLE 1**

$$3 \cdot (4 \cdot 7) \overset{(1)}{=} 3 \cdot (7 \cdot 4)$$
$$\overset{(2)}{=} (3 \cdot 7) \cdot 4$$

**SOLUTION**

(1) The Commutative Principle of Multiplication. (Point out the specific place at which this principle was used.)

(2) The Associative Principle of Multiplication. (Point out the specific place at which this principle was used.)

**EXAMPLE 2**

$$(2 + 7) + \tfrac{1}{3} + 13 \cdot 0 + 23 \cdot 1$$
$$\overset{(1)}{=} (7 + 2) + \tfrac{1}{3} + 13 \cdot 0 + 23 \cdot 1$$
$$\overset{(2)}{=} 7 + (2 + \tfrac{1}{3}) + 13 \cdot 0 + 23$$
$$\overset{(3)}{=} 7 + (\tfrac{1}{3} + 2) + 0 + 23$$

**SOLUTION**

(1) The Commutative Principle of Addition. (Point out the specific place at which this principle was used.)

(2) The Associative Principle of Addition and the Principle of One of Multiplication. (Point out the specific places at which these principles were used.)

(3) The Commutative Principle of Addition and the Principle of Zero of Multiplication. (Point out the specific places at which these principles were used.)

**a.** $3 + 7 \overset{(1)}{=} 7 + 3$

**b.** $(3 + \frac{1}{2}) + \frac{1}{3} \overset{(1)}{=} 3 + (\frac{1}{2} + \frac{1}{3})$

**c.** $4 \cdot 125 \overset{(1)}{=} 125 \cdot 4$

**d.** $(\frac{1}{2} \cdot \frac{1}{4}) \cdot \frac{1}{7} \overset{(1)}{=} \frac{1}{2} \cdot (\frac{1}{4} \cdot \frac{1}{7})$

**e.** $(3 \cdot 5) \cdot 7 \overset{(1)}{=} (5 \cdot 3) \cdot 7$

**f.** $(10 + 3) + 27 \overset{(1)}{=} (3 + 10) + 27$

**g.** $(\frac{2}{7} + \frac{3}{4}) + \frac{1}{2} \overset{(1)}{=} \frac{2}{7} + (\frac{3}{4} + \frac{1}{2})$

**h.** $3 \cdot 0 + (\frac{1}{2} \cdot \frac{1}{3}) \cdot \frac{1}{4} \overset{(1)}{=} 0 + (\frac{1}{2} \cdot \frac{1}{3}) \cdot \frac{1}{4}$

$\overset{(2)}{=} (\frac{1}{2} \cdot \frac{1}{3}) \cdot \frac{1}{4} + 0$

$\overset{(3)}{=} (\frac{1}{2} \cdot \frac{1}{3}) \cdot \frac{1}{4}$

$\overset{(4)}{=} \frac{1}{2} \cdot (\frac{1}{3} \cdot \frac{1}{4})$

**i.** $[6(5 + 8)] + 0 \overset{(1)}{=} [6(8 + 5)] + 0$

$\overset{(2)}{=} [6(8) + 6(5)] + 0$

$\overset{(3)}{=} 6(8) + 6(5)$

**j.** $3 \cdot (1 + 4) + 4 \cdot 7 \overset{(1)}{=} (3 \cdot 1) + (3 \cdot 4) + 4 \cdot 7$

$\overset{(2)}{=} 3 + (3 \cdot 4) + 4 \cdot 7$

$\overset{(3)}{=} 3 + (4 \cdot 3) + (4 \cdot 7)$

$\overset{(4)}{=} 3 + 4(3 + 7)$

**k.** $5 \cdot [(3 + 9) + 7] \overset{(1)}{=} 5 \cdot [(9 + 3) + 7]$

$\overset{(2)}{=} 5 \cdot [9 + (3 + 7)]$

$\overset{(3)}{=} 5 \cdot (9 + 10)$

**l.** $5[(3 + 4) + 6] \overset{(1)}{=} 5[3 + (4 + 6)]$

$\overset{(2)}{=} 5[(4 + 6) + 3]$

$\overset{(3)}{=} 5(4 + 6) + 5(3)$

$\overset{(4)}{=} 5(4) + 5(6) + 5(3)$

**m.** $1 \times [6 \times 3 + 6 \times 7] \overset{(1)}{=} 1 \times [6(3 + 7)]$

$\overset{(2)}{=} [6(3 + 7)] \times 1$

$\overset{(3)}{=} 6(3 + 7)$

## 7 · Inverse Operations

From your study of arithmetic you know that the most frequently used operations are addition, subtraction, multiplication, and division. The operations of addition and subtraction are closely related to each other. To see this relationship, observe the following examples:

1. $5 - 2 = 3$           1′. $3 + 2 = 5$
2. $17 - 3 = 14$         2′. $14 + 3 = 17$
3. $3.5 - .7 = 2.8$      3′. $2.8 + .7 = 3.5$
4. $\frac{1}{3} - \frac{1}{4} = \frac{1}{12}$    4′. $\frac{1}{12} + \frac{1}{4} = \frac{1}{3}$

From the examples above you can see that every subtraction problem can be changed into a related addition problem. Actually, if you did not know how to subtract, you could still find answers to subtraction problems. For instance, the example $17 - 9 = ?$ would be changed to $? + 9 = 17$. Now, you need to answer the question, "what number added to 9 gives 17?" In this case you will have no difficulty in giving the answer immediately. In more difficult problems, you might need to try a few numbers before finding the one which will work.

We can again go back to our frames to portray the relationship which exists between addition and subtraction. It can be shown as follows:

$$\text{If } \square - \triangle = \bigcirc \text{, then } \bigcirc + \triangle = \square.$$

We say that subtraction is the inverse operation of addition.

There is a similar relationship between the operations of multiplication and division. Observe the examples below to see what this relationship is.

1. $16 \div 2 = 8$ or $\frac{16}{2} = 8$     1′. $8 \cdot 2 = 16$
2. $34 \div 4 = 8\frac{1}{2}$ or $\frac{34}{4} = 8\frac{1}{2}$     2′. $8\frac{1}{2} \cdot 4 = 34$
3. $\frac{1}{2} \div \frac{1}{3} = \frac{3}{2}$ or $\frac{\frac{1}{2}}{\frac{1}{3}} = \frac{3}{2}$     3′. $\frac{3}{2} \cdot \frac{1}{3} = \frac{1}{2}$
4. $.5 \div 3 = \frac{1}{6}$ or $\frac{.5}{3} = \frac{1}{6}$     4′. $\frac{1}{6} \cdot 3 = .5$

From the above you can see that a division problem can be changed into a related multiplication problem. For instance, the answer to example **1,** "What is the answer when 16 is divided by 2?" is the same as the answer to the question, "What number multiplied by 2 gives 16?" Formulate for yourself questions to fit examples **2, 3** and **4** above.

Using the frames again, we can portray the relationship between multiplication and division as follows:

$$\text{If } \square \div \triangle = \bigcirc$$
$$\text{then } \bigcirc \cdot \triangle = \square$$

We say that multiplication is the inverse operation of division.

You will note that there is a close similarity between the two frame expressions above. The only difference is in the operation signs. Now, using $\odot$ and $\oplus$ we can write a general expression for two operations which are inverses of each other.

$$\text{``}\odot \text{ is an inverse of } \oplus \text{'' means}$$
$$\text{if } \square \odot \triangle = \bigcirc \text{ then } \bigcirc \oplus \triangle = \square$$

You should replace the frames $\square$, $\bigcirc$, and $\triangle$ above by numerals and the symbols $\odot$ and $\oplus$ by operation symbols to see what pairs of operations have the inverse relationship.

# EXERCISES

Change each of the following subtraction problems into a related addition problem, and solve it.

**EXAMPLE**  $\quad \frac{1}{2} - \frac{1}{3} = \triangle$

**SOLUTION** 
$$\triangle + \frac{1}{3} = \frac{1}{2}$$
$$\triangle + \frac{2}{6} = \frac{3}{6}$$
$$\frac{1}{6} + \frac{2}{6} = \frac{3}{6}$$

Therefore, $\frac{1}{6}$ in place of $\triangle$ makes the statement true.
$$\frac{1}{2} - \frac{1}{3} = \frac{1}{6}$$

1.  $17 - 12 = \square$
2.  $25 - 5 = \triangle$
3.  $13 - .5 = \bigcirc$
4.  $.73 - .03 = \square$
5.  $998 - 97 = \triangle$
6.  $21\frac{3}{4} - 19\frac{1}{4} = \bigcirc$
7.  $\frac{3}{4} - \frac{1}{2} = \square$
8.  $\frac{3}{7} - \frac{1}{3} = \triangle$
9.  $14 - \triangle = 5$
10. $111 - \square = 11$
11. $\square - 10 = 5$
12. $\bigcirc - 73 = 71$
13. $\frac{1}{2} - \square = \frac{1}{4}$
14. $.75 - \triangle = .03$
15. $\bigcirc - .99 = .02$
16. $\triangle - \frac{3}{7} = \frac{1}{5}$

Change each of the following division exercises into a related multiplication exercise, and solve it. Two of them have no answer!

**EXAMPLE 1**     $48 \div 6 = \bigcirc$

**SOLUTION**      $\bigcirc \cdot 6 = 48$

$8 \cdot 6 = 48$

Therefore, 8 in place of $\bigcirc$ makes the statement true.

$48 \div 6 = 8$

**EXAMPLE 2**     $\frac{8}{9} \div \frac{2}{3} = \triangle$

**SOLUTION**      $\triangle \cdot \frac{2}{3} = \frac{8}{9}$

$\frac{4}{3} \cdot \frac{2}{3} = \frac{8}{9}$

Therefore, $\frac{4}{3}$ in place of $\triangle$ makes the statement true.

$\frac{8}{9} \div \frac{2}{3} = \frac{4}{3}$

17. $40 \div 8 = \triangle$

18. $625 \div 25 = \bigcirc$

19. $56 \div 7 = \square$

20. $156 \div 13 = \bigcirc$

21. $.5 \div 1 = \triangle$

22. $.3 \div .1 = \square$

23. $\frac{1}{4} \div \frac{1}{2} = \bigcirc$

24. $\frac{9}{32} \div \frac{3}{4} = \triangle$

25. $280 \div \bigcirc = 35$

26. $165 \div \square = 5$

27. $\triangle \div 11 = 133$

28. $\square \div \frac{3}{7} = \frac{2}{5}$

29. $\frac{3}{2} \div \triangle = \frac{1}{2}$

30. $\bigcirc \div 1.2 = 14.7$

31. $101 \div \square = \frac{1}{2}$

32. $\frac{0}{2} = \triangle$

33. $\frac{3}{0} = \square$

34. $\frac{0}{7} = \bigcirc$

35. $\frac{11}{0} = \triangle$

Let us invent two new operations: *alphation* and *betation*. All you know about these two operations is that one is the inverse of the other. The symbol for alphation is $\alpha$ and the symbol for betation is $\beta$.

Change each of the alphation problems below to a related betation problem.

**EXAMPLE**       $7 \, \alpha \, 3 = 10\frac{1}{2}$

**SOLUTION**      A related betation problem is

$10\frac{1}{2} \, \beta \, 3 = 7$

36. $2 \, \alpha \, 2 = 2$

37. $3 \, \alpha \, 4 = 6$

38. $12 \, \alpha \, 5 = 30$

39. $\frac{1}{2} \, \alpha \, \frac{1}{3} = \frac{1}{12}$

40. $.1 \, \alpha \, .02 = .001$

41. $50 \, \alpha \, 10 = 250$

42. $\frac{2}{3} \, \alpha \, \frac{1}{3} = \frac{1}{9}$

43. $10 \, \alpha \, .01 = .05$

44. $4 \, \alpha \, 8 = 16$

45. $\frac{1}{3} \, \alpha \, \frac{1}{4} = \frac{1}{24}$

**46.** Look carefully at your answers in Exercises 36-45. Can you tell how the operations of alphation and betation are related to the operations you are familiar with. That is, change the expressions below to expressions involving the familiar operations:

$$\square \; \alpha \; \bigcirc \; = \; ?$$
$$\square \; \beta \; \bigcirc \; = \; ?$$

## VOCABULARY

associative (30)

braces (26)

brackets (26)

closure (33)

commutative (29)

commutative operation (30)

counter-example (37)

distributive (36)

inverse operations (42)

non-commutative operations (30)

parentheses (26)

punctuation symbols (26)

········································································································

## REVIEW EXERCISES

**1.** Simplify each of the following:

**a.** $4[13(5 + 7)]$

**b.** $7\{[6(9) - 8] \div 23\}$

**c.** $\frac{1}{2}[(\frac{1}{2} - \frac{1}{3}) \div \frac{1}{6}]$

**d.** $(3.5 + 1.6)[(5.1 - 1.3)(5.1 + 1.3)]$

**e.** $1.1\{[1.1(1.1 + 1.1) + 1.1]1.1\}$

**f.** $3 + 7 \times 4$

**g.** $12 \div 4 \times 2 \div 6$

**h.** $21 - 2 \cdot 3 \cdot 3$

**i.** $5 \cdot 0 + 4 - 2 \cdot 2$

**j.** $17 + 2 - 6 - 2 + 4$

**2.** Name the principle or principles used in going from one statement to another:

**a.** $[2 \cdot 0 + 3(4 + 6)] \times 7 \overset{(1)}{=} [0 + 3(4 + 6)] \times 7$

$$\overset{(2)}{=} [3(4 + 6)] \times 7$$

$$\overset{(3)}{=} 7 \times [3(4 + 6)]$$

$$\overset{(4)}{=} 7[3(4) + 3(6)]$$

**b.** $13 \times [(4 \times 7) \times 11] \overset{(1)}{=} 13 \times [4 \times (7 \times 11)]$

$\overset{(2)}{=} 13 \times [(7 \times 11) \times 4]$

$\overset{(3)}{=} 13 \times [7 \times (11 \times 4)]$

$\overset{(4)}{=} [7 \times (11 \times 4)] \times 13$

$\overset{(5)}{=} [(7 \times 11) \times 4] \times 13$

**c.** $7[(5 + 3) + 6] \overset{(1)}{=} 7[(3 + 5) + 6]$

$\overset{(2)}{=} 7[3 + (5 + 6)]$

$\overset{(3)}{=} 7(3) + 7(5 + 6)$

3. Phrase the commutative, associative, and distributive principles in your own words. Give a numerical illustration of each principle.

4. Replace the frames $\triangle$, $\square$, and $\bigcirc$ with numerals to obtain true statements. (In some cases there is more than one such replacement, in one case there is none!)

   **a.** $\triangle + 7 = 7 + \triangle$          **b.** $6 \cdot \square = \square \cdot 6$

   **c.** $7 \cdot (6 + \bigcirc) = 7 \cdot (6) + 7 \cdot (13)$

   **d.** $\triangle + (3 + \square) = (\triangle + 3) + \square$

   **e.** $2 \cdot \triangle + 2 \cdot \bigcirc = 2 \cdot (\triangle + \bigcirc)$

   **f.** $(3 \times \square) \times 13 = 3 \times (\square \times 13)$

   **g.** $13 \times (11 + 7) = 13 \times \square + 13 \times \triangle$

   **h.** $\bigcirc \times [6 + \triangle] = [6 + \triangle] \times \bigcirc$

   **i.** $4 \cdot \triangle + 17 = 17 + 4 \cdot \triangle$

   **j.** $\frac{4}{3} - \frac{4}{5} = \triangle$     **l.** $\frac{2}{3} \div \frac{1}{4} = \triangle$     **n.** $\frac{5}{6} = \triangle$

   **k.** $\square - 13 = 39$     **m.** $\frac{1}{5} \div \square = \frac{1}{20}$     **o.** $\frac{9}{6} = \square$

5. For each problem determine whether the given set of numbers is closed under the given operations:

   **a.** Set: $\{\frac{1}{2}, 0\}$
   Operations: addition and multiplication

   **b.** Set: all natural numbers and all fractions
   Operations: addition, subtraction, multiplication, and division

   **c.** Set: $\{1, 10, 100, 1000, 10000, \cdots\}$
   Operations: multiplication and division

   **d.** Set: all even natural numbers
   Operation: average of a pair of numbers

   **e.** Set: $\{\cdots 16, 8, 4, 2, 1, \frac{1}{2}, \frac{1}{4}, \frac{1}{8}, \cdots\}$
   Operations: addition and multiplication

# CHAPTER TEST

**1.** Write the simplest numeral for each of the following:

   **a.** $6 \cdot [3 + 5 \cdot 6 - 2]$

   **b.** $[5(2) + 11] \div 3$

   **c.** $4 \times \{78 - [5 \cdot 4 + (15 \div 3)] \times (3)\} \cdot 2$

**2.** Name the principle illustrated by each of the following:

   **a.** $3\frac{1}{3} + 7 = 7 + 3\frac{1}{3}$

   **b.** $(2 \cdot 4) \cdot 15 = 2 \cdot (4 \cdot 15)$

   **c.** $(3 + 7) + 11 = 3 + (7 + 11)$

   **d.** $6 \cdot 7 + 6 \cdot 11 = 6(7 + 11)$

   **e.** $(3 \cdot 7) \cdot 2\frac{1}{3} = 2\frac{1}{3} \cdot (3 \cdot 7)$

   **f.** $5 \cdot (6 + 13) = 5 \cdot 6 + 5 \cdot 13$

   **g.** $(13 + 79) + 0 = 13 + 79$

   **h.** $(.6 \times 39) \times 1 = .6 \times 39$

   **i.** $6[(5 + 7) + 9] = 6[9 + (5 + 7)]$

   **j.** $5 + (6 \cdot 7 + 6 \cdot 11) = 5 + 6(7 + 11)$

   **k.** $(4 \times 13) \times 0 = 0$

**3.** In the following exercises, the frames $\triangle$, $\square$, and $\bigcirc$ hold a place for a numeral. Give replacements for $\triangle$, $\square$, and $\bigcirc$ to obtain true statements. (In one case there is no such replacement! In some cases there are several.)

   **a.** $13 \times (\triangle + 4) = 13 \times 11 + 13 \times 4$

   **b.** $\triangle \times (6 + \square) = 7\frac{1}{2} \times 6 + 7\frac{1}{2} \times 17$

   **c.** $4\frac{1}{2} \times (\square + \bigcirc) = 4\frac{1}{2} \times 9 + 4\frac{1}{2} \times 2\frac{1}{3}$

   **d.** $(7 \cdot \triangle) \cdot 3\frac{1}{2} = 7 \cdot (5 \cdot 3\frac{1}{2})$

   **e.** $\triangle + \frac{1}{4} = \frac{1}{3}$

   **f.** $11 - \square = 4\frac{1}{4}$

   **g.** $\frac{0}{5} = \triangle$

   **h.** $113 \div \square = 22.6$

   **i.** $\bigcirc - \frac{2}{9} = \frac{3}{5}$

   **j.** $\frac{6}{0} = \square$

   **k.** $\triangle + (7 + 6) = (7 + 6) + \triangle$

   **l.** $(3 + \square) \div 1 = 3 + \square$

   **m.** $17\frac{1}{3} + 6\frac{1}{2} \times 2\frac{1}{2} + 6\frac{1}{2} \times 4\frac{1}{4} = 17\frac{1}{3} + \triangle(2\frac{1}{2} + 4\frac{1}{4})$

   **n.** $5 \cdot \triangle + 10 \cdot \square = (\triangle + 2 \cdot \square) \cdot 5$

   **o.** $3(\triangle + \square + \bigcirc) = 3 \cdot \triangle + 3 \cdot \square + 3 \cdot \bigcirc$

**4.** Answer the following questions and give an example to help justify your answer:

**a.** Is multiplication distributive with respect to subtraction?
**b.** Is subtraction distributive with respect to division?
**c.** Is subtraction associative?

**5.** Name the principle involved in going from one statement to the next:

**a.** $1 \times [7 \times 6 + 7 \times 11] \overset{(1)}{=} 1 \times [7 \times (6 + 11)]$
$$\overset{(2)}{=} [7 \times (6 + 11)] \times 1$$
$$\overset{(3)}{=} 7 \times (6 + 11)$$

**b.** $(3 + 5\frac{1}{2}) \cdot 5 + 9 \cdot 6 \overset{(1)}{=} 9 \cdot 6 + (3 + 5\frac{1}{2}) \cdot 5$
$$\overset{(2)}{=} 9 \cdot 6 + 5 \cdot (3 + 5\frac{1}{2})$$
$$\overset{(3)}{=} 9 \cdot 6 + (5 \cdot 3 + 5 \cdot 5\frac{1}{2})$$

**6.** Tell whether every replacement of $\triangle$, $\square$, and $\bigcirc$ by the arithmetic number names produces a true sentence:

**a.** If $\triangle - \square = \bigcirc$, then $\bigcirc + \square = \triangle$
**b.** If $\square \div \bigcirc = \triangle$, then $\bigcirc = \square \cdot \triangle$

**7.** Suppose that $\odot$ and $\oplus$ are inverse operations. Label each statement as true or false:

**a.** If $\frac{1}{3} \odot \frac{1}{2} = \frac{5}{6}$, then $\frac{5}{6} \oplus \frac{1}{3} = \frac{1}{2}$
**b.** If $\frac{3}{8} \oplus \frac{1}{3} = \frac{3}{4}$, then $\frac{3}{4} \odot \frac{1}{3} = \frac{3}{8}$

**8.** Is the set of odd natural numbers closed under **a.** Addition? **b.** Subtraction? **c.** Multiplication? **d.** Division?

## CUMULATIVE REVIEW

★**1.** Given a universal set containing seven elements and two subsets $A$ and $B$. $A$ contains four elements, $B$ contains two elements and $A \cap B$ contains one element. Indicate how many elements there are in the following sets:

**a.** $A \cup B$ **b.** $\overline{A}$ **c.** $\overline{A \cap B}$ **d.** $\overline{B}$ **e.** $\overline{A} \cap B$

**2.** Are sets $A$ and $C$ matching sets?

$$A = \{g, k, l, m, n, r\}$$
$$C = \{t, p, g, y, d\}$$

**3.** Give examples of three sets $G$, $K$, and $L$ such that $G$ and $K$ are both subsets of $L$, and also $K$ is a subset of $G$.

**4.** Given a universal set $U$ with $B$, $H$, and $M$ subsets of $U$, as follows:

$$U = \{4, 6, 7, 9, 11, 13, 19, 21\}$$
$$B = \{4, 7, 9, 11, 13\}$$
$$H = \{4, 9, 13\}$$
$$M = \{9, 6, 11, 19, 21\}$$

Determine the following sets:

**a.** $B \cap H$      **d.** $(M \cup H) \cap B$

**b.** $B \cup M$      ★**e.** $\overline{H}$

★**c.** $\overline{H \cap M}$      ★**f.** $\overline{H \cup M}$

**g.** Using Venn diagrams depict the sets described in **c** and **f**.

**5.** Give one example demonstrating that

**a.** Addition is *not* distributive with respect to multiplication.

**b.** Division is *not* distributive with respect to multiplication.

**6.** Replace $\square$, $\triangle$, and $\bigcirc$ with number names to obtain true sentences:

**a.** $\square(7 + 3) = 35 + 15$      **c.** $(1.9 + \triangle) + .6 = 3.7 + .6$

**b.** $\bigcirc \cdot \frac{1}{2} + \square \cdot \frac{1}{2} = 30 + 6.5$      **d.** $(\bigcirc + \frac{1}{2}) + \frac{1}{4} = \frac{1}{4} + 13\frac{3}{4}$

# BIBLIOGRAPHY

Bakst, A., *Mathematics—Its Magic and Mastery*, D. Van Nostrand, Toronto, 1952, "Numerals and Numeration"—pages 1–30, "Cryptography"—pages 79–101.

Bakst, A., *Mathematical Puzzles and Pastimes*, D. Van Nostrand, Toronto, 1954, "Notch Arithmetic"—pages 22–43.

De Grazia, J., *Math is Fun*, Emerson Books, New York, 1954

Johnson, D. A., and Glenn, W. A., *Sets, Sentences, and Operations*, Webster, St. Louis, 1960, pages 48–58.

Johnson, D. A., and Glenn, W. A., *Understanding Numeration Systems*, Webster, St. Louis, 1960.

School Mathematics Study Group, *Mathematics for High School: First Course in Algebra, Part 1 (Revised Edition)*, SMSG, New Haven, 1960, pages 23–34.

University of Illinois Committee on School Mathematics, *Unit 1*, "*The Arithmetic of Real Numbers*," UICSM, Urbana, Illinois, 1960.

# 3

# The Real Numbers

## I · The Number Line

From your previous experience, you no doubt have some idea of what a straight line is. Now that you know something about sets, we will consider a line to be a set of points. To be sure, for a set of points to be a straight line they have to be arranged in a certain fashion. Here is a picture of a straight line:

The arrows on both ends suggest that there is no end to this set of points. We can extend the picture as far as we please in either direction and all the points thus included will be on the line.

It is *convenient* to assign numbers to the points on a line so that we can refer to the points by the use of numbers. To do this, we choose one point and assign to it the number 0. Then we mark off equal distances to the left and right of the point corresponding to the number 0 and assign numbers to them, as in the picture below.

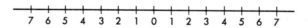

Now you will notice that there are two points corresponding to each number (except 0). Thus, if you should want to call your friend's attention to the point corresponding to, say, the number 4, he would not know which point you intended. We would like to have only one point for each number. Conversely, each point should have only one number associated with it. When this is accomplished, we say that we have a one-to-one correspondence between points on the number line and the numbers.

50

In order to establish a one-to-one correspondence between the points
on the number line and the numbers, we will have to make a distinction
between the points to the left of the point corresponding to 0 and those to
its right. Let us put letters of identification above the points on the line,
and agree to write the numerals below the line, preceded by the *raised
symbol* + for the points to the right of zero and by the *raised symbol* − for
the points to the left of zero.

$$\begin{array}{ccccccccccccccc} J & E & H & C & L & K & F & A & N & P & M & I & B & G & D \end{array}$$
$$^-7\ ^-6\ ^-5\ ^-4\ ^-3\ ^-2\ ^-1\ \ 0\ ^+1\ ^+2\ ^+3\ ^+4\ ^+5\ ^+6\ ^+7$$

Now there is only one point corresponding to a given number. For example,
point $N$ corresponds to the number $^+1$ (positive 1) and $H$ corresponds to
the number $^-5$ (negative 5). Conversely, there is only one number corresponding to a given point. For example, the number $^-2$ (negative 2)
corresponds to the point $K$ and the number $^+7$ (positive 7) corresponds
to the point $D$.

We call numbers of this type **directed numbers.** By means of directed
numbers, we can answer not only the question "how many?" but also the
question "in what direction?"

For example, instead of saying "5 degrees above zero" we may say "$^+5$
degrees" (positive 5 degrees); or, instead of saying "17 degrees below zero"
we may say "$^-17$ degrees" (negative 17 degrees).

Having directed numbers, we are now in a position to discuss more
fully a one-to-one correspondence between the points on the number line
and the new numbers.

negative direction   positive direction

$$\begin{array}{ccccccccccccccc} J & E & H & C & L & K & F & A & N & P & M & I & B & G & D \end{array}$$
$$^-7\ ^-6\ ^-5\ ^-4\ ^-3\ ^-2\ ^-1\ \ 0\ ^+1\ ^+2\ ^+3\ ^+4\ ^+5\ ^+6\ ^+7$$

We must understand that the choice of the direction to the right to be the
positive direction is quite arbitrary. We could choose the direction to the
left as the positive direction; we could even choose to picture the line in a
vertical position, or slanted in some other direction. But once a direction is
chosen as positive, the opposite direction must be the negative direction.
You will note that the symbols + and − are now used to mean two
different things; + may mean to add or it may mean that a positive
number is used. Explain the two meanings of the symbol −.

For example: $^+3 - {}^-4$ means "subtract negative four from positive three."

To make this distinction quite clear we will elevate the symbols "+" and "−" whenever they are used to indicate a positive or negative number, respectively. To indicate addition or subtraction, the symbols will not be elevated.

# EXERCISES

Think of at least ten situations in which the idea of a direction and its opposite can be used. Then choose one of the directions to be positive and the opposite direction to be negative. Describe a specific case in words, then restate it using directed numbers.

**EXAMPLE**

**SOLUTION**

Situation: business transactions in which gain or loss may take place

Directions: gain—positive

loss—negative

A case: gain of 5 dollars, followed by loss of $12\frac{1}{2}$ dollars

Directed numbers: $^+5$ dollars plus $^-12\frac{1}{2}$ dollars

## 2 · Integers

In the first chapter you worked with the counting numbers, or natural numbers. These are whole numbers 1, 2, 3, 4, 5, and so on, which we use to do our counting. You are so used to these numbers that it does not take much thought on your part to tell, for example, which one of two given natural numbers is greater.

For example, of the two numbers 195 and 375, obviously 375 is greater than 195.

Now we have a system of numbers which consists of positive whole numbers $^+1$, $^+2$, $^+3$, $^+4$, $^+5$, $^+6$, and so on, negative whole numbers $^-1$, $^-2$, $^-3$, $^-4$, $^-5$, $^-6$, and so on, and the number 0. We say that all of these numbers, together, make up the set of numbers called the **integers.** Having the integers, we now should be able to compare them. That is, we need to be able to tell which of two given integers is the greater. To decide this, we will use the number line and agree that in comparing any two integers the one which is farther to the right is the greater.

Suppose the two given numbers are ⁻5 and ⁺1. We locate the two points corresponding to the two numbers: point $H$ corresponds to ⁻5, point $N$ corresponds to ⁺1. Point $N$ is to the right of the point $H$, therefore ⁺1 is greater than ⁻5.

We shall use the symbol $>$ to mean *greater than*, and the symbol $<$ to mean *less than*. Thus ⁺1 $>$ ⁻5 is read "positive one is greater than negative five." We can also write ⁻5 $<$ ⁺1, which is read "negative five is less than positive one."

You see that the number line comes in very handy when you need to compare two numbers. Of course, it would be impractical to have a picture of a line long enough to locate on it points very far away from the **origin** (the point corresponding to the number 0), but once you get the concept well in mind, you should have no trouble telling which one of two given numbers is the greater.

Use the picture of the number line above to verify each of the following. One of the statements below is false. Find it!

$$^-6 < {}^-5$$
$$0 < {}^+6$$
$$^-1 > {}^-5$$
$$^+7 < {}^-7$$
$$0 > {}^-1$$
$$^-5 > {}^-7$$
$$0 < {}^+1$$
$$^+1 > {}^-1$$

Having the two symbols of inequality, $<$ and $>$, we can obtain two more new symbols: $\not<$, which means *not less than*, and $\not>$, which means *not greater than*.

Examine each of the statements below. One is false. Find it!

$$^-3 \not< {}^-5$$
$$0 \not> {}^+7$$
$$^-1 \not> {}^+3$$
$$^+2 \not< {}^+2$$
$$^-1 \not< 0$$
$$^+25 \not> {}^+100$$

Of course, you probably can easily guess that the symbol "$\neq$" means *is not equal to.* For example, $^+3 \neq {}^+4$ and $^+6 + {}^+3 \neq {}^+6 + {}^+7$ are true statements, while $^+6 \neq {}^+6$ is a false statement. Explain.

We can obtain two more symbols of comparison by combining " $<$ " with " $=$ " and " $>$ " with " $=$ ".

The two symbols thus obtained are $\cdot\leq$ (read "is less than or equal to,") and $\geq$ (read "is greater than or equal to.") For example, $^+5 \leq {}^+7$ (read "positive five is less than or equal to positive seven") and $^+3 \geq {}^+3$ (read "three is greater than or equal to positive three") are true statements.

Note that each statement above consists of two parts. For example, the first statement has the parts:

    (1)   positive five is less than positive seven
    (2)   positive five is equal to positive seven

The two parts are connected by the word *or.* We have agreed to consider the whole statement true if one of the parts is true. Also the whole statement is true if both parts are true. If both parts are false, the entire statement is false. Thus, $^+4 \geq {}^+7$ (read "positive four is greater than or equal to positive seven") is false, because "positive four is greater than positive seven" is false and "positive four is equal to positive seven" is false.

## EXERCISES

1. List the letters **a** through **p** on your paper; then indicate by writing F or T whether each corresponding statement is false or true.

   **a.** $^-5 \neq {}^+5$                     **i.** $^+6 \geq {}^+8$
   **b.** $^-2 > {}^+3$                      **j.** $^-3 \leq {}^-3$
   **c.** $0 < {}^-17$                      **k.** $^-2 \geq {}^-2$
   **d.** $^-8 > {}^+11$                   **l.** $^-100 \leq {}^+100$
   **e.** $^-7 \not> {}^+8$                   **m.** $0 \not> 0$
   **f.** $^-1 \not< {}^+1$                   **n.** $0 < {}^-1150$
   **g.** $^-10 \not< {}^-15$               **o.** $0 > {}^+25$
   **h.** $^+5 \leq {}^+7$                   **p.** $^+10 \not< {}^+10$

2. Replace the frames with integer names to obtain
       (1)   a true statement
       (2)   a false statement

**EXAMPLE**         $\triangle < {}^+2$

**SOLUTION**      (1)    $^-1 < {}^+2$ is a true statement
                         (2)    $^+5 < {}^+2$ is a false statement

(Note:  There are many different replacements to produce true statements, and many different replacements to produce false statements. You need to give only one replacement for each case.)

a.  $\bigcirc \neq {}^-3$  
b.  $\triangle < {}^-1$  
c.  $\square > 0$  
d.  ${}^-2 \not< \square$  
e.  ${}^-12 \not> \triangle$  
f.  ${}^+5 \leq \bigcirc$  

g.  $\square \leq {}^-1$  
h.  ${}^-1000 \neq \triangle$  
i.  ${}^+125 \not> \bigcirc$  
j.  $\square \not> {}^+12$  
k.  $\triangle \geq 0$  
l.  $\bigcirc \leq {}^-17$  

3.  True or false?

a.  ${}^+3 = {}^+4$ or ${}^+7 < {}^+9$  
b.  ${}^-5 < {}^+3$ and ${}^+9 \neq {}^-7$  
c.  ${}^-13 \leq {}^+4$ or ${}^+5 \leq {}^+5$  
d.  ${}^+6 > {}^+2$ and ${}^-6 < {}^+3$  
e.  ${}^+6 \neq {}^+5$ or ${}^-3 = {}^+3$  
f.  ${}^-11 < {}^+9$ and ${}^+1 < {}^+2$  

g.  ${}^-9 \leq {}^-8$ or ${}^-12 > {}^-3$  
h.  $0 < {}^+3$ and ${}^+4 \leq {}^+4$  
i.  ${}^+7 \not< {}^+6$ or ${}^-15 > {}^-19$  
j.  ${}^+3 < {}^+4$ and ${}^+1 \leq {}^+2$  
k.  ${}^-9 \not> {}^+3$ or ${}^-7 \neq {}^-6$  
l.  ${}^+4 > {}^+12$ and ${}^-6 < {}^-7$  

4.  Replace the frames with numerals to obtain true statements. In the cases where  there  is  more than one such replacement, give only one replacement.

a.  $\square \neq {}^+5$ or ${}^+6 < {}^+9$  
b.  ${}^+1 < {}^+2$ and ${}^-6 < \triangle$  
c.  $\bigcirc > {}^+3$ or ${}^-11 \not< {}^+11$  

d.  ${}^+15 \geq {}^+8$ and $\square \neq {}^-7$  
e.  $\triangle \leq {}^-2$ or ${}^+5 > {}^+6$  
f.  ${}^-6 \neq {}^+6$ and ${}^+5 \geq \triangle$  

# 3 · Absolute Value

Look at the pairs of numbers listed below:

$$
\begin{array}{rr}
{}^+5, & {}^-5 \\
{}^-3, & {}^+3 \\
{}^+100, & {}^-100 \\
{}^-17, & {}^+17
\end{array}
$$

You should not have any trouble adding other pairs which would fit into this pattern.

In each pair above:

$$
\begin{array}{l}
{}^-5 \text{ is the opposite of } {}^+5 \\
{}^+3 \text{ is the opposite of } {}^-3 \\
{}^-100 \text{ is the opposite of } {}^+100 \\
{}^+17 \text{ is the opposite of } {}^-17
\end{array}
$$

You have probably discovered that the opposite of a positive number is a negative number and the opposite of a negative number is a positive number. Zero is the only number which is its own opposite.

It is frequently useful to associate with each directed number its absolute value. For example, the absolute value of $^-5$ is $^+5$, the absolute value of $^-7$ is $^+7$, the absolute value of $^+3$ is $^+3$, the absolute value of $^+5$ is $^+5$, and the absolute value of 0 is 0.

Thus, the **absolute value** of a positive number is the number itself, whereas the absolute value of a negative number is its opposite (which, of course, is a positive number). To abbreviate, we write

$$| \, ^-5 \, | = {}^+5 \quad \text{(read ``the absolute value of negative five is positive five'')}$$

$$| \, ^+5 \, | = {}^+5 \quad \text{(read ``the absolute value of positive five is positive five'')}$$

$$| \, ^+3 \, | = {}^+3 \quad \text{(read ``the absolute value of positive three is positive three'')}$$

$$| \, 0 \, | = 0 \quad \text{(read ``the absolute value of zero is zero'')}$$

Generally, we can say:

Whenever $\triangle$ is replaced by a name of a positive number or zero, $| \, \triangle \, | = \triangle$.
Whenever $\triangle$ is replaced by a name of a negative number, $| \, \triangle \, | =$ the opposite of $\triangle$.

## EXERCISES

1. List the letters **a** through **t** on your paper; then indicate by writing F or T whether each corresponding statement is false or true:

   **a.** $^-2 \neq {}^+2$

   **b.** $| \, ^-2 \, | \neq | \, ^+2 \, |$

   **c.** $^-7 > {}^+8$

   **d.** $| \, ^-7 \, | > {}^+8$

   **e.** $| \, ^+17 \, | < 0$

   **f.** $| \, ^-21 \, | < | \, ^+20 \, |$

   **g.** $| \, 0 \, | > {}^-2$

   **h.** $^-3 \not> {}^-5$

   **i.** $^-1 < | \, ^-17 \, |$

   **j.** $^-3 > {}^-256$

   **k.** $| \, ^-10 \, | \neq | \, ^+10 \, |$

   **l.** $| \, ^-156 \, | = | \, ^+156 \, |$

   **m.** $0 < | \, ^-1137 \, |$

   **n.** $| \, ^+11 \, | > | \, ^+2 \, |$

   **o.** $| \, ^-211 \, | \not< | \, ^+10 \, |$

   **p.** $| \, ^-100 \, | \not> | \, ^+100 \, |$

   **q.** $| \, ^-337 \, | < | \, ^-2 \, |$

   **r.** $0 \neq | \, 0 \, |$

   **s.** $| \, ^-1 \, | < | \, ^-100 \, |$

   **t.** $| \, ^-2 \, | \not> | \, ^+2 \, |$

**2.** On your paper, replace the frames with integer names to obtain

        (1)  a true statement
        (2)  a false statement

**a.** $\bigcirc \neq {}^+3$                   **h.** ${}^-6 \not< \triangle$

**b.** $\triangle > {}^+4$                   **i.** $\bigcirc < {}^-5$

**c.** $\square \not> {}^-6$                   **j.** $|\triangle| < {}^+2$

**d.** ${}^+4 < |\triangle|$                 **k.** $\square \leq |{}^-100|$

**e.** $\bigcirc < |{}^-7|$                **l.** $|{}^-10| \geq \triangle$

**f.** $|{}^+3| \neq \triangle$               **m.** $|{}^+15| \leq \bigcirc$

**g.** $|{}^-21| > \square$               **n.** $\triangle \geq |{}^-1|$

## 4 · Addition of Integers

Once new numbers are invented, man is eager to put them to use. You know from your study of arithmetic that you cannot use numbers to good advantage unless you know how to operate on these numbers. You need to know at least how to add, subtract, multiply, and divide numbers.

    We shall first learn to add directed numbers. For this, we shall use the number line.

We shall imagine making moves along the number line. A move to the right will be described by a positive number and a move to the left by a negative number. Study the following examples:

   (1) A move from $A$ to $M$ is described by ${}^+3$. (Explain why.)

   (2) A move from $N$ to $B$ is described by ${}^+4$.

   (3) A move from $C$ to $F$ is described by ${}^+3$.

   (4) A move from $E$ to $B$ is described by ${}^+11$.

   (5) A move from $A$ to $C$ is described by ${}^-4$.

   (6) A move from $L$ to $E$ is described by ${}^-3$.

   (7) A move from $B$ to $I$ is described by ${}^-1$.

   (8) A move from $M$ to $H$ is described by ${}^-8$.

    How would you describe a move from $J$ to $D$? From $D$ to $J$? From $J$ to $A$? From $D$ to $A$?

Now let us use the idea of moves in adding directed numbers. Suppose we have the following problem:

$$^+2 + {}^+3 = ?$$

Study the picture below until you understand what has been done.

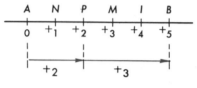

Therefore,                        $^+2 + {}^+3 = {}^+5$

Study each of the problems and pictures below to see how they are worked.

**EXAMPLE**        $^-1 + {}^-4 = ?$

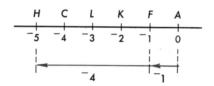

**SOLUTION**        $^-1 + {}^-4 = {}^-5$

**EXAMPLE**        $^+3 + {}^-1 = ?$

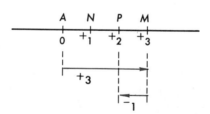

**SOLUTION**        $^+3 + {}^-1 = {}^+2$

**EXAMPLE**        $^+2 + {}^-5 = ?$

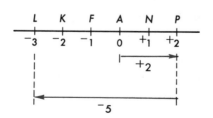

**SOLUTION**        $^+2 + {}^-5 = {}^-3$

# EXERCISES

1. Find the sum in each of the following, using the number line as in the examples above, as long as you feel you need it.

| | |
|---|---|
| **a.** $^+1 + {}^+5$ | **k.** $^+3 + {}^-4$ |
| **b.** $^+3 + {}^+3$ | **l.** $^-4 + {}^+3$ |
| **c.** $0 + {}^+5$ | **m.** $^-4 + {}^-7$ |
| **d.** $0 + {}^+7$ | **n.** $^-7 + {}^-4$ |
| **e.** $0 + {}^-5$ | **o.** $^-2 + {}^+6$ |
| **f.** $0 + {}^-3$ | **p.** $^+6 + {}^-2$ |
| **g.** $^-1 + {}^-2$ | **q.** $0 + {}^-7$ |
| **h.** $^-2 + {}^-4$ | **r.** $^-7 + 0$ |
| **i.** $^-1 + {}^+7$ | **s.** $^-8 + {}^-1$ |
| **j.** $^-7 + {}^+2$ | **t.** $^-1 + {}^-8$ |

2.
| | |
|---|---|
| **a.** $^-19 + {}^+13$ | **i.** $^+573 + {}^+335$ |
| **b.** $^+91 + {}^-47$ | **j.** $^+13 + {}^-173$ |
| **c.** $^-16 + {}^-19$ | **k.** $^+105 + {}^-205$ |
| **d.** $^-16 + {}^+42$ | **l.** $^-366 + {}^-42$ |
| **e.** $^+37 + {}^-13$ | **m.** $^-378 + {}^-112$ |
| **f.** $^+42 + {}^+38$ | **n.** $^-85 + {}^+12$ |
| **g.** $^-41 + {}^-32$ | **o.** $^-105 + {}^+15$ |
| **h.** $^+176 + {}^+133$ | **p.** $^-987 + {}^+88$ |

3. Replace the frames with integer names to make the statement true.

**EXAMPLE** $^+3 + \bigcirc = {}^-4$

**SOLUTION** On the number line we would go seven units to the left from $^+3$ to reach $^-4$. If $\bigcirc$ is replaced by $^-7$, we obtain a true statement.
$^+3 + {}^-7 = {}^-4$

| | |
|---|---|
| **a.** $\square + {}^+3 = {}^+7$ | **d.** $\triangle + {}^-9 = {}^-13$ |
| **b.** $^+5 + \triangle = {}^-3$ | **e.** $^+7 + \square = {}^+2$ |
| **c.** $^-6 + {}^+14 = \bigcirc$ | **f.** $^-13 + \triangle = {}^+22$ |

**g.** $\bigcirc + {}^+12 = {}^-3$

**h.** ${}^+13 + {}^-7 = \triangle$

**i.** ${}^-19 + \square = {}^-11$

**j.** $\triangle + {}^+12 = {}^+3$

**k.** $\square + {}^-5 = {}^-10$

**l.** $\triangle + {}^-9 = {}^-9$

**m.** ${}^+11 + \bigcirc = 0$

**n.** ${}^-4 + \triangle = {}^-4$

4. Label each of the following statements as true or false:

  **a.** $|\,{}^+2\,| + |\,{}^-3\,| < {}^-3 + {}^+2$

  **b.** ${}^+4 + ({}^-8) \neq {}^-4$

  **c.** ${}^+6 + {}^-3 > {}^-2$

  **d.** ${}^+6 + |\,{}^-5\,| > {}^+11$

  **e.** ${}^-3 + {}^+2 < |\,{}^-5\,|$

  **f.** $|\,{}^-5\,| + {}^-5 \neq 0$

  **g.** $(|\,{}^+6\,| + {}^-5) + {}^-1 \not< {}^+2$

  **h.** $|\,{}^-3\,| + |\,{}^-2\,| \not< {}^-3 + {}^-2$

5. Replace the frames with integer names to produce

  (1) a true statement

  (2) a false statement

  **a.** $\triangle + {}^-7 < {}^+13$

  **b.** ${}^-11 + \bigcirc \neq {}^+6$

  **c.** ${}^+22 + \square \not< {}^+13$

  **d.** $\triangle + {}^-6 > {}^+3$

  **e.** ${}^-3 + {}^+7 \neq \square$

  **f.** ${}^+6 + \triangle \not> {}^-6$

  **g.** ${}^+7 + \square < {}^+11$

## 5 · Rational Numbers

Let us return to a picture of the number line.

You recall that there is a one-to-one correspondence between some points on the number line and the integers. So far we have paid attention only to integers (whole directed numbers) and their associated points. But you know that there are many more points on the number line. Let us enlarge the portion of the number line between the points $A$ and $N$, including $A$ and $N$:

Now let us mark some points corresponding to numbers between 0 and $^+1$.

We could go on marking more points, because there is always at least one more point between any two that we marked. For example, to find a point between $A$ and $X$, you could take 0 and $^+\frac{1}{10}$ and find a number between the two; $^+\frac{1}{20}$ will do because $0 < {}^+\frac{1}{20} < {}^+\frac{1}{10}$. $0 < {}^+\frac{1}{20} < {}^+\frac{1}{10}$ is an abbreviation for $0 < {}^+\frac{1}{20}$ *and* $^+\frac{1}{20} < {}^+\frac{1}{10}$. Can you devise a method which will never fail to give you a number which is between two given numbers?

Numbers such as those described above are called **rational numbers.** Each rational number has a number symbol which can be expressed generally in the form

$$\frac{^+\square}{\triangle} \quad \text{or} \quad \frac{^-\square}{\triangle}$$

where the frames $\square$ and $\triangle$ can be replaced by the natural number names. (We can also replace $\square$ by zero.) Let us make a few replacements:

$$3 \text{ for } \square, 7 \text{ for } \triangle: {}^+\tfrac{3}{7}, {}^-\tfrac{3}{7}$$
$$2 \text{ for } \square, 5 \text{ for } \triangle: {}^+\tfrac{2}{5}, {}^-\tfrac{2}{5}$$
$$4 \text{ for } \square, 1 \text{ for } \triangle: {}^+\tfrac{4}{1}, {}^-\tfrac{4}{1}$$

Of course, simpler names for the last two numbers are $^+4$ and $^-4$. These two numbers happen to be integers. What can you tell about any number obtained by replacing $\triangle$ in $\frac{^+\square}{\triangle}$ or $\frac{^-\square}{\triangle}$ by 1?

Rational numbers probably remind you of fractions. You should notice that the set of rational numbers includes the integers. Thus the set of integers is a subset of the set of rational numbers.

On the number line below there are marked a few points which correspond to some of the rational numbers:

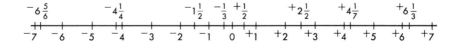

You will recall from arithmetic that all rational numbers have decimal number names. For example, $^+\frac{1}{2}$ is the same as $^+.5$, $^+2\frac{1}{2}$ is the same as $^+2.5$, and $^-4\frac{1}{4}$ is the same as $^-4.25$. Some of the rational numbers, however, have more complicated decimal number names. For example, $^+\frac{1}{3}$ is the same as $^+.33\dot{3}$, where the dot above the last 3 means that the digit 3 repeats on and on. Similarly, $^-6\frac{5}{6}$ is the same as $^-6.833\dot{3}$, and $^+4\frac{1}{7}$ is the same as $^+4.142857142857$, where the dots above 142857 mean that this sequence of six digits repeats. These numbers might also appear as $^+.\dot{3}$, $^-6.8\dot{3}$ and $^+4.\dot{1}4285\dot{7}$.

You see, then, that a rational number may be represented in the form of a decimal which either ends (**terminating decimal**), or is a **repeating decimal**. Terminating decimals could be considered to be repeating decimals, since they can be thought to have a zero repeating.

It is also true that a terminating decimal names a rational number. Therefore, a terminating decimal also has a number symbol of the form $^+\frac{\square}{\triangle}$ or $^-\frac{\square}{\triangle}$; that is, a fractional numeral. For example, $^+3.16507$ is the same as $^+\frac{316.507}{100.000}$.

Furthermore, a repeating decimal names a rational number. Therefore it also has a number symbol of the form $^+\frac{\square}{\triangle}$ or $^-\frac{\square}{\triangle}$. For example, $^+.\dot{1}35\dot{1}35$ is a repeating decimal. The number $^+.\dot{1}35\dot{1}35$ is the same as $^+\frac{135}{999}$. We can verify this by dividing 135 by 999.

It is obvious that '135' will repeat on and on. Thus we see that $^+.\dot{1}35\dot{1}35$ is the same as $^+\frac{135}{999}$.

```
          .135135
999 | 135.000000
      99 9
      35 10
      29 97
       5 130
       4 995
        1350
         999
        3510
        2997
        5130
        4995
        1350
```

Of course, you are wondering how we knew in the first place that $.\dot{1}35\dot{1}35$ is the same as $\frac{135}{999}$. Here is one way of arriving at this.

Let $\triangle = .\dot{1}35\dot{1}35$

then $1000 \times \triangle = 135.\dot{1}35\dot{1}35$

Now it follows that

$1000 \times \triangle - \triangle = 135.\dot{1}35\dot{1}35 - .\dot{1}35\dot{1}35$

or, $999 \times \triangle = 135$

$\triangle = \frac{135}{999}$

To simplify our work, we kept in mind the fact that the number was positive, and did not write the plus sign.

## EXERCISES

**1.** Change the following fractional numerals into decimal numerals, and state whether it is a terminating or repeating decimal.

**EXAMPLE 1**   $\frac{3}{8}$

**SOLUTION**   8 | 3.000
               .375

Therefore, $\frac{3}{8}$ expressed as a decimal is a terminating decimal.

**EXAMPLE 2**   $\frac{1}{7}$

**SOLUTION**   7 | 1.00000000
               .142857142857

Therefore, $\frac{1}{7}$ expressed as a decimal is a repeating decimal.

| | | | |
|---|---|---|---|
| **a.** $\frac{5}{8}$ | **e.** $\frac{1}{6}$ | **i.** $\frac{5}{6}$ | **m.** $\frac{7}{19}$ |
| **b.** $\frac{4}{9}$ | **f.** $\frac{7}{9}$ | **j.** $\frac{4}{13}$ | **n.** $\frac{3}{11}$ |
| **c.** $\frac{2}{3}$ | **g.** $\frac{6}{7}$ | **k.** $\frac{2}{15}$ | **o.** $\frac{5}{9}$ |
| **d.** $\frac{3}{8}$ | **h.** $\frac{2}{11}$ | **l.** $\frac{6}{17}$ | **p.** $\frac{5}{18}$ |

**2.** Express the following in the form $\frac{\square}{\triangle}$ where $\triangle$ and $\square$ are replaceable by the counting number names and zero ($\triangle \neq O$).

**EXAMPLE 1**   2.35

**SOLUTION**   $2.35 = 2 + \frac{35}{100}$
                    $= \frac{200}{100} + \frac{35}{100}$
                    $= \frac{235}{100}$
                    $= \frac{47}{20}$

**EXAMPLE 2**   .6333

**SOLUTION**   Let        $\triangle = .6333$
        Then $10 \cdot \triangle = 6.333$
        $10 \cdot \triangle - \triangle = 6.333 - .6333$
             $9 \cdot \triangle = 5.7$
                $\triangle = \frac{5.7}{9} = \frac{57}{90} = \frac{19}{30}$
                $\triangle = \frac{19}{30}$

| | | |
|---|---|---|
| **a.** .7 | **c.** 1.3 | **e.** $2\frac{3}{4}$ |
| **b.** 2.97 | **d.** $2\frac{1}{6}$ | **f.** .1250 |

g. .8333̇  n. .8750  u. 3.22̇2̇  $\frac{29}{9}$

h. .166̇6̇  o. .44̇4̇  v. 1.36̇

i. 2.33̇3̇  p. $3\frac{1}{9}$  w. 2.66̇6̇  $\frac{8}{3}$

j. 3.17  q. 7.06  x. .3̇0̇7̇6̇9̇2̇307692̇

k. 5.9  r. .77̇7̇  y. 2.181̇8̇  $\frac{24}{11}$

l. .11̇1̇  s. .365  z. 3.121̇2̇

m. 4.66̇6̇  t. $1\frac{2}{9}$  a'. 4.272̇7̇  $\frac{47}{11}$

## 6 · Irrational Numbers

In the previous section you learned that between any two rational numbers there is another rational number. You should see that this is true no matter how close the two rational numbers are. For example, take the rational numbers $\frac{2}{37}$ and $\frac{2}{38}$. These two numbers are very close together. To find a number which is between the two, we can simply find the average (arithmetic mean) of the two numbers:

$$\frac{\frac{2}{37} + \frac{2}{38}}{2} = \frac{\frac{76}{1406} + \frac{74}{1406}}{2} = \frac{\frac{150}{1406}}{2} = \frac{75}{1406}$$

To see that $\frac{75}{1406}$ is indeed between $\frac{2}{37}$ and $\frac{2}{38}$, all you need to do is to observe that $\frac{2}{37}$ is the same as $\frac{76}{1406}$ and $\frac{2}{38}$ is the same as $\frac{74}{1406}$. Now it is easy to see that:

$$\frac{74}{1406} < \frac{75}{1406} < \frac{76}{1406}$$

There is another, somewhat simpler way, of locating a rational number between two given rational numbers. Consider the same two numbers $\frac{2}{37}$ and $\frac{2}{38}$.

To obtain a number between these two, we simply do the following $\frac{2+2}{37+38}$, or $\frac{4}{75}$

Check to see that the statement $\frac{2}{38} < \frac{4}{75} < \frac{2}{37}$ is true. That is, that $\frac{4}{75}$ is indeed between $\frac{2}{38}$ and $\frac{2}{37}$. Here we again remembered that both numbers were positive, without writing the plus sign over and over again.

Between any two rational numbers, there is another rational number. Therefore, the set of rational numbers is called *dense*. In fact, it might appear to you that every point on the number line has a rational number associated with it, but this is not so.

Let us consider a number which, when multiplied by itself, gives 2. Multiplying a number by itself is called "squaring the number." For example, $3^2 = 9$ is read "three squared equals nine" or "the square of three is nine." You will see later that in the system of directed numbers there are two numbers whose square is positive nine; they are $^+3$ and $^-3$.

The positive number that makes the statement $\triangle^2 = 2$ true is $^+\sqrt{2}$. We will keep in mind that we are dealing with a positive number, and omit the plus sign to simplify writing. Thus, we have $(\sqrt{2})^2 = \sqrt{2} \times \sqrt{2} = 2$. For the present, we will be concerned only with the positive number.

You should note that:

$$\sqrt{2} \text{ is not equal to } 1.4$$
$$\text{because } 1.4 \times 1.4 = 1.96 \neq 2$$

Similarly,

$$\sqrt{2} \text{ is not equal to } 1.42$$
$$\text{because } 1.42 \times 1.42 = 2.0164 \neq 2$$

and

$$\sqrt{2} \text{ is not equal to } 1.41$$
$$\text{because } 1.41 \times 1.41 = 1.9881 \neq 2$$

We can devise a method for finding numbers which are very close to $\sqrt{2}$. This method is based on the fact that we want a number which when multiplied by itself gives a number as close to 2 as possible. We start out with 1 as a trial number:

$$\tfrac{2}{1} = 2$$

From your study óf the relationship between multiplication and division, you know that the problem above is related to the multiplication problem:

$$2 = 1 \cdot 2$$

We have now two numbers, 1 and 2, whose product is 2, but these two numbers differ by 1:

$$2 - 1 = 1$$

Our problem, of course, is to find a number such that if it is multiplied by *itself*, the result will be 2 or very close to it. This number is between 1 and 2, therefore, we take the number half-way between, or the average of 1 and 2:

$$\tfrac{1}{2}(1 + 2) = \tfrac{1}{2} \times 3 = 1.5$$

Now, we repeat the step above: $\frac{2}{1.5} = 1.3$. Next, take the average of 1.5 and 1.3: $\frac{1}{2}(1.5 + 1.3) = 1.4$, and repeat the steps over and over again:

$$\frac{2}{1.40} = 1.42$$
$$\tfrac{1}{2}(1.40 + 1.42) = 1.41$$
$$\frac{2}{1.410} = 1.418$$
$$\tfrac{1}{2}(1.410 + 1.418) = 1.414$$

$$\frac{2}{1.4140} = 1.4144$$
$$\tfrac{1}{2}(1.4140 + 1.4144) = 1.4142$$
$$\frac{2}{1.41420} = 1.41422$$
$$\tfrac{1}{2}(1.41420 + 1.41422) = 1.41421$$
$$\frac{2}{1.414210} = 1.414217$$
$$\tfrac{1}{2}(1.414210 + 1.414217) = 1.4142135$$
and so on.

To check to see how close the number 1.4142135 is to $\sqrt{2}$, we multiply it by itself:

$$1.4142135 \times 1.4142135 = 1.999999825358225$$

The result differs from 2 by

$$0.00000017641775$$

which is a very small number. The square of each of these estimates is getting closer to 2, but it appears from this method that there is no decimal representation of $\sqrt{2}$ whose square is exactly 2.

If there is no decimal representation for $\sqrt{2}$, then it follows that $\sqrt{2}$ has no name of the form $\frac{\square}{\triangle}$, where $\square$ and $\triangle$ are replaceable by natural number names. Then it follows that $\sqrt{2}$ is not a rational number, because every rational number has a name of the form $\frac{\square}{\triangle}$. A number which is not a rational number is called an **irrational number.**

Now, assuming that $\sqrt{2}$ is an irrational number, we will show that there is a point on the number line which corresponds to $\sqrt{2}$. Thus, we will show that there are points on the number line in addition to those corresponding to the rational numbers.

Consider the part of the number line between the points $A$ and $N$, the points corresponding to the numbers 0 and 1, respectively. Also extend the line a little to the right of $N$.

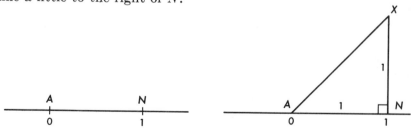

Now, the length of the line segment $AN$ is 1. Draw the line segment $NX$ perpendicular to $AN$, and also of 1 unit length. In the diagram on page 67, you can compute the length of the line segment $AX$ if you recall that in a right triangle the square of the length of the side opposite the right angle is equal to the square of the length of one side adjacent to the right angle plus the square of the other. That is:

$$(AX)^2 = (AN)^2 + (NX)^2 = 1^2 + 1^2 = 2$$

Thus, $$AX = \sqrt{2}$$

Now, imagine swinging an arc with the radius of $AX$, and center at $A$, down on the number line, like this

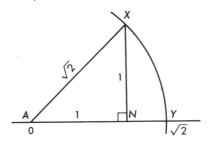

Since $AX$ and $AY$ are two radii of the same circle, they are of the same length. Thus, the length of $AY$ is $\sqrt{2}$ and the number $\sqrt{2}$ corresponds to the point $Y$.

Even though $\sqrt{2}$ is an irrational number, we have demonstrated the existence on the number line of a point which corresponds to an irrational number. Of course, there are many more points on the number line which correspond to other irrational numbers.

Previously you learned that every rational number has a name in a form of a terminating or repeating decimal. However, an irrational number has no such name. For example, if you examine the decimal

$$.172172217222172222 \cdots$$

you should discover that it is a non-repeating, non-terminating decimal; that is, no group of digits is repeating on and on. Thus,

$$.172172217222172222 \cdots$$

is an irrational number.

Let us take another irrational number:

$$.261261126111261111 \cdots$$

It is easy to see that there is another irrational number between these two. For example, $.182182218222182222 \cdots$ is such a number, because

$$.172172217222172222 \cdots < .182182218222182222 \cdots$$
$$< .261261126111261111 \cdots$$

In fact, it is possible to find an irrational number between any two irrational numbers.

*If you take the set of rational numbers and the set of irrational numbers and form the union of these two sets, the result is the set of **real** numbers. Thus, real numbers consist of rational and irrational numbers.* Since no rational number is irrational, and no irrational number is rational, the two sets are disjoint sets.

## EXERCISES

1. Find the rational number midway between

   **a.** $+\frac{1}{2}$ and $+\frac{6}{4}$

   **b.** $+\frac{5}{8}$ and $+\frac{4}{16}$

   **c.** $+\frac{28}{37}$ and $+\frac{13}{74}$

   **d.** $+4.17$ and $+4.96$

   **e.** $+\frac{11}{2}$ and $+\frac{5}{6}$

   **f.** $+2.19$ and $+1.11$

   **g.** $+3.12$ and $+3.76$

2. Approach the positive square root. In each case, carry out the computations to four decimal places and round-off to three decimal places (if the fourth decimal place is 5 or more, add 1 to the third decimal place; if the fourth place is less than 5 just drop the fourth decimal place).

**EXAMPLE**     $\sqrt{3} = ?$

**SOLUTION**     Choose 1 as the first trial number.

$\frac{3}{1} = 3$

$\frac{1}{2}(1 + 3) = \frac{1}{2} \times 4 = 2$

$\frac{3}{2.0} = 1.5$

$\frac{1}{2}(2.0 + 1.5) = 1.75$

$\frac{3}{1.75} = 1.714$

$\frac{1}{2}(1.750 + 1.714) = 1.732$

$\frac{3}{1.732} = 1.7321$

Thus 1.732 is the square root of 3 correct to three decimal places.

$\sqrt{3} = 1.732 \cdots$

$1.732 \times 1.732 = 2.999824$

a. $\sqrt{5}$      f. $\sqrt{19}$      k. $\sqrt{361}$

b. $\sqrt{7}$      g. $\sqrt{5.2}$      l. $\sqrt{42.4}$

c. $\sqrt{225}$      h. $\sqrt{6.25}$      m. $\sqrt{1.96}$

d. $\sqrt{13}$      i. $\sqrt{17.6}$      n. $\sqrt{31.7}$

e. $\sqrt{529}$      j. $\sqrt{139.8}$      o. $\sqrt{2.89}$

**3.** The following decimal representations of rational numbers are repeating. Change to irrational numbers by inserting number symbols after each repeating "block."

**EXAMPLE**      .281281281 · · ·

**SOLUTION**      The repeating "block" is 281. We choose to insert 3, 4, 5, 6, 7, · · · after each repeating block.
.2813281428152816 · · ·
Thus, .281328142815 · · · is an irrational number.

a. .14141414 · · ·      c. .987198719871 · · ·

b. .289289 · · ·      d. .142857142857142857 · · ·

## 7 · Subtraction of Real Numbers

In arithmetic you learned how to subtract arithmetic numbers. But, even if you knew only how to add, you could change every subtraction problem to a related addition problem and obtain your answer. This is possible because addition and subtraction are inverse operations.

From previous chapters, you will remember that the problem $7 - 2 = ?$ can be changed into $? + 2 = 7$; and since $5 + 2 = 7$ the answer to the original problem is 5, or $7 - 2 = 5$.

The relation between subtraction and addition of *real* numbers is the same as the relation between subtraction and addition of *arithmetic* numbers.

Study the following examples:

(1)      $^+9 - {}^+4 = ?$      (1')      $? + {}^+4 = {}^+9$
**or,** what number added to $^+4$ gives $^+9$?
**Answer:** $^+5$.      *Therefore,* $^+9 - {}^+4 = {}^+5$.

(2)      $^+16 - {}^+9 = ?$      (2')      $? + {}^+9 = {}^+16$
**or,** what number added to $^+9$ gives $^+16$?
**Answer:** $^+7$.      *Therefore,* $^+16 - {}^+9 = {}^+7$.

(3)      $^+5 - {}^+8 = ?$      (3')      $? + {}^+8 = {}^+5$
**or,** what number added to $^+8$ gives $^+5$?
**Answer:** $^-3$.      *Therefore,* $^+5 - {}^+8 = {}^-3$.

(4) $^+12 - {}^+20 = ?$     (4') $? + {}^+20 = {}^+12$
**or,** what number added to $^+20$ gives $^+12$?
**Answer:** $^-8$.     *Therefore,* $^+12 - {}^+20 = {}^-8$.

(5) $^+3 - {}^-6 = ?$     (5') $? + {}^-6 = {}^+3$
**or,** what number added to $^-6$ gives $^+3$?
**Answer:** $^+9$.     *Therefore,* $^+3 - {}^-6 = {}^+9$.

(6) $^+7 - {}^-2 = ?$     (6') $? + {}^-2 = {}^+7$
**or,** what number added to $^-2$ gives $^+7$?
**Answer:** $^+9$.     *Therefore,* $^+7 - {}^-2 = {}^+9$.

(7) $^-5 - {}^-2 = ?$     (7') $? + {}^-2 = {}^-5$
**or,** what number added to $^-2$ gives $^-5$?
**Answer:** $^-3$.     *Therefore,* $^-5 - {}^-2 = {}^-3$.

(8) $^+\frac{1}{5} - {}^-\frac{3}{5} = ?$     (8') $? + {}^-10 = {}^-6$
**or,** what number added to $^-\frac{3}{5}$ gives $^+\frac{1}{5}$?
**Answer:** $^+\frac{4}{5}$     *Therefore,* $^+\frac{1}{5} - {}^-\frac{3}{5} = {}^+\frac{4}{5}$.

(9) $^-2 - {}^!5 = ?$     (9') $? + {}^+5 = {}^-2$
**or,** what number added to $^+5$ gives $^-2$?
**Answer:** $^-7$.     *Therefore,* $^-2 - {}^+5 = {}^-7$.

(10) $^-.25 - {}^+.3 = ?$     (10') $? + {}^+.3 = {}^-.25$
**or,** what number added to $^+.3$ gives $^-.25$?
**Answer:** $^-.55$.     *Therefore,* $^-.25 - {}^+.3 = {}^-.55$.

## EXERCISES

Find the answer to each subtraction problem below by changing it to the related addition problem.

**EXAMPLE**     $^-3 - {}^-28 = ?$

**SOLUTION**     $^-3 - {}^-28 = ?$
or,
$? + {}^-28 = {}^-3$
or,
What number added to $^-28$ gives $^-3$?
Answer: $^+25$.
Therefore, $^-3 - {}^-28 = {}^+25$.

1. $^+3 - {}^+1$        4. $^+3 - {}^+13$
2. $^+17 - {}^+10$      5. $^+27 - {}^+136$
3. $^+2 - {}^+7$        6. $^+132 - {}^+36$

7.  $^+216 - {}^+18$
8.  $^+78 - {}^+92$
9.  $^+320 - {}^+185$
10. $^+6 - {}^-12$
11. $^+3 - {}^-42$
12. $^+7 - {}^-39$
13. $^+100 - {}^-12$
14. $^-17 - {}^+17$
15. $^-85 - {}^+13$
16. $^-199 - {}^+99$
17. $^-85 - {}^-15$
18. $^-17 - {}^-53$
19. $^-55 - {}^-116$
20. $^-168 - {}^-32$
21. $^+\frac{3}{2} - {}^+\frac{1}{2}$

22. $^+1.8 - {}^+1.2$
23. $^+\frac{1}{3} - {}^+\frac{1}{2}$
24. $^+\frac{2}{5} - {}^+\frac{2}{7}$
25. $^-.5 - {}^+.2$
26. $^-\frac{2}{3} - {}^+\frac{1}{3}$
27. $^-2.14 - {}^+1.14$
28. $^-115.5 - {}^+105.4$
29. $^+1.2 - {}^-.8$
30. $^+3.52 - {}^-7.48$
31. $^+\frac{2}{9} - {}^-\frac{1}{3}$
32. $^+\frac{11}{12} - {}^-\frac{3}{4}$
33. $^-\frac{1}{2} - {}^-\frac{3}{2}$
34. $^-\frac{3}{4} - {}^-\frac{3}{4}$
35. $^-1.7 - {}^-3.3$
36. $^-.333 - {}^-.444$

Examine thoughtfully the exercises above. Try to formulate in your mind a theory as to how the subtraction of real numbers works. This theory should be suggestive of a way to work subtraction problems by using the opposite of subtraction. Do not tell your theory to anyone. Let your teacher check your theory by telling you whether or not your answers to the exercises below are correct.

37. $^+113 - {}^+14$
38. $^+17 - {}^+56$
39. $^+\frac{1}{2} - {}^+\frac{1}{3}$
40. $^+\frac{7}{8} - {}^+\frac{3}{8}$
41. $^+1.3 - {}^+.7$
42. $^+17.9 - {}^+34.9$
43. $^-16 - {}^-3$

44. $^-35 - {}^-78$
45. $^-\frac{3}{4} - {}^-\frac{1}{4}$
46. $^-\frac{2}{5} - {}^-\frac{3}{5}$
47. $^+100 - {}^-12$
48. $^+200 - {}^-300$
49. $^+\frac{1}{2} - {}^-\frac{1}{3}$
50. $^+\frac{9}{15} - {}^-\frac{13}{15}$

## 8 · A Different Look at Subtraction

On the next page are a number of examples of subtraction problems worked out for you. To the right of each subtraction problem is an addition problem. Study all of these examples and see if you can discover how each addition problem is related to the subtraction problem on its left. There is one problem which does not fit into the pattern. Find it!

| | | | |
|---|---|---|---|
| 1. | $^+4 - {}^+11 = {}^-7$ | 1′. | $^+4 + {}^-11 = {}^-7$ |
| 2. | $^+17 - {}^+9 = {}^+8$ | 2′. | $^+17 + {}^-9 = {}^+8$ |
| 3. | $^+7 - {}^-10 = {}^+17$ | 3′. | $^+7 + {}^+10 = {}^+17$ |
| 4. | $^+18 - {}^-12 = {}^+30$ | 4′. | $^+18 + {}^+12 = {}^+30$ |
| 5. | $^-6 - {}^+17 = {}^-23$ | 5′. | $^-6 + {}^-17 = {}^-23$ |
| 6. | $^-\frac{1}{2} - {}^+\frac{1}{2} = {}^-1$ | 6′. | $^-\frac{1}{2} + {}^-\frac{1}{2} = {}^-1$ |
| 7. | $^-\frac{5}{7} - {}^-\frac{5}{7} = 0$ | 7′. | $^-\frac{5}{7} + {}^+\frac{5}{7} = 0$ |
| 8. | $^+11.3 - {}^-11.2 = {}^+22.5$ | 8′. | $^+11.3 + {}^+11.2 = {}^+22.5$ |
| 9. | $^-25.1 - {}^-3.4 = {}^-21.7$ | 9′. | $^+25.1 + {}^-3.4 = {}^+21.7$ |
| 10. | $^-\frac{3}{8} - {}^+\frac{5}{8} = {}^-1$ | 10′. | $^-\frac{3}{8} + {}^-\frac{5}{8} = {}^-1$ |

You must have observed that every problem on the right is an addition problem. Every problem on the left is a subtraction problem. In changing a subtraction problem to an addition problem, we have used the opposite of the subtrahend. For example, in the first problem instead of subtracting $^+11$ from $^+4$ we added $^-11$ to $^+4$.

$$^-11 \text{ is the opposite of } {}^+11$$

In the third problem, instead of subtracting $^-10$ from $^+7$, we added $^+10$ to $^+7$.

$$^+10 \text{ is the opposite of } {}^-10$$

Thus we have a principle concerning addition and subtraction of directed numbers:

Subtracting a directed number is the same as adding its opposite. This principle can be stated using frames, as follows:

$$\square - \triangle = \square + \text{(the opposite of } \triangle)$$

where $\square$ and $\triangle$ are replaced by names of real numbers. We shall call this the Principle of Subtraction. For example, 1 and 1′, above, are instances of this principle. Replace $\square$ by $^+4$ and $\triangle$ by $^+11$ to obtain

$$^+4 - {}^+11 = {}^+4 + \text{(the opposite of } {}^+11)$$

Now, we know that the opposite of $^+11$ is $^-11$, hence we have

$$^+4 - {}^+11 = {}^+4 + {}^-11$$

*Every real number has an opposite.* The opposite of a positive number is a negative number. The opposite of a negative number is a positive number. The opposite of 0 is 0.

Now look at the following examples:

$$^+5 + {}^-5 = 0$$
$$^+\tfrac{3}{7} + {}^-\tfrac{3}{7} = 0$$
$$^-13.7 + {}^+13.7 = 0$$
$$0 + 0 = 0$$

What principle is illustrated by these examples? The principle can be stated using frames, as follows:

$$\square + (\text{the opposite of } \square) = 0$$

for every replacement of $\square$ by a name of a real number. Thus, the sum of any real number and its opposite is zero.

## EXERCISES

**1.** Give the opposite of each of the following numbers:

   **a.** $^-13$        **f.** $^-1.078$

   **b.** $^-176$       **g.** the opposite of $^+12$

   **c.** $^+398$       **h.** the opposite of $^-17$

   **d.** $^-\tfrac{9}{4}$        **i.** the opposite of the opposite of $^+1$

   **e.** $^+\tfrac{17}{3}$      **j.** the opposite of the opposite of $^-3$

**2.** For each pair of numbers below, tell whether or not one number in each pair is the opposite of the other number:

**EXAMPLE 1**     $^+37.5,\ ^-73.5$

**SOLUTION**     No.

**EXAMPLE 2**     $^-13\tfrac{1}{2},\ ^+13\tfrac{1}{2}$

**SOLUTION**     Yes.

   **a.** $^+27,\ ^-27$        **f.** $^+.4,\ ^-\tfrac{2}{5}$

   **b.** $^-325,\ ^+325$     **g.** $|\,^-13\tfrac{1}{2}\,|,\ ^-\tfrac{27}{2}$

   **c.** $^+136,\ ^-163$     **h.** $^+1,\ ^+3 + {}^-4$

   **d.** $^-1221,\ ^+2112$    **i.** $|\,^+5 - {}^+7\,|,\ |\,^-2\,|$

   **e.** $^+\tfrac{3}{7},\ ^-\tfrac{7}{3}$       **j.** $|\,^-\tfrac{1}{2} + {}^-\tfrac{1}{2}\,|,\ |\,^+\tfrac{1}{4}\,|$

**3.** Compute the sum of each pair of numbers given in Exercise 2 above.

**EXAMPLE 1**     $^+37.5,\ ^-73.5$

**SOLUTION**     $^+37.5 + {}^-73.5 = {}^-36.0$

**EXAMPLE 2**   $^-13\frac{1}{2}, \, ^+13\frac{1}{2}$

**SOLUTION**   $^-13\frac{1}{2} + \, ^+13\frac{1}{2} = 0$

4. In each case, replace the frames with a real number symbol to result in a true statement:

a. $^+7 - \triangle = \, ^+2$

b. $\square - \, ^-6 = \, ^+9$

c. $^+16 - \triangle = \, ^-11$

d. $\bigcirc - \, ^+9 = \, ^+14$

e. $^-9 - \, ^-7 = \triangle$

f. $^+2 - \square = \, ^-5$

g. $\triangle - \, ^-5 = \, ^-16$

h. $^+\frac{1}{2} + \triangle = 0$

i. $^-\frac{2}{3} + \square = \, ^-\frac{4}{3}$

j. $^+1.75 - \bigcirc = \, ^+1.15$

k. $^-3.5 + \, ^-1.6 = \triangle$

l. $^-\frac{1}{7} + \triangle = \, ^-\frac{4}{21}$

m. $^+\frac{2}{9} - \, ^-\frac{3}{4} = \square$

n. $\bigcirc - \, ^-\frac{3}{5} = \, ^+1$

5. In each case, replace the frames with a real number name to result in

  (1)  a true statement
  (2)  a false statement

a. $^+7 - \, ^+3 < |\triangle|$

b. $^+4 - \, ^-7 > \square$

c. $\triangle - \, ^+5 \neq \, ^+7$

d. $^-4 - \bigcirc < \, ^+3$

e. $\triangle - \, ^+2 > \, ^+5$

f. $\triangle + \, ^-7 = 0$

g. $\square + \, ^+11 = 0$

h. $^-3 + \triangle = 0$

i. $\square + \, ^-9 \neq 0$

j. $^-9 + \, ^+9 = \triangle$

k. $\triangle < \, ^-\frac{1}{2} + \, ^+\frac{1}{3}$

l. $\square + \, ^+.5 > \, ^+17.6$

m. $\bigcirc - \, ^-\frac{1}{3} > \, ^+\frac{1}{3}$

n. $^+\frac{2}{3} + \, ^+\frac{1}{4} = \square$

o. $^+.67 - \, ^-.34 > \triangle$

p. $\triangle - \, ^-1.78 = \, ^+1.12$

q. $\square + \, ^-1015 > \, ^+1015$

r. $|\bigcirc| - \, ^+\frac{3}{4} = 0$

s. $^+\frac{1}{2} - |\triangle| = 0$

t. $^+2 \cdot |\square| - \, ^+\frac{8}{7} = 0$

u. $^+23 - |\triangle| \not< \, ^+2$

v. $|\bigcirc| - \, ^+\frac{1}{2} \not> \, ^+\frac{3}{4}$

6. Change each statement to its equivalent involving addition, then give the answer:

**EXAMPLE**   $^+3 - \, ^-7$

**SOLUTION**   $^+3 - \, ^-7 = \, ^+3 + \, ^+7 = \, ^+10$

a. $^+4 - \, ^+1$

b. $^+21 - \, ^+17$

c. $^+39 - \, ^+121$

d. $^+16 - \, ^+215$

e. $^-13 - \, ^-4$

f. $^-12 - \, ^-8$

g. $^-25 - \, ^-72$

h. $^-98 - \, ^-113$

**i.** $^+12 - ^-4$

**j.** $^+25 - ^-23$

**k.** $^+29 - ^-37$

**l.** $^+41 - ^-68$

**m.** $^-16 - ^+4$

**n.** $^-58 - ^+13$

**o.** $^-62 - ^+85$

**p.** $^-75 - ^+109$

**q.** $0 - ^+156$

**r.** $0 - ^-76$

**s.** $^-\frac{1}{2} - ^+\frac{3}{4}$

**t.** $^-\frac{3}{5} - ^-\frac{17}{5}$

**u.** $^-\frac{6}{7} - ^-\frac{13}{7}$

**v.** $^+\frac{3}{5} - ^-\frac{1}{5}$

**w.** $^+\frac{6}{11} - ^+\frac{17}{11}$

**x.** $^-13.6 - ^-2.3$

**y.** $^-19.8 - ^-36.3$

**z.** $^-29.2 - ^+13.5$

**a'.** $^-40.9 - ^+90.4$

**b'.** $^+13.9 - ^-12.8$

**c'.** $^+58.45 - ^-67.54$

## 9 · Multiplication of Real Numbers

In order to learn how to multiply real numbers, we shall now argue that positive numbers "behave" like the numbers of arithmetic. Furthermore, we can establish a one-to-one correspondence between the numbers of arithmetic and the positive numbers. This correspondence for whole numbers is indicated below.

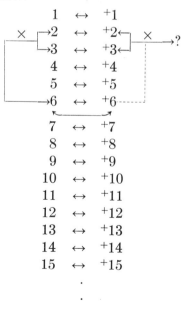

The dots indicate that this array can be continued on and on. Two-headed arrows indicate that to each arithmetic number there corresponds a positive number, and to each positive number there corresponds an arithmetic number. That is, there is a correspondence both ways, or a one-to-one correspondence.

Now, suppose we have the following problem $^+2 \cdot {}^+3 = ?$ To determine the answer, we enlist the aid of the figure. First, we find the arithmetic number corresponding to $^+2$. It is 2. Then we find the arithmetic number corresponding to $^+3$. It is 3. Now we know that $2 \cdot 3 = 6$, and we find that to the arithmetic number 6 there corresponds the positive number $^+6$. So, if our positive numbers are to behave like arithmetic numbers, $^+2 \cdot {}^+3 = {}^+6$. Study the display to interpret the meaning of arrows in it.

On a sheet of paper, make a display like the one above. Use it, in the same manner as above, to show that $^+3 \cdot {}^+4 = {}^+12$ and $^+5 \cdot {}^+3 = {}^+15$.

It is apparent that *a positive number multiplied by a positive number gives a positive number for a product.*

Next, we make use of a very important characteristic of mathematics. One mathematician said that "Mathematics is a study of patterns." We can learn a great deal of mathematics by keeping our eyes open for patterns.

Study the following examples and look for a pattern:

$$^+2 \cdot {}^+4 = {}^+8$$
$$\downarrow \quad \downarrow \quad \downarrow$$
$$^+2 \cdot {}^+3 = {}^+6$$
$$\downarrow \quad \downarrow \quad \downarrow$$
$$^+2 \cdot {}^+2 = {}^+4$$

Would you know what to write next? Here it is:

$$\downarrow \quad \downarrow \quad \downarrow$$
$$^+2 \cdot {}^+1 = {}^+2$$
$$\downarrow \quad \downarrow \quad \downarrow$$
$$^+2 \cdot \ 0 = \ 0$$

What comes next? (Answer the question before reading further.)

$$\downarrow \quad \downarrow \quad \downarrow$$
$$^+2 \cdot {}^-1 = {}^-2$$
$$\downarrow \quad \downarrow \quad \downarrow$$
$$^+2 \cdot {}^-2 = {}^-4$$
$$\downarrow \quad \downarrow \quad \downarrow$$
$$^+2 \cdot {}^-3 = {}^-6$$
$$\downarrow \quad \downarrow \quad \downarrow$$
$$^+2 \cdot {}^-4 = {}^-8$$

and so on.

Do you know how to continue? Try building a few more such patterns using numbers different from those above. What do you discover about multiplication of numbers like the ones above?

Now that you know that, for example, $^+2 \cdot {}^-3 = {}^-6$, you also know that $^-3 \cdot {}^+2 = {}^-6$, because we shall retain all of the basic principles for the numbers of arithmetic stated in Chapter 2. All of these principles also hold for the real numbers. Thus, $^+2 \cdot {}^-3 = {}^-3 \cdot {}^+2$ according to the Commutative Principle of Addition.

Therefore, we can agree that *the product of a positive number and a negative number is a negative number.*

Let us now build another pattern:

$$^-2 \cdot {}^+4 = {}^-8$$
$$\downarrow \quad \downarrow \qquad \downarrow$$
$$^-2 \cdot {}^+3 = {}^-6$$
$$\downarrow \quad \downarrow \qquad \downarrow$$
$$^-2 \cdot {}^+2 = {}^-4$$

What would you write next? Here it is:

$$\downarrow \quad \downarrow \qquad \downarrow$$
$$^-2 \cdot {}^+1 = {}^-2$$
$$\downarrow \quad \downarrow \qquad \downarrow$$
$$^-2 \cdot \ 0 = \ 0$$

What comes next? Be sure to answer this question for yourself before reading on. Continuing the pattern, we would have the following:

$$^-2 \cdot {}^-1 = {}^+2$$
$$\downarrow \quad \downarrow \qquad \downarrow$$
$$^-2 \cdot {}^-2 = {}^+4$$
$$\downarrow \quad \downarrow \qquad \downarrow$$
$$^-2 \cdot {}^-3 = {}^+6$$
$$\downarrow \quad \downarrow \qquad \downarrow$$
$$^-2 \cdot {}^-4 = {}^+8$$

and so on.

Thus, *a negative number multiplied by a negative number is a positive number.*

This can be shown to be a consequence of previous facts and the Distributive Principle. Suppose for a moment that we do not know what $^-5 \times {}^-7$ is.

Consider the following:

$$^-5 \times ({}^+7 + {}^-7)$$

According to the Distributive Principle,

$$^-5 \times ({}^+7 + {}^-7) = ({}^-5 \times {}^+7) + ({}^-5 \times {}^-7)$$

We already know that $^-5 \times ^+7 = ^-35$

Therefore, $(^-5 \times ^+7) + (^-5 \times ^-7) = ^-35 + (^-5 \times ^-7)$

We also know that

$$^-5 \times (^+7 + ^-7) = ^-5 \times 0 = 0$$

The Principle of Zero of Multiplication holds for real numbers

Therefore, $\qquad ^-35 + (^-5 \times ^-7) = 0$

or

$$^-35 + \text{?} = 0$$

The question is: What number added to $^-35$ gives 0? It is $^+35$.

Thus, $\qquad\qquad\qquad ^-5 \times ^-7 = ^+35$

Later we shall prove that for all negative real numbers, the product of two negative numbers is a positive number. For the present, we shall accept it as reasonable.

Here are some products worked out for you. Check each one to see if it is correct.

$^+6 \cdot ^+5 = ^+30$ $\qquad\qquad$ $^-1 \cdot ^+12 = ^-12$

$^+2 \cdot ^+\frac{1}{3} = ^+\frac{2}{3}$ $\qquad\qquad$ $^-5 \cdot ^+\frac{3}{4} = ^-\frac{15}{4}$ or $^-3\frac{3}{4}$

$^+\frac{2}{5} \cdot ^+\frac{3}{7} = ^+\frac{6}{35}$ $\qquad\qquad$ $^-\frac{7}{8} \cdot ^+\frac{2}{9} = ^-\frac{14}{72}$ or $^-\frac{7}{36}$

$^+.2 \times ^+1.3 = ^+.26$ $\qquad\qquad$ $^-10.4 \times ^+1.5 = ^-15.6$

$^+2 \cdot ^-7 = ^-14$ $\qquad\qquad$ $^-3 \cdot ^-12 = ^+36$

$^+7 \cdot ^-\frac{2}{3} = ^-\frac{14}{3}$ or $^-4\frac{2}{3}$ $\qquad$ $^-8 \cdot ^-\frac{5}{6} = ^+\frac{40}{6}$ or $^+\frac{20}{3}$ or $^+6\frac{2}{3}$

$^+\frac{2}{5} \cdot ^-\frac{1}{3} = ^-\frac{2}{15}$ $\qquad\qquad$ $^-\frac{4}{3} \cdot ^-\frac{2}{5} = ^+\frac{8}{15}$

$^+2.5 \times ^-.3 = ^-.75$ $\qquad\qquad$ $^-2.5 \times ^-1.5 = ^+3.75$

## EXERCISES

1. Work each of the following multiplication problems:

  **a.** $^+6 \cdot ^+8$ $\qquad\qquad\qquad$ **d.** $^-12 \cdot ^-7$

  **b.** $^+12 \cdot ^-3$ $\qquad\qquad\qquad$ **e.** $^+\frac{1}{2} \cdot ^-2$

  **c.** $^-4 \cdot ^+15$ $\qquad\qquad\qquad$ **f.** $^+\frac{2}{3} \cdot ^+\frac{2}{7}$

g. $\frac{-4}{5} \cdot \frac{+2}{7}$

h. $\frac{-11}{12} \cdot \frac{-2}{5}$

i. $^{-}.5 \times \frac{-2}{5}$

j. $^{+}1.6 \times \frac{-1}{3}$

k. $\frac{-4}{5} \times {}^{+}10.5$

l. $^{+}.7 \times \frac{+4}{5}$

m. $^{-}1.3 \times {}^{+}.5$

n. $^{+}2.7 \times {}^{-}1.4$

o. $^{-}.6 \times {}^{+}36.5$

p. $^{-}.5 \times {}^{-}.12$

q. $^{+}12 \times \frac{-1}{12}$

r. $^{-}3 \times \frac{-1}{3}$

s. $^{-}7 \times \frac{+1}{7}$

t. $^{-}.1 \times {}^{+}10$

u. $^{+}.01 \times {}^{-}100$

v. $\frac{-2}{7} \times \frac{-7}{2}$

w. $\frac{+4}{9} \times \frac{-9}{4}$

x. $\frac{-11}{5} \times \frac{-5}{11}$

y. $\frac{+3}{2} \times \frac{-2}{3}$

z. $^{-}11 \times {}^{+}111$

a'. $^{-}.02 \times {}^{-}.1$

b'. $\frac{-1}{4} \times \frac{-1}{4}$

c'. $^{-}.07 \times {}^{-}.07$

d'. $^{-}.8 \times {}^{+}.8$

2. Replace the frames with real number names to obtain true sentences:

a. $^{+}2 \cdot \square = {}^{+}16$

b. $\triangle \cdot {}^{+}4 = {}^{-}24$

c. $^{-}3 \times \bigcirc = {}^{-}6$

d. $^{-}16 \times {}^{+}\frac{1}{2} = \triangle$

e. $^{+}5 \times \square = {}^{-}25$

f. $^{+}2 \cdot \bigcirc = {}^{+}7$

g. $^{-}16 \times {}^{+}\frac{5}{2} = \bigcirc$

h. $\left({}^{+}\frac{2}{3}\right) \cdot \triangle = {}^{-}\frac{6}{7}$

i. $\square \cdot \left({}^{-}\frac{5}{8}\right) = {}^{+}\frac{3}{7}$

j. $\left({}^{+}\frac{5}{9}\right) \cdot \left({}^{-}\frac{6}{7}\right) = \triangle$

k. $\bigcirc \cdot \left({}^{+}\frac{4}{3}\right) = {}^{-}\frac{11}{9}$

l. $\square \cdot {}^{-}\frac{1}{6} = {}^{+}\frac{1}{2}$

3. Insert one of the symbols $=$, $<$, $>$, between each pair of expressions below to make true statements:

EXAMPLE $\qquad$ $|\, {}^{+}7 \cdot {}^{-}5 \,|$ $\qquad$ $|\, {}^{+}7 \,| \cdot |\, {}^{-}5 \,|$

SOLUTION $\qquad$ $|\, {}^{+}7 \cdot {}^{-}5 \,| = |\, {}^{-}35 \,| = {}^{+}35$

$\qquad\qquad\quad$ $|\, {}^{+}7 \,| \cdot |\, {}^{-}5 \,| = {}^{+}7 \cdot {}^{+}5 = {}^{+}35$

$\qquad$ Therefore,

$\qquad\qquad$ $|\, {}^{+}7 \cdot {}^{-}5 \,| = |\, {}^{+}7 \,| \cdot |\, {}^{-}5 \,|$

a. $|\, {}^{+}2 \cdot {}^{+}3 \,|$ $\qquad$ $|\, {}^{+}2 \,| \cdot |\, {}^{+}3 \,|$

b. $|\, {}^{+}\frac{1}{2} \cdot {}^{+}\frac{3}{4} \,|$ $\qquad$ $|\, {}^{+}\frac{1}{2} \,| \cdot |\, {}^{+}\frac{3}{4} \,|$

c. $|\, {}^{-}5 \cdot {}^{-}12 \,|$ $\qquad$ $|\, {}^{-}5 \,| \cdot |\, {}^{-}12 \,|$

d. $|\, {}^{-}1.2 \cdot {}^{-}2.5 \,|$ $\qquad$ $|\, {}^{-}1.2 \,| \cdot |\, {}^{-}2.5 \,|$

e. $|\, {}^{+}30 \cdot {}^{-}6 \,|$ $\qquad$ $|\, {}^{+}30 \,| \cdot |\, {}^{-}6 \,|$

f. $|\, {}^{-}12 \cdot {}^{+}12 \,|$ $\qquad$ $|\, {}^{-}12 \,| \cdot |\, {}^{+}12 \,|$

g. $|\, {}^{-}\frac{1}{2} \cdot {}^{+}\frac{1}{2} \,|$ $\qquad$ $|\, {}^{-}\frac{1}{2} \,| \cdot |\, {}^{+}\frac{1}{2} \,|$

4. Examine your answers to Exercise 3. What generalization is suggested by your answers. State it using frames.

## 10 · Basic Principles and Real Numbers

We have already made use of the desire to have all of the basic principles for operations with the numbers of arithmetic hold also for real numbers. It is very easy for you to see that, for example, the operations of addition and multiplication of real numbers are commutative.

What about associativity? Let·us check a few examples.

**EXAMPLE 1**   $(^-2 + {}^+3) + {}^-7 = {}^+1 + {}^-7 = {}^-6$
$^-2 + ({}^+3 + {}^-7) = {}^-2 + {}^-4 = {}^-6$
Therefore, $(^-2 + {}^+3) + {}^-7 = {}^-2 + ({}^+3 + {}^-7)$

**EXAMPLE 2**   $(^-\frac{1}{2} + {}^-\frac{3}{4}) + {}^-\frac{2}{5} = (^-\frac{10}{20} + {}^-\frac{15}{20}) + {}^-\frac{8}{20}$
$= {}^-\frac{25}{20} + {}^-\frac{8}{20} = {}^-\frac{33}{20}$
$= {}^-1\frac{13}{20}$
$^-\frac{1}{2} + ({}^-\frac{3}{4} + {}^-\frac{2}{5}) = {}^-\frac{10}{20} + ({}^-\frac{15}{20} + {}^-\frac{8}{20})$
$= {}^-\frac{10}{20} + {}^-\frac{23}{20}$
$= {}^-\frac{33}{20} = {}^-1\frac{13}{20}$
Therefore, $(^-\frac{1}{2} + {}^-\frac{3}{4}) + {}^-\frac{2}{5} = {}^-\frac{1}{2} + ({}^-\frac{3}{4} + {}^-\frac{2}{5})$

**EXAMPLE 3**   $(^-.3 + {}^+5.7) + {}^-17.3 = {}^+5.4 + {}^-17.3$
$= {}^-11.9$
$^-.3 + ({}^+5.7 + {}^-17.3) = {}^-.3 + {}^-11.6$
$= {}^-11.9$
Therefore, $(^-.3 + {}^+5.7) + {}^-17.3 = {}^-.3 + ({}^+5.7 + {}^-17.3)$

It seems quite reasonable to assume that the Associative Principle for Addition holds for real numbers. That is, for every replacement of $\square$, $\triangle$, and $\bigcirc$ by *real* number symbols,

$$(\square + \triangle) + \bigcirc = \square + (\triangle + \bigcirc)$$

yields a true statement.

## EXERCISES

1. In each exercise below there are two parts to be worked out. If you get the same answer to each part, state the principle or principles which justify your answers.

   **a.** $(^-3 + {}^+4) + {}^-2; {}^-3 + ({}^+4 + {}^-2)$
   **b.** $^-2 \cdot (^-6 + {}^+5); (^-2 \cdot {}^-6) + (^-2 \cdot {}^+5)$

**c.** $^-3 \cdot (^+2 \cdot {}^-7); (^-3 \cdot {}^+2) \cdot {}^-7$

**d.** $^-\frac{1}{2} + {}^-\frac{1}{4}; {}^-\frac{1}{4} + {}^-\frac{1}{2}$

**e.** $^-1.3 \times (^+2.9 + {}^-3.2); (^-1.3 \times {}^+2.9) + (^-1.3 \times {}^-3.2)$

**f.** $^-8 + |^-4|; |^-4| + {}^-8$

**g.** $|^-\frac{3}{5}| + |^-\frac{3}{4}|; |^-\frac{3}{4}| + |^-\frac{3}{5}|$

**h.** $^-\frac{1}{2} \cdot {}^-\frac{1}{4}; {}^-\frac{1}{4} \cdot {}^-\frac{1}{2}$

**i.** $^-5 \times {}^-3.4 + (^-5 \times {}^+3.6); {}^-5 \times (^-3.4 + {}^+3.6)$

**j.** $(^-6 + {}^+5) \cdot {}^-1; {}^+6 + {}^+5$

2. Make up three examples, and work them out to demonstrate that the Associative Principle of Multiplication holds for real numbers.
3. Using frames, state the Associative Principle of Multiplication.
4. Make up three examples and work them out to demonstrate that the multiplication of real numbers is distributive with respect to addition.
5. Using frames, state the Distributive Principle.

## 11 · Division of Real Numbers

From arithmetic you know that multiplication and division of the numbers of arithmetic are related. Any division problem can be changed to a related multiplication problem. For example:

$$12 \div 6 = 2 \text{ or } 2 \cdot 6 = 12$$
$$2 \div 6 = \tfrac{1}{3} \text{ or } \tfrac{1}{3} \cdot 6 = 2$$
$$\tfrac{1}{2} \div \tfrac{2}{3} = \tfrac{3}{4} \text{ or } \tfrac{3}{4} \cdot \tfrac{2}{3} = \tfrac{1}{2}$$

The same relationship exists between division and multiplication of real numbers. On the basis of this relationship, we shall be able to learn how to divide real numbers once we know how to multiply them. Study carefully each example below in order to learn how to divide directed numbers.

**(1)** $^+15 \div {}^+3 = ?$ **(1′)** $? \cdot {}^+3 = {}^+15$
**or,** what number multiplied by $^+3$ gives $^+15$?
**Answer:** $^+5.$ *Therefore,* $^+15 \div {}^+3 = {}^+5.$

**(2)** $^+2 \div {}^+6 = ?$ **(2′)** $? \cdot {}^+6 = {}^+2$
**or,** what number multiplied by $^+6$ gives $^+2$?
**Answer:** $^+\frac{1}{3}.$ *Therefore,* $^+2 \div {}^+6 = {}^+\frac{1}{3}.$

**(3)** $^+8 \div {}^-4 = ?$ **(3′)** $? \cdot {}^-4 = {}^+8$
**or,** what number multiplied by $^-4$ gives $^+8$?
**Answer:** $^-2.$ *Therefore,* $^+8 \div {}^-4 = {}^-2.$

(4) $^+6 \div ^-18 = ?$     (4') $? \cdot ^-18 = ^+6$
**or,** what number multiplied by $^-18$ gives $^+6$?
**Answer:** $^-\frac{1}{3}$.     *Therefore,* $^+6 \div ^-18 = ^-\frac{1}{3}$.

(5) $^-14 \div ^+7 = ?$     (5') $? \cdot ^+7 = ^-14$
**or,** what number multiplied by $^+7$ gives $^-14$?
**Answer:** $^-2$.     *Therefore,* $^-14 \div ^+7 = ^-2$.

(6) $^-5 \div ^+10 = ?$     (6') $? \cdot ^+10 = ^-5$
**or,** what number multiplied by $^+10$ gives $^-5$?
**Answer:** $^-\frac{1}{2}$.     *Therefore,* $^-5 \div ^+10 = ^-\frac{1}{2}$.

(7) $^-18 \div ^-3 = ?$     (7') $? \cdot ^-3 = ^-18$
**or,** what number multiplied by $^-3$ gives $^-18$?
**Answer:** $^+6$.     *Therefore,* $^-18 \div ^-3 = ^+6$.

(8) $^-5 \div ^-25 = ?$     (8') $? \cdot ^-25 = ^-5$
**or,** what number multiplied by $^-25$ gives $^-5$?
**Answer:** $^+\frac{1}{5}$.     *Therefore,* $^-5 \div ^-25 = ^+\frac{1}{5}$.

The pattern above can be stated generally as

$$\triangle \div \square = \bigcirc \text{ means } \bigcirc \times \square = \triangle$$

for every replacement of $\triangle$, $\square$, and $\bigcirc$, except zero for $\square$.

Now let us take a different look at the division of numbers of arithmetic. Here are some examples to point out an interesting relationship.

$$18 \div 3 = 6 \text{ and } 18 \cdot \frac{1}{3} = 6$$
$$26 \div 2 = 13 \text{ and } 26 \cdot \frac{1}{2} = 13$$
$$5 \div \frac{2}{3} = 7\frac{1}{2} \text{ and } 5 \cdot \frac{3}{2} = 7\frac{1}{2}$$

The examples above show that division can be replaced by multiplication in a way different from the one you already considered.

In this relationship certain pairs of numbers recur. Let us look at these pairs:

$$3, \tfrac{1}{3}; \ 2, \tfrac{1}{2}; \ \tfrac{2}{3}, \tfrac{3}{2}$$

3 is the **reciprocal** of $\frac{1}{3}$; 2 is the reciprocal of $\frac{1}{2}$; $\frac{2}{3}$ is the reciprocal of $\frac{3}{2}$. What is the product of a number and its reciprocal?

Thus, we can say that dividing a number by another number can be replaced by multiplication of the first number by the reciprocal of the divisor. Using frames,

$$\square \div \triangle = \square \times \frac{1}{\triangle}$$

We shall call this the Principle of Division. Like the other principles, it also holds for the real numbers.

# EXERCISES

**1.** Change each problem below to the related multiplication problem, then find the answer:

**EXAMPLE**      $^+12 \div {}^-2 = ?$

**SOLUTION**      $^+12 \div {}^-2 = ?$

The related multiplication problem is:

$? \cdot {}^-2 = {}^+12$

or,

"What number multiplied by $^-2$ gives $^+12$?"

The answer, of course, is $^-6$.

Therefore, $^+12 \div {}^-2 = {}^-6$

**a.** $^-16 \div {}^-4$

**b.** $^+100 \div {}^-2$

**c.** $^-100 \div {}^+50$

**d.** $^-17 \div {}^+17$

**e.** $^+35 \div {}^+1$

**f.** $^+35 \div {}^-1$

**g.** $^-35 \div {}^+1$

**h.** $^-35 \div {}^-1$

**i.** $^+99 \div {}^-11$

**j.** $^-99 \div {}^-11$

**k.** $^+99 \div {}^+11$

**l.** $^-99 \div {}^+11$

**m.** $^-1 \div {}^-1$

**n.** $^+1 \div {}^-1$

**o.** $^-1 \div {}^+1$

**p.** $^+1 \div {}^+1$

**q.** $^-\frac{1}{2} \div {}^-\frac{1}{2}$

**r.** $^-3.673 \div {}^-3.673$

**s.** $^+4.006 \div {}^-4.006$

**t.** $^-111.12 \div {}^+111.12$

**2.** Examine your answers in Exercise 1. If you have a theory about the division of one real number by another, use it on the exercises below. Tell no one your theory. Let your teacher check your answers.

**a.** $^-17 \div {}^+2$

**b.** $^+52 \div {}^-4$

**c.** $^-21 \div {}^-3$

**d.** $^+10 \div {}^-20$

**e.** $^-255 \div {}^+3$

**f.** $^-1000 \div {}^-100$

**g.** $^-\frac{1}{3} \div {}^+4$

**h.** $^-2 \div {}^-\frac{1}{3}$

**i.** $^-\frac{1}{2} \div {}^+\frac{1}{2}$

**j.** $^+5.6 \div {}^-2.8$

**k.** $^-.1 \div {}^-10$

**l.** $^-2 \div {}^+.1$

**m.** $^+\frac{3}{4} \div {}^-\frac{2}{3}$

**n.** $^-\frac{1}{2} \div {}^-\frac{7}{8}$

**o.** $^-4 \div {}^-.003$

**p.** $0 \div {}^-125$

**q.** $0 \div {}^+136$

**r.** $^-\frac{1}{2} \div {}^+5$

**s.** $^+.7 \div {}^-10$

**t.** $^-.33 \div {}^-\frac{1}{16}$

**u.** $^+17.305 \div {}^+\frac{1}{2}$

**v.** $^+\frac{3}{10} \div {}^-\frac{17}{2}$

3. Replace the frames with real number symbols to obtain true statements:

a. $\triangle \div {}^+2 = {}^+6$

b. $\square \div {}^-4 = {}^+10$

c. $\bigcirc \div {}^+10 = {}^-12$

d. $\triangle \div {}^-15 = {}^-4$

e. $^+20 \div \triangle = {}^+1$

f. $^-10 \div \square = {}^+2$

g. $^-5 \div \bigcirc = {}^-2.5$

h. $^+10 \div {}^-2.5 = \triangle$

i. $^-25 \div {}^-75 = \square$

j. $\frac{-1}{2} \div \frac{-1}{4} = \bigcirc$

k. $^+\frac{7}{8} \div \frac{-4}{5} = \square$

l. $^-7 \div \square = {}^+\frac{6}{7}$

m. $\bigcirc \div {}^+3 = {}^-7$

n. $^-9 \div \triangle = {}^+\frac{5}{7}$

o. $^+5 \div {}^+7 = \square$

p. $\triangle \div {}^-5 = {}^+9$

q. $^-13 \div \square = {}^+17$

r. $^+14 \div {}^+\frac{5}{3} = \triangle$

s. $\square \div {}^+\frac{6}{7} = \frac{-5}{9}$

t. $\triangle \div {}^-3.5 = {}^-1$

4. Compute the answer to each pair of exercises below:

a. $^+16 \div {}^+4;\ {}^+16 \cdot {}^+\frac{1}{4}$

b. $^+27 \div {}^+3;\ {}^+27 \cdot {}^+\frac{1}{3}$

c. $^+49 \div {}^-7;\ {}^+49 \cdot {}^-\frac{1}{7}$

d. $^-72 \div {}^+8;\ {}^-72 \cdot {}^+\frac{1}{8}$

e. $^+144 \div {}^-12;\ {}^+144 \cdot {}^-\frac{1}{12}$

f. $^-85 \div {}^-5;\ {}^-85 \cdot {}^-\frac{1}{5}$

g. $^-91 \div {}^+7;\ {}^-91 \cdot {}^+\frac{1}{7}$

h. $^+70 \div {}^-5;\ {}^+70 \cdot {}^-\frac{1}{5}$

i. $^-102 \div {}^-6;\ {}^-102 \cdot {}^-\frac{1}{6}$

j. $^-48 \div {}^-\frac{1}{2};\ {}^-48 \cdot {}^-2$

5. The product of a number and its reciprocal is 1. Give the reciprocal of each of the following numbers:

a. $^+4$

b. $^+3$

c. $^-7$

d. $^+8$

e. $^-12$

f. $^-5$

g. $^+7$

h. $^-6$

i. $\frac{-1}{2}$

j. $^+\frac{1}{4}$

k. $\frac{-2}{3}$

l. $^+\frac{4}{7}$

m. $-\frac{6}{13}$

n. $^+1.6$

o. $^-1.1$

p. $\frac{-5}{6}$

q. $^+\frac{17}{18}$

r. $\frac{-3}{4}$

s. $^+3.4$

t. $^-4.23$

u. $^-1.01$

v. $^+2.04$

w. $^-1.05$

x. $^-2.78$

6. What can you tell about the reciprocal of a positive number?

7. What can you tell about the reciprocal of a negative number?

8. What can you tell about the reciprocal of a number between 0 and $^+1$?

9. Does 0 have a reciprocal?

# VOCABULARY

absolute value (55)
dense (64)
directed number (51)
greater than ($>$) (53)
integer (52)
irrational number (64)
less than ($<$) (53)
negative number (51)
not equal to ($\neq$) (53)
not greater than ($\not>$) (53)
not less than ($\not<$) (53)

number line (50)
opposite of a number (55)
origin (53)
positive number (51)
rational number (60)
real number (68)
reciprocal (82)
repeating decimal (62)
square root 65
terminating decimal (62)

. . . . . . . . . . . . . . . . . . . . . . . . . . . . . . . . . . . . . . . . . . . . . . . . . . . . . . . . . . . . .

# REVIEW EXERCISES

1. Work each of the following:

   a. $^+4 + {}^+3$

   b. $^-7 + {}^+24$

   c. $^+89 + {}^-120$

   d. $^-36 + {}^-112$

   e. $^+7 - {}^+15$

   f. $^+36 - {}^+17$

   g. $^-3 - {}^+21$

   h. $^-7 - {}^-29$

   i. $^+3 \cdot {}^+9$

   j. $^+10 \cdot {}^-23$

   k. $^-12 \cdot {}^-12$

   l. $^-150 \cdot 0$

   m. $0 \div {}^-199$

   n. $^-17 \div {}^+17$

   o. $^+52 \div {}^-4$

   p. $^-99 \div {}^-11$

   q. $\frac{^-1}{2} \cdot {}^-4$

   r. $^-9 \cdot {}^-\frac{1}{27}$

   s. $^+\frac{2}{3} \cdot {}^-\frac{4}{7}$

   t. $^+.6 \times {}^-1.7$

   u. $\frac{^-3}{4} \div {}^+4$

   v. $^+\frac{1}{3} \div {}^+\frac{1}{100}$

   w. $\frac{^-7}{3} \div {}^+\frac{3}{8}$

   x. $^+\frac{20}{17} \div {}^-\frac{1}{2}$

   y. $\frac{^-1}{2} - {}^+\frac{1}{3}$

   z. $^+\frac{2}{7} - {}^-\frac{3}{5}$

   a'. $^-8.5 - {}^+9.7$

   b'. $^-100.1 + {}^-\frac{4}{5}$

   c'. $^+\frac{3}{4} + {}^-\frac{4}{6}$

   d'. $\frac{^-1}{2} + {}^-7.65$

   e'. $\frac{^-7}{11} + {}^-\frac{3}{2}$

   f'. $^+6.66 + {}^-3.3$

2. Indicate which of the following statements are true and which are false:

   a. $^-17 < {}^-137$

   b. $| {}^-17 | < | {}^-137 |$

   c. $| {}^+\frac{1}{2} | > | {}^-\frac{1}{3} |$

   d. $| {}^-45 | \leq {}^+100$

**e.** $|\frac{-3}{+3}| \neq {}^{+}1$

**f.** $|{}^{-}7 + {}^{-}2| \geq |{}^{-}7| + |{}^{-}2|$

**g.** $|{}^{-}2| \cdot |{}^{-}3| = |{}^{-}2 \cdot {}^{-}3|$

**h.** $|{}^{-}6 \div {}^{+}3| \neq |{}^{-}6| \div |{}^{+}3|$

**i.** $|{}^{-}4 - {}^{+}16| \nleq |{}^{-}4| - |{}^{+}16|$

**j.** $|{}^{-}2| \leq |{}^{+}2|$

**3.** Replace the frames with real number names to obtain true statements:

**a.** $\square + {}^{-}7 = {}^{-}9$

**b.** ${}^{-}9 - \triangle = {}^{-}13$

**c.** $\frac{-3}{2} \cdot \square = {}^{+}\frac{8}{9}$

**d.** $\bigcirc \div {}^{+}2 = {}^{+}5$

**e.** ${}^{+}13 - \triangle = {}^{-}13$

**f.** $\triangle \cdot {}^{+}4 = {}^{+}\frac{7}{9}$

**g.** ${}^{-}9 + \square = {}^{-}13$

**h.** ${}^{-}7 \div \triangle = {}^{-}4$

**i.** $\bigcirc - {}^{-}3 = {}^{+}5$

**4.** Replace the frames with real number names to obtain

       (1)   a true statement

       (2)   a false statement

**a.** $|\triangle| < {}^{+}2$

**b.** $\square + {}^{-}3 \neq {}^{-}7$

**c.** ${}^{-}9 \cdot \triangle = {}^{+}27$

**d.** $\triangle - {}^{-}9 \neq {}^{+}5$

**e.** ${}^{+}8 + \triangle < {}^{-}3$

**f.** ${}^{+}6 \cdot \square > {}^{-}3$

**5.** Simplify each of the following:

**EXAMPLE 1**     $({}^{+}10 + {}^{-}15 - {}^{-}3) \cdot {}^{-}2$

**SOLUTION**

$$({}^{+}10 + {}^{-}15 - {}^{-}3) \cdot {}^{-}2$$
$$= ({}^{-}5 - {}^{-}3) \cdot {}^{-}2$$
$$= {}^{-}2 \cdot {}^{-}2$$
$$= {}^{+}4$$

**EXAMPLE 2**     $(-\frac{1}{4} + -\frac{1}{4}) \cdot (-3 - {}^{+}1)$

**SOLUTION**     $(-\frac{1}{4} + -\frac{1}{4}) \cdot (-3 - {}^{+}1)$

$$= (-\frac{1}{2}) \cdot (-4)$$
$$= {}^{+}2$$

**a.** ${}^{-}3 + {}^{-}17 - {}^{+}2 - {}^{-}6$

**b.** ${}^{-}4 \cdot {}^{-}2 + {}^{-}3 + {}^{-}1.5$

**c.** ${}^{+}3 + {}^{-}1.5 - {}^{+}7 \cdot {}^{-}4$

**d.** $({}^{+}3 + {}^{-}4) \cdot -\frac{1}{2}$

**e.** ${}^{-}.75 \times ({}^{-}3 + {}^{-}4) \cdot ({}^{-}2 - {}^{+}3)$

**f.** $(-\frac{1}{2} + -\frac{1}{2}) \cdot (-\frac{1}{3} + -\frac{1}{3} + -\frac{1}{3})$

**g.** $\frac{-1.6}{1.6} \times \frac{-3.5}{3.5} + (^+176 + {}^-176) \cdot {}^-\frac{1}{176}$

**h.** $[(^-6 + {}^-13) \cdot (^+\frac{1}{2} + {}^-\frac{7}{14})] \div {}^+\frac{1}{3}$

**i.** $[(^+\frac{1}{2} \div {}^-\frac{3}{7}) \div {}^-\frac{1}{2}] \cdot {}^-\frac{2}{3}$

**6.** *(Optional)* Solve each of the following problems. You should give careful thought to each problem because there may be several answers or no answer to some problems.

**a.** A real number multiplied by $^+2$ yields the same answer as that number divided by $^+2$. What is the number?

**b.** The sum of a real number and $^+5$ is the same as the product of that number and 0. What is the number?

**c.** The product of $^+2$ and the absolute value of a real number is $^+10$. How many such numbers are there? Find them.

**d.** Can you find two real numbers such that the product of the absolute values of these numbers is a negative number?

**e.** The sum of two different positive even integers is $^+12$. What are the two integers? How many pairs of such integers can you find?

**f.** Repeat Exercise **e** when the sum of the two positive even integers is $^+13$.

**g.** The sum of two positive odd integers is $^+12$. How many pairs of such integers can you find?

**h.** Repeat Exercise **g** when the sum of the two positive odd integers is $^+13$.

**i.** The sum of two different numbers is the same as the product of these numbers. How many pairs of such numbers can you find?

Note: $^+2$ and $^+2$ are *not two* different numbers.

One such pair is, for example,

$^+5$ and $^+\frac{5}{4}$, because

$$^+5 + {}^+\tfrac{5}{4} = {}^+5\tfrac{5}{4} = {}^+6\tfrac{1}{4}$$

$$\text{and } {}^+5 \cdot {}^+\tfrac{5}{4} = {}^+\tfrac{25}{4} = {}^+6\tfrac{1}{4}$$

**j.** (1) What is the product of $^+6$ and its absolute value?

(2) What is the product of $^-6$ and its absolute value?

(3) What can you tell about the product of a positive number and its absolute value?

(4) What can you tell about the product of a negative number and its absolute value?

**k.** Answer questions 1, 2, 3, and 4 in Exercise **j** concerning quotients of the same numbers.

**l.** Twice a real number subtracted from the number is $^+3$. What is the number?

**m.** Using a directed number, express the financial standing of a company which has assets of $1,756,000 and liabilities of $879,167.

**n.** Your watch is 7 minutes faster than the radio time. The clock in your school is 3 minutes slower than your watch. Is the clock in your school faster or slower than the radio time? By how much?

**o.** Write names for the numbers 0, 1, 2, 3, and so on using four and only four symbols "4". You are allowed to use any operations you wish.

$$\text{Hint: } 0 = \tfrac{4}{4} - \tfrac{4}{4}$$
$$1 = \tfrac{4+4}{4+4}$$
$$2 = \tfrac{4}{4} + \tfrac{4}{4}$$
$$3 = \tfrac{4}{\sqrt{4}} + \tfrac{4}{4}$$

Keep going!

**p.** In Canada, tides are measured in the following way: '0' level is selected just above the lowest possible tide, and all tides are measured from this '0'. Suppose a tugboat captain knows he cannot go through a certain channel until the tide level is 5 feet 6 inches. If the present tide level is $^-6''$, and the tide is going up at the rate of $20''$ per hour, how long will he have to wait for the channel to be safe?

**q.** A driver drives 1 mile uphill at 30 mph. How fast must he drive a second mile downhill in order to average 60 mph on the two-mile stretch?

## CHAPTER TEST

**1.** Replace the frames with real number names to obtain true statements:

| | | |
|---|---|---|
| **a.** $^+1 + {}^+13 = \triangle$ | **i.** $^-5 - \triangle = {}^-1$ | **q.** $^-18 \div {}^-3 = \square$ |
| **b.** $^+4 + {}^-3 = \square$ | **j.** $\square - {}^-5 = {}^-5$ | **r.** $^-24 \div {}^+8 = \bigcirc$ |
| **c.** $^+9 + \triangle = {}^-16$ | **k.** $^+10 - {}^-4 = \bigcirc$ | **s.** $^+5 \div \square = {}^-5$ |
| **d.** $\bigcirc + {}^-10 = {}^-3$ | **l.** $\triangle - {}^-25 = {}^+20$ | **t.** $\triangle \div {}^+8 = {}^+30$ |
| **e.** $^+17 - {}^+3 = \triangle$ | **m.** $^+3 \times {}^+25 = \square$ | **u.** $0 \div {}^-3 = \triangle$ |
| **f.** $\bigcirc - {}^+30 = {}^-20$ | **n.** $^-4 \times \triangle = {}^+21$ | **v.** $\square \div {}^-2 = 0$ |
| **g.** $^-2 - \square = {}^+3$ | **o.** $\square \times {}^-8 = {}^-32$ | **w.** $^-\tfrac{1}{2} \div {}^-\tfrac{1}{4} = \triangle$ |
| **h.** $^-3 - {}^+2 = \bigcirc$ | **p.** $^+12 \times {}^-2 = \triangle$ | **x.** $\square \div {}^+\tfrac{6}{7} = {}^-\tfrac{5}{9}$ |

**2.** Which statements are true and which are false?

   **a.** $^-3 < ^-117$

   **b.** $^+1 > ^-225$

   **c.** $0 > ^-100$

   **d.** $^+13 < 0$

   **e.** $^+\frac{1}{2} > ^+1.5$

   **f.** $^-12 \geq ^-12$

   **g.** $^+\frac{3}{4} \leq ^+\frac{3}{4}$

   **h.** $|\ ^-2 \div ^+2\ | \neq ^+1$

   **i.** $|\ ^-8 \div ^+4\ | \neq |\ ^-8\ | \div |\ ^+4\ |$

   **j.** $|\ ^-3\ | \times |\ ^-4\ | \neq |\ ^-3 \times ^-4\ |$

   **k.** $|\ ^-3 + ^+4\ | < |\ ^-3\ | + |\ ^+4\ |$

   **l.** $|\ ^+1\ | + |\ ^-4\ | \leq |\ ^+1 + ^-4\ |$

   **m.** $|\ ^-11.78 + ^+\frac{3}{17}\ | > 0$

   **n.** $|\ ^-17 + ^-3\ | \times 0 \leq 0$

   **o.** $|\ ^+3\ | - |\ ^-3\ | = 0$

   **p.** $^+\frac{3}{7}$ and $^-\frac{7}{3}$ are opposites of each other.

   **q.** $\sqrt{2} = 1.414$

**3.** When $\frac{5}{33}$ is written in the form of a decimal, is it a repeating or terminating decimal? Determine your answer by calculation.

**4.** Determine $\sqrt{13}$ to two decimal places.

**5.** Replace the frames with real number symbols to obtain

(1) a true statement; (2) a false statement:

   **a.** $^-3 \not< \triangle$

   **b.** $^-2 \cdot \square \geq ^+17$

   **c.** $\frac{\triangle}{^-4} < ^+17$

   **d.** $^-9 + \bigcirc > ^-4$

   **e.** $\triangle + ^-3 > 0$

   **f.** $^-2 \cdot \triangle - ^+7 = ^-11$

   **g.** $\frac{\square + ^+6}{^-2} = ^+8$

   **h.** $^+3(\triangle + ^-3) = ^-12$

   **i.** $^-6 \cdot \square + ^+5 = ^+29$

   **j.** $|\ \triangle\ | < ^+3$

**6.** What is the rational number midway between $^-3.19$ and $^+2.11$?

**7.** Express the following in the form $\frac{^+\square}{\triangle}$ or $\frac{^-\square}{\triangle}$, where $\triangle$ and $\square$ are replaced by natural number names.

   **a.** $^-3.29$     **b.** $^+.111$     **c.** $^-3\frac{2}{7}$

8. Tell whether the following numbers are rational or irrational:

   **a.** $+.135135\dot{1}\dot{3}\dot{5}$

   **b.** $-.26126112611126 \cdots$

   **c.** $-.141414\dot{1}\dot{4}$

   **d.** $+\sqrt{3}$

   **e.** $-.1497813$

9. Find replacements for $\square$ and $\triangle$ from real numbers to obtain true statements:

   **a.** $+\frac{4}{3} \cdot \square + {}^+11 = {}^+35$

   **b.** $\dfrac{{}^+12 - {}^+6 \cdot \triangle}{{}^+5} = {}^-6$

# CUMULATIVE REVIEW

1. Suppose $B = \{g, k, l, m\}$. List all the possible subsets of $B$.

2. Give an example of a pair of finite sets which are matching.

3. Let $U = \{1, 3, 5, 7, 9, 11\}$

   $A = \{1, 5, 7\}$    $B = \{3, 7, 9, 11\}$    $C = \{1, 7, 9\}$

   Determine the following sets:

   **a.** $A \cap B$

   **b.** $B \cap A$

   **c.** $B \cup A$

   **d.** $A \cup B$

   **e.** $(A \cup B) \cup C$

   **f.** $A \cup (B \cup C)$

   **★g.** $\bar{A} \cap \bar{B}$

   **★h.** $\bar{A} \cup \bar{B}$

4. $F = \{1, 4, 7, 11, 13\}$, $G = \{4, 7, 11, 13\}$, $K = \{4, 6, 7, 13, 11\}$. Are the following statements true of false?

   **a.** $F \subset G$

   **b.** $G \subset K$

   **c.** $G \subset F$

   **d.** $K \subset K$

5. $H = \{2, 6, 12, 16, 22\}$; is $H$ a subset of the set of even integers? Why?

6. Let $R$ stand for the set of real numbers, $I$ stand for the set of integers, $Ra$ stand for the set of rational numbers.
   Are the following statements true or false?

   **a.** $I \subset R$?        **b.** $Ra \subset I$?        **c.** $I \subset Ra$?

7. Name the principle illustrated by each of the following:

   **a.** $^-4 + (^-6\frac{1}{3} + 5\frac{1}{9}) = (^-4 + {}^-6\frac{1}{3}) + 5\frac{1}{9}$

   **b.** $[5 \cdot (^-2)] \cdot (^-2\frac{1}{4}) = (^-2\frac{1}{4}) \cdot [5 \cdot (^-2)]$

   **c.** $(^-7) \cdot [(^-2\frac{1}{8}) + (^-5\frac{1}{9})] = (^-7) \cdot (^-2\frac{1}{8}) + (^-7) \cdot (^-5\frac{1}{9})$

   **d.** $(\frac{7}{3} \cdot \frac{8}{11}) \cdot 1 = (\frac{7}{3} \cdot \frac{8}{11})$

★8. Let $R$ stand for the set of real numbers, $Ra$ stand for the set of rational numbers, $Ir$ stand for the set of irrational numbers, $I$ stand for the set of integers.

Are the following true or false?

   **a.** $R \subset I$

   **b.** $Ra \subset Ir$

   **c.** $I \subset Ra$

   **d.** $Ra \subset R$

9. Give replacements for the frames which make the statements true:

   **a.** $(^-4\frac{1}{2}) \cdot [^+13\frac{1}{3} + (^-7\frac{2}{5})] = (^-4\frac{1}{2}) \cdot (\triangle) + (^-4\frac{1}{2}) \cdot (^-7\frac{2}{5})$

   **b.** $[(^-7\frac{1}{7}) \cdot \triangle] \cdot {}^+3\frac{1}{6} = {}^+3\frac{1}{6} \cdot [(^-7\frac{1}{7}) \cdot (^+8\frac{1}{4})]$

   **c.** $[(^-4) + (^-2\frac{1}{9})] + \square = (^-4) + [(^-2\frac{1}{9}) + \square]$

   **d.** $^-7 + \bigcirc = 0$

   **e.** $^-6 - \triangle = {}^-11\frac{1}{4}$

   **f.** $\square \cdot [(^-3\frac{2}{7}) + \triangle] = (^-5\frac{3}{8}) \cdot (^-3\frac{2}{7}) + (^-5\frac{3}{8}) \cdot (^+7\frac{5}{7})$

# BIBLIOGRAPHY

Adler, I., *The Magic House of Numbers*, The John Day Company, New York, 1957.

Bakst, A., *Mathematics—Its Magic and Mastery*, D. Van Nostrand, Toronto, 1952, "How the Number Magician Does It"—pages 150–157.

Bakst, A., *Mathematical Puzzles and Pastimes*, D. Van Nostrand, Toronto, 1954, "Billiard Ball Computer"—pages 10–21.

School Mathematics Study Group, *Mathematics for High School: First Course in Algebra, Part 1*, (Revised Edition), SMSG, New Haven, Connecticut, 1960, pages 97–120.

School Mathematics Study Group, *Mathematics for Junior High School: Supplementary Units*, SMSG, New Haven, Connecticut, 1960, "Repeating Decimals and Tests for Divisibility,"—pages 49–66.

# 4

# Open Sentences

## I · True and False Mathematical Sentences

In your English classes you have studied sentence construction. Much of what you learned there can also be applied to mathematical sentences. There is a similarity between some English sentences and some mathematical sentences.

It is easy to tell whether some English sentences are true or false. Consider the sentence "Babe Ruth was a famous baseball figure." If you know something of the history of baseball, you can tell whether this sentence is true or false.

The mathematical sentence "$\frac{1}{2} = \frac{2}{4}$" can similarly be judged true or false if you know something about arithmetic. You will say that this sentence is true because $\frac{1}{2}$ is $\frac{2}{4}$, or because $\frac{1}{2}$ and $\frac{2}{4}$ are two symbols for the same number. Thus,

$$\frac{1}{2} = \frac{2}{4}$$

can be read as                  "$\frac{1}{2}$ is equal to $\frac{2}{4}$"

or

"$\frac{1}{2}$ equals $\frac{2}{4}$"

or

"$\frac{1}{2}$ is $\frac{2}{4}$"

On the other hand, the sentence $\frac{3}{5} = .5$ is false because $\frac{3}{5}$ and $.5$ are numerals naming two different numbers.

If we should write $\frac{3}{5} \neq .5$ this would be a true sentence. Explain.

Another true sentence is $\frac{3}{5} > .5$ which we read "$\frac{3}{5}$ is greater than $.5$."

92

We can find English sentences which are analogous to mathematical sentences. For example, the sentence "The Saskatchewan is the longest river in Canada" is such a sentence. This sentence gives you two names for the same river. You can say "The Saskatchewan," or you can say "the longest river in Canada," and in each case you will be referring to the same river. Of course, you must know some geography to be able to tell whether or not this sentence is true. This sentence may be written as "The Saskatchewan = the longest river in Canada" in order to see the analogy between this sentence and the mathematical sentence "$\frac{1}{2} = \frac{2}{4}$."

You have already worked with mathematical sentences containing the symbols $<$, $>$, and $\neq$. For example, $^+5 < {}^+273$, $^-3 > {}^-13\frac{1}{2}$, and $^-17 \neq {}^+5$ are such sentences. They are read as follows:

$^+5 < {}^+273$     "positive 5 is less than positive 273"

$^-3 > {}^-13\frac{1}{2}$     "negative 3 is greater than negative $13\frac{1}{2}$"

$^-17 \neq {}^+5$     "negative 17 is unequal to positive 5"

## EXERCISES

1. Label each sentence as either true or false:

  **a.** Lewis Carroll = the author of the book *Alice in Wonderland*
  **b.** Chicago = the largest city in the world
  **c.** Brussels = the city of the World's Fair of 1958
  **d.** Nile = the longest river in Egypt
  **e.** Venus = the farthest planet from the earth
  **f.** The Empire State Building = the tallest building in the world
  **g.** Cain = the first-born of Adam and Eve
  **h.** Montreal = the city of the World's Fair in 1967.
  **i.** Belgium = the smallest country in the world
  **j.** Prince Edward Island = the smallest province in Canada.
  **k.** Yugoslavia = the only Communist country in the world
  **l.** $^+\frac{17}{10} = {}^+1.7$
  **m.** $^+3.03\frac{1}{2} = {}^+3\frac{7}{200}$
  **n.** $^+1\% = {}^+.1$
  **o.** $^+\frac{1050}{100} = {}^+10.5$
  **p.** $^+.2\% = {}^+20$
  **q.** $^+.01\% = {}^+\frac{1}{10,000}$
  **r.** $^+17^2 = {}^+289$
  **s.** $^+\sqrt{50,625} = {}^+225$
  **t.** $^+\sqrt{9} = {}^+3$
  **u.** $^-2 \cdot {}^-2 = {}^-4$
  **v.** $^+\sqrt{1024} = {}^+32$

**2.** Label each sentence as either true or false:

**a.** $^-2 < ^-3$

**b.** $^+5 > ^-\frac{1}{2}$

**c.** $|^-2| > |^+1|$

**d.** $|^-4| \neq |^+4|$

**e.** $^-\frac{1}{2} + ^-\frac{1}{2} < ^+\frac{1}{2} + ^+\frac{1}{2}$

**f.** $|^-3 \cdot ^-4| > |^+3 \cdot ^+4|$

**g.** $|^+3 - ^+7| = |^-7 - ^-3|$

**h.** $|^-1 - ^+6| = |^+6 - ^-1|$

**i.** $^+100\% > ^+100$

**j.** $^+.5\% < ^+.5$

**k.** $^+200\% \neq ^+2$

**l.** $^+\frac{3}{4} = ^+.75$

**m.** $^+\frac{1}{3} \neq ^+.3$

**n.** $^+\frac{1}{9} = ^+\frac{90}{810}$

**o.** $^+.0032 \neq ^+\frac{8}{2500}$

**p.** $^+\frac{1}{7} = ^+.14285714285\overset{.......}{7}$

**q.** $^+\frac{3}{8} \neq ^+.375$

## 2 · Open Sentences

The sentences we discussed in the previous section were either true or false. In some cases you might have had to look up certain facts in books. But, once you located the information you were looking for, you were able to decide whether the sentence was true or false.

There are some sentences which are neither true nor false. No amount of information will enable you to decide about the truth of such a sentence. Consider, for example, the sentence "She is a queen." Is this sentence true or false? Of course, you cannot decide, because you do not know who *she* is. But if you replace the pronoun "she" with a name of a person, then you obtain a sentence which is either true or false. For example, if you replace "she" with "Elizabeth II," then the sentence "She is a queen" is a true sentence. Similarly, if "she" is replaced by "Mary Jones," then the resulting sentence, "Mary Jones is a queen" is false.

$$x + ^+5 = ^+7$$

This sentence is neither true nor false because we do not know what $x$ is.

Suppose we replace the letter $x$ in the sentence above by $^+3$. Is the resulting sentence,

$$^+3 + ^+5 = ^+7,$$

true or false? It is false, because $^+3 + ^+5$ and $^+7$ are not numerals for the same number.

Let us replace $x$ by $^+2$ in the sentence

$$x + ^+5 = ^+7.$$

We obtain $^{+}2 + {^{+}5} = {^{+}7}$ which is a true sentence, because $^{+}2 + {^{+}5}$ and $^{+}7$ are names for the numeral.

Mathematical sentences which contain letters or other symbols like frames to be replaced by number names and which are neither true nor false are called *open sentences*. Examples of such sentences are

$$y - {^{+}7} = {^{+}1}$$
$$\frac{^{+}5}{a} = {^{+}3}$$
$$^{-}7 \cdot f = {^{-}\tfrac{1}{2}}$$
$$^{+}3 \cdot d < {^{+}16}$$
$$^{+}5 \cdot m - {^{+}3} > {^{+}16}$$
$$^{+}\tfrac{1}{3} \cdot n + {^{+}14} = {^{+}16} \cdot n - {^{+}3}$$
$$\triangle + {^{-}13} = {^{-}22}$$
$$^{-}2 \cdot \square + {^{-}7} = {^{+}21}$$

## EXERCISES

1. In each sentence below, replace the letter by a numeral so that a false sentence is obtained; then replace the letter by another numeral so that a true sentence is obtained.

**EXAMPLE 1**   $^{-}2 + y = {^{+}3}$

**SOLUTION**
(1)   $^{-}4$ for $y$
      $^{-}2 + {^{-}4} = {^{+}3}$; False
(2)   $^{+}5$ for $y$
      $^{-}2 + {^{+}5} = {^{+}3}$; True

**EXAMPLE 2**   $\dfrac{^{-}2}{a} = {^{+}2}$

**SOLUTION**
(1)   $^{+}2$ for $a$
      $\frac{^{-}2}{^{+}2} = {^{+}2}$; False
(2)   $^{-}1$ for $a$
      $\frac{^{-}2}{^{-}1} = {^{+}2}$; True

**a.** $^{+}3 + x = {^{+}7}$

**b.** $c + {^{-}5} = 0$

**c.** $^{-}1 + m = {^{-}5}$

**d.** $d + {^{+}2} = {^{-}10}$

**e.** $^{+}5 - t = {^{+}4}$

**f.** $s - {^{+}9} = {^{+}1}$

**g.** $d - {}^-3 = {}^+17$

**n.** $\dfrac{r}{{}^-3} = {}^+\frac{2}{3}$

**h.** ${}^-12 - p = {}^-11$

**o.** ${}^+\frac{1}{2} = \dfrac{{}^+7}{t}$

**i.** ${}^+3 \cdot u = {}^-9$

**p.** ${}^-.5 = {}^+100 \cdot w$

**j.** $b \cdot {}^-2 = {}^-4$

**q.** $\dfrac{{}^+5}{a} = {}^-.1$

**k.** ${}^-7 \cdot f = {}^-\frac{1}{2}$

**l.** $g \cdot {}^+21 = {}^-42$

**r.** $x \cdot {}^-2 = {}^-1$

**s.** ${}^-16 \div y = {}^-2$

**m.** $\dfrac{{}^+11}{n} = {}^-2$

**t.** $f \div {}^-1.1 = {}^+2.2$

**2.** In each inequality below make two different replacements for the letter, so that two true sentences result. Then make two more replacements, so that two false sentences result.

**EXAMPLE**    ${}^-5 \cdot r + {}^+2 > {}^+2 \cdot r - {}^+1$

**SOLUTION**    (1)  ${}^-2$ for $r$
$\quad\quad {}^-5 \cdot {}^-2 + {}^+2 > {}^+2 \cdot {}^-2 - {}^+1$
$\quad\quad {}^+10 + {}^+2 > {}^-4 - {}^+1$
$\quad\quad {}^+12 > {}^-5; \text{ True}$

(2)  $0$ for $r$
$\quad\quad {}^-5 \cdot 0 + {}^+2 > {}^+2 \cdot 0 - {}^+1$
$\quad\quad 0 + {}^+2 > 0 - {}^+1$
$\quad\quad {}^+2 > {}^-1; \text{ True}$

(3)  ${}^+3$ for $r$
$\quad\quad {}^-5 \cdot {}^+3 + {}^+2 > {}^+2 \cdot {}^+3 - {}^+1$
$\quad\quad {}^-15 + {}^+2 > {}^+6 - {}^+1$
$\quad\quad {}^-13 > {}^+5; \text{ False}$

(4)  ${}^+1$ for $r$
$\quad\quad {}^-5 \cdot {}^+1 + {}^+2 > {}^+2 \cdot {}^+1 - {}^+1$
$\quad\quad {}^-5 + {}^+2 > {}^+2 - {}^+1$
$\quad\quad {}^-3 > {}^+1; \text{ False}$

**a.** $m > {}^-1$

**b.** $x < {}^+3$

**c.** $n > {}^-\frac{1}{2}$

**d.** $r + {}^-5 < {}^-2$

**e.** ${}^+3 + y > {}^+2$

**f.** ${}^-1 - c < {}^-1$

**g.** ${}^-3 + d > {}^-200$

**h.** ${}^+2 \cdot p + {}^+1 < p$

**i.** ${}^-3 \cdot t + {}^+7 > {}^+1 + t$

**j.** $|\, u \,| > {}^+10$

**k.** $|\, w \,| < {}^+99$

**l.** ${}^+3 \cdot |\, a \,| > {}^+3$

**m.** $|\, f \,| = f$

**n.** ${}^+2 \cdot |\, v \,| - |\, v \,| < {}^+5$

### 3 · Some Simplification in Writing

You have already agreed that positive numbers "behave" just like the numbers of arithmetic. Therefore, as you have already observed, no error will be committed in working problems involving positive numbers, if, in the names for positive numbers, you omit the plus symbol. For example, you can write 2 for $^+2$, $\frac{1}{2}$ for $^+\frac{1}{2}$, 1.6 for $^+1.6$ and so on. A problem like $7 + {}^-6 = 1$ then will be the same as $^+7 + {}^-6 = {}^+1$.

Another agreement which we shall make concerns ways of writing problems which involve multiplication. You are already familiar with the symbol "·". It has been used in ways exemplified by the following:

$$^-2 \cdot {}^-3 = {}^+6$$
$$3 \cdot y = 17$$
$$a \cdot b = 20$$

Frequently the symbol "$\times$" is used in place of the dot. The three examples above could be written as

$$^-2 \times {}^-3 = {}^+6$$
$$3 \times y = 17$$
$$a \times b = 20$$

You will also find that both the dot and the cross are frequently omitted altogether, and still multiplication is intended. Thus, the examples above could be written as follows:

$$(^-2)(^-3) = {}^+6$$
$$3y = 17$$
$$ab = 20$$

You should note that it is not always possible to omit "$\times$" or "·" without changing the meaning of what we intend to write. For example: $2 \times 3 = 6$ and $2 \cdot 3 = 6$ cannot be written as $23 = 6$. It should not take much thought to tell what is wrong with just omitting $\times$ or · in the last example. We can write, however, $(2)(3) = 6$.

## EXERCISES

1. Rewrite each multiplication problem using a different multiplication symbol and also omitting the symbols.

**EXAMPLE 1**    $^-2 \times {}^-3 = {}^+6$

**SOLUTION**    (1)  $^-2 \cdot {}^-3 = {}^+6$

(2)  $(^-2)(^-3) = {}^+6$

**EXAMPLE 2**   $5 \times 7 = 35$

**SOLUTION**   (1)   $5 \cdot 7 = 35$
(2)   $(5)(7) = 35$

**EXAMPLE 3**   $7 \cdot y = 156$

**SOLUTION**   (1)   $7 \times y = 156$
(2)   $7y = 156$

**EXAMPLE 4**   $a \cdot b \cdot m = x \cdot y$

**SOLUTION**   (1)   $a \times b \times m = x \times y$
(2)   $abm = xy$

**a.** $^-1 \times {}^+6$
**b.** $^+\frac{1}{3} \cdot {}^-\frac{1}{2}$
**c.** $5 \times 6 \times 7$
**d.** $x \cdot m$
**e.** $a \times b + m \times r$

**f.** $17 \times x - 1.6 \times y$
**g.** $a \times (b \times c) = (a \times b) \times c$
**h.** $x \cdot (y + z) = (x \cdot y) + (x \cdot z)$
**i.** $1 \cdot x = x$
**j.** $0 \cdot x = 0$

## 4 · Statement of Basic Principles

In Chapter 2 you studied a number of basic principles. Review those parts of the chapter to refresh your memory on what you have already learned. We shall retain these basic principles for real numbers.

Now that you know how letters are used in algebra, you will be able to state these principles in brief form. On page 29 the following examples are given:

$$2 + 7 = 7 + 2$$
$$\tfrac{1}{2} + 3 = 3 + \tfrac{1}{2}$$
$$.7 + 1.2 = 1.2 + .7$$
$$\tfrac{3}{2} + \tfrac{7}{2} = \tfrac{7}{2} + \tfrac{3}{2}$$

We called the pattern suggested by these examples The Commutative Principle of Addition.

Let us state the Commutative Principle of Addition as follows:

For every $x$ and $y$, $x + y = y + x$

What does this sentence mean? To answer this question, let us replace the letters $x$ and $y$ in it by some numerals.

(1)   $^-1$ for $x$, 2 for $y$
      The resulting sentence is $^-1 + 2 = 2 + ^-1$
      or, $1 = 1$

(2)   2.5 for $x$, $^-3.1$ for $y$
      The resulting sentence is $2.5 + ^-3.1 = ^-3.1 + 2.5$
      or, $^-.6 = ^-.6$

(3)   $^-\frac{5}{7}$ for $x$, $\frac{4}{3}$ for $y$
      The resulting sentence is $^-\frac{5}{7} + \frac{4}{3} = \frac{4}{3} + ^-\frac{5}{7}$
      or, $\frac{13}{21} = \frac{13}{21}$

Note that, no matter what replacements you make, you obtain a true sentence.

Now we are ready to describe the meaning of the sentence

$$\text{For every } x \text{ and } y, \; x + y = y + x.$$

*No matter what number name is put in place of "$x$" and in place of "$y$" in $x + y = y + x$, a true sentence will be obtained. The numeral replacing "$x$" on the left of "$=$" must name the same number as the numeral for "$x$" on the right of "$=$". The same must be true for "$y$".*

Do you see that the sentence "For every $x$ and $y$, $x + y = y + x$" is a convenient abbreviation for the long explanation above?

When letters are used in sentences or expressions in the way we have used them so far, we call them **variables.** A sentence which contains one or more variables and is neither true nor false is an **open sentence.**

Now, consider the sentence

$$\text{For some } x, \; x + 3 < ^-2$$

Let us make some replacements for $x$ in $x + 3 < ^-2$.

$$^-10 \text{ for } x: \; ^-10 + 3 < ^-2$$
$$\text{or}$$
$$^-7 < ^-2; \text{ True}$$

$$^-6 \text{ for } x: \; ^-6 + 3 < ^-2$$
$$\text{or}$$
$$^-3 < ^-2; \text{ True}$$

$$^-5 \text{ for } x: \; ^-5 + 3 < ^-2$$
$$^-2 < ^-2; \text{ False}$$

$$0 \text{ for } x: \; 0 + 3 < ^-2$$
$$3 < ^-2; \text{ False}$$

Not every replacement in this case gives us a true sentence. This is the reason for not saying "for every $x$, $x + 3 < {}^-2$," but rather saying

$$\text{"for some } x, x + 3 < {}^-2\text{."}$$

How many different replacements for $x$ could you find so that resulting sentences are true? Are false?

You should note that, in these open sentences, it does not matter what letters of the alphabet we use. You could also use some other symbols, as you have already done. For example, the Commutative Principle of Addition could be stated in any one of the following ways:

$$\text{For every } a \text{ and } b, a + b = b + a$$
$$\text{For every } c \text{ and } m, c + m = m + c$$
$$\text{For every } \beta \text{ and } \theta, \beta + \theta = \theta + \beta$$
$$\text{For every } \square \text{ and } \bigcirc, \square + \bigcirc = \bigcirc + \square$$

Each of the symbols: $a$, $b$, $c$, $m$, $\beta$, $\theta$, $\square$, and $\bigcirc$ is a variable.

Now you should be ready to state all the basic principles with which you are familiar, using variables like those in the statement of the Commutative Principle of Addition above. State each principle by yourself, then compare your statements with those given below.

The Commutative Principle of Multiplication:
$$\text{For every } x \text{ and } y, xy = yx$$
The Associative Principle of Addition:
$$\text{For every } x, y, \text{ and } z, (x + y) + z = x + (y + z)$$
The Associative Principle of Multiplication:
$$\text{For every } x, y, \text{ and } z, (xy)z = x(yz)$$
The Distributive Principle:
$$\text{For every } x, y, \text{ and } z, x(y + z) = xy + xz$$
The Principle of Multiplication by One.
$$\text{For every } x, x \cdot 1 = x$$
The Principle of Division by One.
$$\text{For every } x, x \div 1 = x$$
The Principle of Addition by One.
$$\text{For every } x, x + 0 = x$$
The Principle of Multiplication by Zero.
$$\text{For every } x, x \cdot 0 = 0$$

You see from the above that it is convenient to use variables in open sentences that yield true sentences for all replacements of variables.

## EXERCISES

**1.** In each sentence below, replace the variables by some numerals. Then state whether or not the resulting sentence is true. Whenever possible, make a general statement describing the numerals which may replace the variable.

**EXAMPLE 1**    $x \cdot x = x^2$

**SOLUTION**    3 for $x$: $3 \cdot 3 = 3^2$ (read: three squared)

$$9 = 9; \text{True}$$

$^-5$ for $x$: $(^-5)(^-5) = (^-5)^2$

$$25 = 25; \text{True}$$

0 for $x$: $0 \cdot 0 = 0^2$

$$0 = 0; \text{True}$$

The resulting sentences are true.
General Statement: For every $x$, $x \cdot x = x^2$

**EXAMPLE 2**    $\left| \dfrac{m}{m} \right| = 1$

**SOLUTION**    4 for $m$: $\left| \dfrac{4}{4} \right| = 1$

$$|\,1\,| = 1$$

$$1 = 1; \text{True}$$

$^-2$ for $m$: $\left| \dfrac{^-2}{^-2} \right| = 1$

$$|\,1\,| = 1$$

$$1 = 1; \text{True}$$

0 for $m$: $\left| \dfrac{0}{0} \right| = 1; ?$

But what does $\dfrac{0}{0}$ mean? To answer this question, we need to recall the relationship between multiplication and division. $\dfrac{a}{b} = c$ means that $cb = a$. Thus, if $\dfrac{0}{0}$ names some number, let this number be $n$.

Then $\dfrac{0}{0} = n$ and $n \times 0 = 0$. But this is true for every number $n$ (according to what principle?). Therefore, $\dfrac{0}{0}$

can be 5 or 10 or $^{-}20$ or any other number you wish. This would be a misleading symbol then, because someone might say that if $\dfrac{0}{0} = 5$ and $\dfrac{0}{0} = 10$, then it follows that $5 = 10$, and you would not like this. Therefore, we will not view the symbol $\dfrac{0}{0}$ as having any meaning.

Thus $\dfrac{0}{0}$ is meaningless. The first two sentences are true. Replacement of $m$ by 0 results in a meaningless symbol.

General Statement: For every $m$ (except 0) $\left|\dfrac{m}{m}\right| = 1$

**EXAMPLE 3**    $a = a + 1$

**SOLUTION**    5 for $a$: $5 = 5 + 1$

$5 = 6$; False

$^{-}6$ for $a$: $^{-}6 = {^{-}6} + 1$

$^{-}6 = {^{-}5}$; False

0 for $a$: $0 = 0 + 1$

$0 = 1$; False

Do you think that you can find a replacement for $a$ so that a true statement will result?
It appears that no replacement for $a$ will yield a true statement.

**EXAMPLE 4**    $c \leq 0$   (read: $c$ is less than *or* equal to 0)
Since the word "or" is used differently by different people, we need to agree on its meaning before we can proceed with this problem. We will agree that to us "or" will mean that if either one of the two mentioned possibilities is true, the whole sentence will be true; also, if *both* possibilities are true, the entire sentence will be true.

**SOLUTION**    1 for $c$: $1 \leq 0$ False, since neither $1 < 0$ nor $1 = 0$ is true.
$^{-}1$ for $c$: $^{-}1 \leq 0$ True, since $^{-}1 < 0$ is true.
0 for $c$: $0 \leq 0$ True, since $0 = 0$ is true.
General Statement: For some $c$, $c \leq 0$

**EXAMPLE 5**   $2y - 3 < 1$

**SOLUTION**   2 for $y$: $2 \cdot 2 - 3 < 1$

$$4 - 3 < 1$$
$$1 < 1; \text{ False}$$

3 for $y$: $2 \cdot 3 - 3 < 1$

$$6 - 3 < 1$$
$$3 < 1; \text{ False}$$

1 for $y$: $2 \cdot 1 - 3 < 1$

$$2 - 3 < 1$$
$$^-1 < 1; \text{ True}$$

0 for $y$: $2 \cdot 0 - 3 < 1$

$$0 - 3 < 1$$
$$^-3 < 1; \text{ True}$$

General Statement: For some $y$, $2y - 3 < 1$

**EXAMPLE 6**   $4p - 2 = 2$

**SOLUTION**   1 for $p$: $4 \cdot 1 - 2 = 2$

$$4 - 2 = 2$$
$$2 = 2; \text{ True}$$

8 for $p$: $4 \cdot 8 - 2 = 2$

$$32 - 2 = 2$$
$$30 = 2; \text{ False}$$

$^-5$ for $p$: $4 \cdot {}^-5 - 2 = 2$

$$^-20 - 2 = 2$$
$$^-22 = 2; \text{ False}$$

General Statement: For some $p$, $4p - 2 = 2$

**a.** $x + x + x = 3x$

**b.** $3m - m = 2m$

**c.** $1.6y - 1.5y = .1y$

**d.** $3\frac{1}{2}a + 7\frac{1}{2}a = 11a$

**e.** $u \cdot u \cdot u = u^3$

**f.** $\dfrac{4z}{2z} = 2$

**g.** $\dfrac{20s}{4} = 5s$

**h.** $\mid d \mid = d$

**i.** $v > 0$

**j.** $^-5n = n$

**k.** $9f - 3 = 6$

**l.** $2 + s < {}^-10$

**m.** $y = y$

**n.** $3x - 1 = 1 - 3x$

**o.** $g = \dfrac{1}{g}$

**p.** $\mid x - y \mid = \mid y - x \mid$

**q.** $(x + y)^2 = x^2 + 2xy + y^2$　　　　**s.** $|\, xy\, | = |\, x\, | \cdot |\, y\, |$

**r.** $(x - y)(x + y) = x^2 - y^2$　　　　**t.** $\left|\, \dfrac{x}{y}\, \right| = \dfrac{|\, x\, |}{|\, y\, |}$

**2.** At each step, identify the basic principle used.

**EXAMPLE 1**　　$(x + y) + 3 \overset{(1)}{=} x + (y + 3)$

**SOLUTION**　　(1)　Associative Principle (Addition)

**EXAMPLE 2**　　$(4x)(3y) \overset{(1)}{=} [(4x) \cdot 3]y$

$\overset{(2)}{=} [4(x \cdot 3)]y$

$\overset{(3)}{=} [4(3 \cdot x)]y$

$\overset{(4)}{=} [(4 \cdot 3)x]y$

$\overset{(5)}{=} [12x]y$

**SOLUTION**　　(1)　Associative Principle (Multiplication)

(2)　Associative Principle (Multiplication)

(3)　Commutative Principle (Multiplication)

(4)　Associative Principle (Multiplication)

(5)　An Arithmetic Fact $(4 \cdot 3 = 12)$

**EXAMPLE 3**　　$5x + 3x \overset{(1)}{=} x \cdot 5 + x \cdot 3$

$\overset{(2)}{=} x(5 + 3)$

$\overset{(3)}{=} x \cdot 8$

$\overset{(4)}{=} 8x$

**SOLUTION**　　(1)　Commutative Principle (Multiplication) (used twice)

(2)　Distributive Principle

(3)　An Arithmetic Fact $(5 + 3 = 8)$

(4)　Commutative Principle (Multiplication)

**a.** $3 \times (5y) \overset{(1)}{=} (3 \times 5)y$

$\overset{(2)}{=} 15y$

**b.** $(a + 3) + 5 \overset{(1)}{=} a + (3 + 5)$

$\overset{(2)}{=} a + 8$

$\overset{(3)}{=} 8 + a$

**c.** $-17(mn) \overset{(1)}{=} -17(nm)$

**d.** $x + x \overset{(1)}{=} x \cdot 1 + x \cdot 1$
$$\overset{(2)}{=} x(1 + 1)$$
$$\overset{(3)}{=} x \cdot 2$$
$$\overset{(4)}{=} 2x$$

**e.** $y(y + y) \overset{(1)}{=} y(y \cdot 1 + y \cdot 1)$
$$\overset{(2)}{=} y \cdot [y(1 + 1)]$$
$$\overset{(3)}{=} y \cdot (y \cdot 2)$$
$$\overset{(4)}{=} y \cdot (2 \cdot y)$$
$$\overset{(5)}{=} (2 \cdot y) \cdot y$$

**f.** $17 \times 15 + 23 \times 15 \overset{(1)}{=} 15 \times 17 + 15 \times 23$
$$\overset{(2)}{=} 15(17 + 23)$$
$$\overset{(3)}{=} 15 \times 40$$

**g.** $(3.9x + 7.9x) + 10.1x \overset{(1)}{=} 3.9x + (7.9x + 10.1x)$
$$\overset{(2)}{=} 3.9x + (x \times 7.9 + x \times 10.1)$$
$$\overset{(3)}{=} 3.9x + x(7.9 + 10.1)$$
$$\overset{(4)}{=} 3.9x + x \cdot 18$$
$$\overset{(5)}{=} x3.9 + x.18$$
$$\overset{(6)}{=} x(3.9 + 18)$$
$$\overset{(7)}{=} 21.9x$$

**3.** Replace the frames with names of real numbers to obtain true sentences:

**a.** $+9 \cdot \square = +1$

**b.** $-3 \cdot \triangle = +1$

**c.** $\bigcirc \cdot +\frac{1}{2} = +1$

**d.** $+\frac{3}{2} \cdot \triangle = +1$

**e.** $-1 \cdot \square = +1$

**f.** $+\frac{1}{9} \cdot \bigcirc = +1$

**g.** $-\frac{6}{7} \cdot \square = +1$

**h.** $+1 \cdot \triangle = +1$

**i.** $-\frac{1}{2} \cdot \bigcirc = +1$

**j.** $+\frac{7}{3} \cdot \square = +1$

**4.** Give the reciprocal of each of the following numbers:

**a.** 2      **b.** 11      **c.** $-1$      **d.** $\frac{1}{4}$      **e.** 1.4      **f.** .29

**5.** What numbers are their own reciprocals?

## 5 · Eleven Basic Properties of Real Numbers

In Chapter 3 you learned that rational and irrational numbers together make up the real numbers. Examples of real numbers are $^-2$, $\sqrt{5}$, $1.351351135111351111 \cdots$, $\frac{1}{3}$. When you thought of the number line as made up of an infinite string of points, you found that every point on the line has a real number corresponding to it, and every real number has a point on the number line. We called this correspondence a one-to-one correspondence.

Now we are going to assemble all of the basic principles of real numbers that we already know and add some new ones. First, we are going to assume that we have two basic operations, addition and multiplication.

You probably have observed that for every pair of real numbers there is a real number which is the sum of the pair of numbers. Thus, given $^-3$ and $\frac{1}{2}$, we have

$$^-3 + \tfrac{1}{2} = ^-2\tfrac{1}{2}$$

or, given .7 and .36, we have

$$.7 + .36 = 1.06$$

Note that a number pair may consist of the same number taken twice. Thus, 3 and 3 is a number pair, although only one number (3) is used. It follows that a number pair does not necessarily require two different numbers.

You will recall from Chapter 2 that if a set of numbers has the property that for every pair there is a number in the set which is the sum of the pair, the set is said to be closed under addition. Or, we say that the property of closure for addition holds for this set of numbers. Thus,

I. The set of real numbers is closed under addition.
> For every $a$ and $b$, there exists exactly one $c$ such that $a + b = c$

It is easy to observe that the same is true for multiplication. Thus,

II. The set of real numbers is closed under multiplication.
> For every $a$ and $b$, there exists exactly one $c$ such that $ab = c$

Let us now list the basic principles of addition and multiplication which are already known to you.

III. Addition is commutative, or
> For every $a$ and $b$, $a + b = b + a$

IV. Multiplication is commutative, or

$$\text{For every } a \text{ and } b, \, ab = ba$$

V. Addition is associative, or

$$\text{For every } a, \, b, \text{ and } c, \, (a + b) + c = a + (b + c)$$

VI. Multiplication is associative, or

$$\text{For every } a, \, b, \text{ and } c, \, (ab)c = a(bc)$$

VII. Multiplication is distributive with respect to addition, or

$$\text{For every } a, \, b, \text{ and } c, \, a(b + c) = ab + ac$$

In addition to the above properties, you know that among real numbers we have the number 1 which has an interesting property. Any number multiplied by 1 gives that number. We, therefore, call the number 1 **the multiplicative identity.** Thus, we have

VIII. There exists a multiplicative identity, (the number 1) such that

$$\text{For every } a, \, a \cdot 1 = a$$

There is also a number among the real numbers which "acts" in addition like the number 1 does in multiplication. That number is 0, because 0 added to any number results in that number. The number 0 is given the name of **additive identity.** Thus,

IX. There exists an additive identity, (the number 0,) such that

$$\text{For every } a, \, a + 0 = a$$

There is another interesting property that every real number (except 0) has. To discover this property, imagine that your friend challenged you to the following battle of wits. He names a number (not 0) and your task is to name a number so that the product of the pair of numbers is 1. He calls 7; you should say, $\frac{1}{7}$, because $7 \cdot \frac{1}{7} = 1$. He calls $^-5$; you should say, $^-\frac{1}{5}$, because $^-5 \cdot ^-\frac{1}{5} = 1$, and so on. Do you see that you cannot fail to name a number for every one that he will call? You are already familiar with this idea. We say:

> $\frac{1}{7}$ is the **reciprocal** of 7, because $\frac{1}{7} \cdot 7 = 1$
> also 7 is the reciprocal of $\frac{1}{7}$.
> $^-\frac{1}{5}$ is the reciprocal of $^-5$, because $^-\frac{1}{5} \cdot ^-5 = 1$
> also $^-5$ is the reciprocal of $^-\frac{1}{5}$.
> $\frac{2}{3}$ and $\frac{3}{2}$ are reciprocals of each other, for $\frac{2}{3} \cdot \frac{3}{2} = 1$.

What is the reciprocal of $\frac{3}{5}$? $^-\frac{4}{7}$? .2? 1.5? Sometimes the phrase **"multiplicative inverse"** is used instead of "reciprocal."

X. For every $a$, there is exactly one reciprocal $\dfrac{1}{a}$ such that

$$a \cdot \frac{1}{a} = 1 \ (a \neq 0).$$

This is called the *Principle of Reciprocals*.

A similar property exists for addition. But here the game is somewhat different. For each number your friend calls, you are to name a number so that the sum of the pair is 0. If he calls 7, you should say ⁻7, because $7 + {}^-7 = 0$. If he calls ⁻5, you should say 5, because ${}^-5 + 5 = 0$. And so on. This is the old familiar opposite of a number, or **additive inverse.**

We recall that

$$^-3 \text{ is the opposite of } 3.$$
$$^+4 \text{ is the opposite of } ^-4.$$

In mathematics we shorten statements of this type by agreeing to replace "the opposite of" with a lowered "$-$" in front of the number symbol.

Thus, since ⁻3 is the opposite of 3, we would write $^-3 = -3$.

We know that ⁺4 is the opposite of ⁻4, so we would write $^+4 = -(^-4)$.

Another way of saying $^-\frac{1}{3}$ is the opposite of $\frac{1}{3}$ is $^-\frac{1}{3} = -\frac{1}{3}$.

It is clear that the raised "⁻" and lowered "$-$" act in the same manner, so we may consistently use the lower "$-$" for both cases; we shall agree to do this.

Thus, $^+4 = -(-4)$ is read "4 is equal to the opposite of the opposite of 4."

The opposite of $-(-4)$ is written $-[-(-4)]$; since we saw that $-(-4) = {}^+4$, the opposite of $-(-4)$ would be $-4$.

We will refer to $-x$ as the "opposite of $x$" instead of "negative $x$," since it is not known whether "$-x$" refers to a negative or positive number.

Thus,

XI. For every number $x$, there is exactly one opposite number $-x$, such that $x + (-x) = 0$.

This is called the *Principle of Opposites*.

*A set of numbers which has the eleven properties is called a* **number field.**

We can also now write a Principle of Subtraction.

$$\text{For every } x \text{ and } y, \ x - y = x + (-y)$$

# EXERCISES

1. Consider the set of natural numbers
$$N = \{1, 2, 3, 4, 5, \cdots\}$$

   **a.** Check each of the eleven properties of real numbers to see whether or not they also hold for natural numbers. State the properties, if there are any, which do not hold for $N$.

   **b.** Is $N$ a number field?

2. Consider the set of integers
$$I = \{\cdots -5, -4, -3, -2, -1, 0, 1, 2, 3, 4, 5, \cdots\}$$

   **a.** Check each of the eleven properties of real numbers to see whether or not they also hold for integers. State the properties, if there are any, which do not hold for $I$.

   **b.** Is $I$ a number field?

3. Consider the set of rational numbers $Ra$; that is, numbers which have names of the form $\frac{a}{b}$ or $-\frac{a}{b}$ where $a$ and $b$ are natural numbers ($a$ may also be zero).

   **a.** Check each of the eleven properties of real numbers to see whether or not they also hold for rational numbers. State the properties, if there are any, which do not hold for $Ra$.

   **b.** Is $Ra$ a number field?

## 6 · Finite Systems of Numbers

The sets of natural numbers, integers, rational numbers, and real numbers are infinite sets. Let us now take a look at a system of numbers which has a finite number of elements. One such system is the clock arithmetic, which is well known to you.

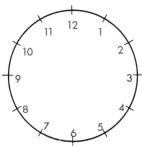

## Clock Arithmetic

In clock arithmetic you count up to 12, then you start over again. This means that, if you add 1 and 12, you get 1. If you add 2 and 12 you get 2, and so on. These are some answers to addition problems in clock arithmetic. Study them carefully.

$$12 + 1 = 1 \qquad\qquad 11 + 2 = 1$$
$$12 + 2 = 2 \qquad\qquad 11 + 4 = 3$$
$$12 + 7 = 7 \qquad\qquad 11 + 10 = 9$$

$$10 + 2 = 12 \qquad\qquad 6 + 6 = 12$$
$$10 + 3 = 1 \qquad\qquad 6 + 7 = 1$$
$$10 + 4 = 2 \qquad\qquad 5 + 12 = 5$$

Let us now make a complete addition table for the clock arithmetic.

| + | 1 | 2 | 3 | 4 | 5 | 6 | 7 | 8 | 9 | 10 | 11 | 12 |
|----|----|----|----|----|----|----|----|----|----|----|----|----|
| 1 | 2 | 3 | 4 | 5 | 6 | 7 | 8 | 9 | 10 | 11 | 12 | 1 |
| 2 | 3 | 4 | 5 | 6 | 7 | 8 | 9 | 10 | 11 | 12 | 1 | 2 |
| 3 | 4 | 5 | 6 | 7 | 8 | 9 | 10 | 11 | 12 | 1 | 2 | 3 |
| 4 | 5 | 6 | 7 | 8 | 9 | 10 | 11 | 12 | 1 | 2 | 3 | 4 |
| 5 | 6 | 7 | 8 | 9 | 10 | 11 | 12 | 1 | 2 | 3 | 4 | 5 |
| 6 | 7 | 8 | 9 | 10 | 11 | 12 | 1 | 2 | 3 | 4 | 5 | 6 |
| 7 | 8 | 9 | 10 | 11 | 12 | 1 | 2 | 3 | 4 | 5 | 6 | 7 |
| 8 | 9 | 10 | 11 | 12 | 1 | 2 | 3 | 4 | 5 | 6 | 7 | 8 |
| 9 | 10 | 11 | 12 | 1 | 2 | 3 | 4 | 5 | 6 | 7 | 8 | 9 |
| 10 | 11 | 12 | 1 | 2 | 3 | 4 | 5 | 6 | 7 | 8 | 9 | 10 |
| 11 | 12 | 1 | 2 | 3 | 4 | 5 | 6 | 7 | 8 | 9 | 10 | 11 |
| 12 | 1 | 2 | 3 | 4 | 5 | 6 | 7 | 8 | 9 | 10 | 11 | 12 |

Let us now work out a few multiplication problems in clock arithmetic.

$$12 \cdot 1 = 12 \qquad\qquad 4 \cdot 2 = 8$$
$$3 \cdot 1 = 3 \qquad\qquad 4 \cdot 3 = 12$$
$$3 \cdot 2 = 6 \qquad\qquad 4 \cdot 4 = 4$$
$$3 \cdot 4 = 12 \qquad\qquad 10 \cdot 2 = 8$$
$$3 \cdot 5 = 3 \qquad\qquad 10 \cdot 3 = 6$$

The complete multiplication table is worked out for you on the next page.

| × | 1 | 2 | 3 | 4 | 5 | 6 | 7 | 8 | 9 | 10 | 11 | 12 |
|---|---|---|---|---|---|---|---|---|---|----|----|----|
| 1 | 1 | 2 | 3 | 4 | 5 | 6 | 7 | 8 | 9 | 10 | 11 | 12 |
| 2 | 2 | 4 | 6 | 8 | 10 | 12 | 2 | 4 | 6 | 8 | 10 | 12 |
| 3 | 3 | 6 | 9 | 12 | 3 | 6 | 9 | 12 | 3 | 6 | 9 | 12 |
| 4 | 4 | 8 | 12 | 4 | 8 | 12 | 4 | 8 | 12 | 4 | 8 | 12 |
| 5 | 5 | 10 | 3 | 8 | 1 | 6 | 11 | 4 | 9 | 2 | 7 | 12 |
| 6 | 6 | 12 | 6 | 12 | 6 | 12 | 6 | 12 | 6 | 12 | 6 | 12 |
| 7 | 7 | 2 | 9 | 4 | 11 | 6 | 1 | 8 | 3 | 10 | 5 | 12 |
| 8 | 8 | 4 | 12 | 8 | 4 | 12 | 8 | 4 | 12 | 8 | 4 | 12 |
| 9 | 9 | 6 | 3 | 12 | 9 | 6 | 3 | 12 | 9 | 6 | 3 | 12 |
| 10 | 10 | 8 | 6 | 4 | 2 | 12 | 10 | 8 | 6 | 4 | 2 | 12 |
| 11 | 11 | 10 | 9 | 8 | 7 | 6 | 5 | 4 | 3 | 2 | 1 | 12 |
| 12 | 12 | 12 | 12 | 12 | 12 | 12 | 12 | 12 | 12 | 12 | 12 | 12 |

Now we are ready to check the eleven properties for real numbers to see which of them hold for the clock arithmetic. Have both tables in front of you as you follow the check of each property.

I.      Closure for Addition: Yes. For every pair of numbers there is exactly one number which is their sum and it is an element of the original system.

II.     Closure for Multiplication: Yes. For every pair of numbers, there is exactly one number which is their product and it is an element of the original system.

III.    Commutativity of Addition: Yes. It does not matter whether you add $10 + 8$ or $8 + 10$, the answer in each case is 6. The same is true for every other pair of numbers.

IV.    Commutativity of Multiplication: Yes.

V.     Associativity of Addition: This needs checking:

(1)   $(4 + 8) + 7 = 12 + 7 = 7$
$4 + (8 + 7) = 4 + 3 = 7$

(2)   $(10 + 1) + 9 = 11 + 9 = 8$
$10 + (1 + 9) = 10 + 10 = 8$

Check a few more cases to convince yourself that the answer is yes.

VI.    Associativity of Multiplication: Work a few examples to see that the answer is yes.

VII.   Distributivity of Multiplication with respect to addition: Let us work out some examples.

(1)   $3 \cdot (5 + 9) = 3 \cdot 2 = 6$
       $(3 \cdot 5) + (3 \cdot 9) = 3 + 3 = 6$
(2)   $7 \cdot (4 + 10) = 7 \cdot 2 = 2$
       $(7 \cdot 4) + (7 \cdot 10) = 4 + 10 = 2$

Check a few more cases to convince yourself that the answer is "yes."

VIII.  Existence of the Multiplicative Identity: Search the multiplication table to see whether there is exactly one number $a$ such that $x \cdot a = x$ for every number $x$ in the table. You will discover that there is one such number, namely the number 1, because

$1 \cdot 1 = 1, 2 \cdot 1 = 2, 3 \cdot 1 = 3$, and so on.

IX.    Existence of the Additive Identity: Here we need to search for one number $a$ such that $x + a = x$ for every number $x$. Look at the addition table. Do you find such a number? It is the number 12, because $1 + 12 = 1, 2 + 12 = 2, 3 + 12 = 3$, and so on.

X.     Existence of a unique reciprocal: Look at the multiplication table. For each number 1 through 12, you should look for another number $a$ such that $x \cdot a = 1$ for every $x$. Let us go down the rows and check this for every number.

   For 1, there is only one number, namely 1, such that $1 \cdot 1 = 1$
   For 2, there is no number such that the product of 2 and that number is 1. Therefore, 2 has no reciprocal.
   This one example is sufficient to conclude that the number system, clock arithmetic, is not a number field.
   From the table, tell which numbers have reciprocals and which do not. Do any numbers have more than one reciprocal?

XI.    Existence of the unique opposite: You found that the additive identity for clock arithmetic is 12. Now your problem is to see whether every number has exactly one opposite. To check this, go to the addition table and start checking each number.

   $1 + 11 = 12$, so the opposite of 1 is 11.
   $2 + 10 = 12$, so the opposite of 2 is 10.
   $3 + \phantom{0}9 = 12$, so the opposite of 3 is 9.

Continue this until you have checked each number.

Do you see that, if 11 is the opposite of 1, then 1 is the opposite of 11? If 9 is the opposite of 3, then 3 is the opposite of 9? And so on.

Which numbers are opposites of themselves? Do you see that the number 12 in this system is like 0 in the system of integers?

Our conclusion now is that the set of clock arithmetic numbers does not meet all of the requirements to be considered a field. Explain.

## EXERCISES

**1.** Consider a finite number system which consists of two elements, say 0 and 1. Here are the addition and multiplication tables for this system.

| + | 0 | 1 |
|---|---|---|
| 0 | 0 | 1 |
| 1 | 1 | 0 |

| × | 0 | 1 |
|---|---|---|
| 0 | 0 | 0 |
| 1 | 0 | 1 |

Check to see whether or not this number system is a field, that is, check to see whether or not each of the eleven properties holds for this number system.

**2.** Suppose we had a "five-hour clock." Three hours after two o'clock the time will be zero o'clock ($2 + 3 = 0$). Three hours after three o'clock will be one o'clock ($3 + 3 = 1$). Finish supplying the numbers in the addition table for the numbers of the "five-hour clock."

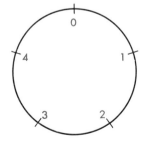

| + | 0 | 1 | 2 | 3 | 4 |
|---|---|---|---|---|---|
| 0 | 0 | 1 | 2 | 3 | 4 |
| 1 | 1 |   |   |   |   |
| 2 | 2 |   |   |   | 1 |
| 3 | 3 | 4 |   | 1 |   |
| 4 | 4 |   | 1 |   |   |

The multiplication table for the numbers of the "five-hour clock" is given partially in the table at the top of page 114. Supply the missing numbers.

| × | 0 | 1 | 2 | 3 | 4 |
|---|---|---|---|---|---|
| 0 | 0 | 0 | 0 | 0 | 0 |
| 1 | 0 |   |   |   |   |
| 2 | 0 | 2 |   |   |   |
| 3 | 0 |   | 1 | 4 | 2 |
| 4 | 0 |   |   |   | 1 |

Check to see whether or not this set of numbers is a field under the operations of addition and multiplication.

**3.** Repeat the approach described above for a "four-hour" clock.

Addition:

| + | 0 | 1 | 2 | 3 |
|---|---|---|---|---|
| 0 | 0 | 1 | 2 | 3 |
| 1 | 1 |   |   | 0 |
| 2 | 2 | 3 |   |   |
| 3 | 3 |   | 1 | 2 |

Multiplication:

| × | 0 | 1 | 2 | 3 |
|---|---|---|---|---|
| 0 | 0 | 0 | 0 | 0 |
| 1 | 0 | 1 |   |   |
| 2 | 0 |   | 0 |   |
| 3 | 0 |   | 2 | 1 |

Complete the tables and determine whether or not the set of numbers is a field under the operations of addition and multiplication.

# 7 · The Replacement Set of a Variable

You already know that an open sentence contains at least one variable. For example, $3x + 5 = 6$ is such a sentence. It is neither true nor false. Upon replacement of $x$ by numerals, we obtain sentences which are true or false. However, before we can proceed to make replacements of this numerical variable $x$ by numerals, we must know what numbers we are allowed to use.

You may be told that you are allowed to use only natural numbers. Then, for example, 2 for $x$ will give you the sentence $3 \cdot 2 + 5 = 6$, which is false. Why? Assuming that you are allowed to use only natural numerals as replacements for $x$, can you find a replacement which will result in a true sentence?

Or, you may be told that the integers are the numbers whose names you may use as replacements for $x$. Then, for example, $-5$ for $x$ will give the sentence $3 \cdot (-5) + 5 = 6$ which is also false. Can you find an integer which will yield a true sentence?

Or, you may be asked to choose your replacements from the set of directed rational numbers. Then, for example, $-\frac{2}{3}$ for $x$ will give you the sentence $3 \cdot (-\frac{2}{3}) + 5 = 6$ which is also false. Why? Can you find a rational number which will yield a true sentence?

Or, it may be specified that the set of real numbers will serve as the set from which replacements for the numerical variable are to come. You could also use a number like $\sqrt{5}$ and obtain $3 \cdot \sqrt{5} + 5 = 6$ which, of course, is also a false sentence.

A set of numbers whose names are to be used as replacements for a numerical variable is called the **replacement set of the variable.**

## EXERCISES

For each open sentence below, there is specified a replacement set of the variable. Make one replacement of the variable resulting in a false sentence and one replacement resulting in a true sentence.

**1.** $2x = 4$; the replacement set of $x$ is the set of natural numbers

**2.** $5x = 15$; the replacement set of $x$ is the set of natural numbers

**3.** $-3a = 87$; the replacement set of $a$ is the set of integers

**4.** $5m = -105$; the replacement set of $m$ is the set of integers

**5.** $n - 7 = 3$; the replacement set of $n$ is the set of natural numbers

**6.** $-12 + y = 14$; the replacement set of $y$ is the set of integers

**7.** $-9 \cdot x = 8$; the replacement set of $y$ is the set of rational numbers

**8.** $r + 9 \neq 21$; the replacement set of $r$ is the set of natural numbers

**9.** $6x < 17$; the replacement set of $x$ is the set of integers

**10.** $\dfrac{|x|}{2} > 3$; the replacement set of $x$ is the set of integers

**11.** $|y| + 3 < 7$; the replacement set of $y$ is the set of integers

**12.** $3 \cdot \bigcirc + 3 < 7$; natural numbers

**13.** $5 + \dfrac{\triangle}{2} \neq 8$; rational numbers

**14.** $|x - 3| > 4$; integers

**15.** $7 + 5 \cdot z > 12$; integers

**16.** $\dfrac{|y|}{3} < 3$; integers

**17.** $7 + 4 \cdot \triangle = 21$; rational numbers

**18.** $3t - (-9) \neq 18$; integers

**19.** $\dfrac{|s|}{5} < 2$; rational numbers

**20.** $-5.8 \times \square = 2.9$; rational numbers

**21.** $-\sqrt{2x} + \sqrt{2} \neq 0$; real numbers

**22.** $2 \cdot x - |x| < 3$; integers

**23.** $2 \cdot \square - 17 \not> 3$; integers

**24.** $\frac{5}{6}y + (-3) > \frac{2}{3}$; rational numbers

**25.** $\sqrt{3} + x = 0$; real numbers

**26.** $x - \frac{1}{2} \neq 0$; rational numbers

**27.** $x - \sqrt{5} \neq 0$; real numbers

**28.** $|x + 1| < 6$; integers

**29.** $|x| + 2 < 3$; integers

**30.** $y + (-7) < |y|$; integers

**31.** $\frac{7}{8} \cdot x + (-\frac{1}{8}) > \frac{2}{3}$; rational numbers

**32.** $3 \cdot y - \dfrac{|y|}{2} \neq \frac{5}{2}$; rational numbers

**33.** $\dfrac{x + 7}{6} < 1$; integers

**34.** $y + 2 = y + 3$; integers

**35.** $\dfrac{4 + |y|}{5 + |y|} \neq \frac{6}{7}$; rational numbers

**36.** $|2 + x| < 7$; integers

**37.** $\dfrac{9 - 4 \cdot \triangle}{5} \neq 7$; rational numbers

**38.** $6 + |9 - 5x| > 7$; rational numbers

**39.** $4.3y - 1.7 \not< 5.1$; rational numbers

**40.** $\frac{1}{2} - x = \frac{1}{2}$; rational numbers

**41.** $|x| \neq \frac{5}{9}$; rational numbers

**42.** $3(y - 7) \not< -14$; rational numbers

**43.** $|7 + y| < 6$; integers

**44.** $7 - 5(x + 3) \neq 8$; rational numbers

**45.** $\dfrac{6}{|x|} < 3$; integers

**46.** $3x = 7$; rational numbers

**47.** $\sqrt{7x} + 6 \neq 13$; real numbers

**48.** $-13 \nless 7 - \mid 2x \mid$; integers

# 8 · Terms and Expressions in Algebra

Examine each of the following:

$$4$$
$$3x$$
$$-7y$$
$$5ax$$

$$-12mv$$
$$\tfrac{1}{2}xyc$$
$$-1.675mp$$

Each of the above is called a **term.** Give a few more examples of terms. Now examine each of the following:

$$7$$
$$5cy$$
$$5x + 7x$$
$$-13y + 16ax$$
$$\tfrac{1}{2}abc - 7.63x + 16u$$
$$4.6xy - \tfrac{3}{7}a + 1.2mn - 3cd$$

Each of the above is called an **expression.** Notice that a term is also an expression.

On the basis of your experience, you should be able to see that, for the third expression in the examples above, the following can be said:

$$\text{For every } x, \ 5x + 7x = 12x.$$

We are agreeing, thus, that for every replacement of $x$, $5x + 7x$ and $12x$ will yield names for the same number. Let us try some replacements.

$$(1) \qquad -2 \text{ for } x$$

| $5x + 7x$ | $12x$ |
|---|---|
| $5(-2) + 7(-2)$ | $12(-2)$ |
| $= -10 -14$ | $= -24$ |
| $= -24$ | |

We shall say that the **value** of $5x + 7x$ when $x$ is replaced by $-2$ is $-24$. Also the *value* of $12x$ when $x$ is replaced by $-2$ is $-24$.

(2)  $\frac{1}{2}$ for $x$ $\qquad$ $5x + 7x$ $\qquad$ $12x$

$$5(\tfrac{1}{2}) + 7(\tfrac{1}{2}) \qquad 12(\tfrac{1}{2})$$

$$= \frac{12}{2} = 6 \qquad = 6$$

Try a few more replacements for $x$ to convince yourself that the expressions $5x + 7x$ and $12x$ have the same value for the same replacements of $x$. Such expressions are called **equivalent expressions.**

In each example below, there are given a number of equivalent expressions. Check to see whether you agree that they are equivalent expressions.

(1)   $13y + 12y$; $25y$

(2)   $17A - A$; $16A$

(3)   $\frac{1}{2}xy + \frac{3}{4}xy$; $\frac{2}{4}xy + \frac{3}{4}xy$; $\frac{5}{4}xy$; $1\frac{1}{4}xy$

(4)   $1.6mpr - \frac{1}{2}mpr + 3mpr$; $1.6mpr - .5mpr + 3mpr$; $4.1mpr$

(5)   $5(4x + 5y)$; $20x + 25y$

You will note that some expressions are "simpler looking" than others. For example, of the two equivalent expressions: $13y + 12y$ and $25y$, $25y$ is certainly "simpler looking" than $13y + 12y$. Since the two expressions *are equivalent*, it is usually more convenient to use the simpler expression. The process of arriving at an equivalent expression which is simpler looking than a given expression is frequently called simplification. For example, in simplifying the expression $-12my + 11my - 3my$ you would probably write $-4my$ as an expression which is equivalent to the given expression and which is simpler.

# EXERCISES

**1.** Find the value of each of the expressions below for the designated replacements of variables:

**EXAMPLE**     $6x - 2m$

(a)   $-2$ for $x$; $\frac{1}{2}$ for $m$

(b)   $0$ for $x$; $7$ for $m$

**SOLUTION**   (a)   $6 \cdot (-2) - 2 \cdot \frac{1}{2} = -12 - 1 = -13$

(b)   $6 \cdot 0 - 2 \cdot 7 = 0 - 14 = -14$

**a.** $4p - 3$ $\qquad\qquad\qquad$ **b.** $11x - 25y$

(1)   $-7$ for $p$ $\qquad\qquad\qquad\qquad$ (1)   $-\frac{1}{2}$ for $x$; $2$ for $y$

(2)   $\frac{1}{3}$ for $p$ $\qquad\qquad\qquad\qquad$ (2)   $0$ for $x$; $0$ for $y$

**c.** $3mv + \frac{1}{2}m$
    (1)  1 for $m$; $-2$ for $v$
    (2)  0 for $m$; 100 for $v$

**d.** $x^2 + x^2$
    (1)  $-1$ for $x$
    (2)  1 for $x$
    (3)  0 for $x$
    (4)  $-5$ for $x$
    (5)  5 for $x$

**e.** $\dfrac{x^3}{x^2}$
    (1)  $-1$ for $x$
    (2)  1 for $x$
    (3)  $-2$ for $x$
    (4)  2 for $x$

**f.** $x + y$
    (1)  $-1$ for $x$; $-2$ for $y$
    (2)  3 for $x$; $-1$ for $y$
    (3)  0 for $x$; 0 for $y$

**g.** $\dfrac{a + b}{a - b}$
    (1)  2 for $a$; $-15$ for $b$
    (2)  $\frac{1}{2}$ for $a$; $-\frac{1}{2}$ for $b$
    (3)  $\frac{2}{3}$ for $a$; $-\frac{1}{3}$ for $b$

**h.** $r^2 - s^2$
    (1)  $-1$ for $r$; $-1$ for $s$
    (2)  3 for $r$; 2 for $s$
    (3)  $\frac{2}{7}$ for $r$; $-\frac{3}{4}$ for $s$

**i.** $\dfrac{m^2 - n^2}{m - n}$
    (1)  1 for $m$; 2 for $n$
    (2)  3 for $m$; 2 for $n$

**j.** $m + n$
    (1)  1 for $m$; 2 for $n$
    (2)  3 for $m$; 2 for $n$

**k.** $x(y - z)$
    (1)  1 for $x$; 2 for $y$; 3 for $z$
    (2)  $-1$ for $x$; $-5$ for $y$; 4 for $z$

**l.** $xy - xz$
    (1)  1 for $x$; 2 for $y$; 3 for $z$
    (2)  $-1$ for $x$; $-5$ for $y$; 4 for $z$

**2.** In each exercise below, there are given two expressions. Make three different replacements of the variables to see whether it is reasonable to suspect that the two given expressions may be equivalent expressions.

**EXAMPLE 1**    $x^2 - y^2$; $(x - y)(x + y)$

**SOLUTION**    (1)  $-2$ for $x$; 5 for $y$

$$\frac{x^2 - y^2}{(-2)^2 - 5^2} \qquad \frac{(x - y)(x + y)}{(-2 - 5)(-2 + 5)}$$
$$= 4 - 25 \qquad\qquad = -7 \cdot 3$$
$$= -21 \qquad\qquad\quad = -21$$

(2)  0 for $x$; $-\frac{1}{2}$ for $y$

$$\frac{x^2 - y^2}{0^2 - (-\frac{1}{2})^2}$$
$$= 0 - \frac{1}{4}$$
$$= -\frac{1}{4}$$

$$\frac{(x - y)(x + y)}{[0 - (-\frac{1}{2})]\,[0 + (-\frac{1}{2})]}$$
$$= \frac{1}{2} \cdot (-\frac{1}{2})$$
$$= -\frac{1}{4}$$

(3)  $-4$ for $x$; $.7$ for $y$

$$\frac{x^2 - y^2}{(-4)^2 - .7^2}$$
$$= 16 - .49$$
$$= 15.51$$

$$\frac{(x - y)(x + y)}{(-4 - .7)(-4 + .7)}$$
$$= 4.7 \cdot (-3 \cdot 3)$$
$$= 15.51$$

There is reason to believe that $x^2 - y^2$ and $(x - y)(x + y)$ are equivalent expressions.

**EXAMPLE 2**     $x \cdot x$; $2x$

**SOLUTION**     (1)  0 for $x$; $\dfrac{x \cdot x}{0 \cdot 0}$    $\dfrac{2x}{2 \cdot 0}$

$$= 0 \qquad\qquad = 0$$

(2)  2 for $x$; $\dfrac{x \cdot x}{2 \cdot 2}$    $\dfrac{2x}{2 \cdot 2}$

$$= 4 \qquad\qquad = 4$$

(3)  $-5$ for $x$;  $\dfrac{x \cdot x}{-5 \cdot (-5\ )}$    $\dfrac{2x}{2 \cdot (-5\ )}$

$$= 25 \qquad\qquad = -10$$

The last replacement is sufficient to dispel any suspicion that $x \cdot x$ and $2x$ are equivalent expressions.

**a.** $x^2 + x$; $x(x + 1)$

**b.** $3x + 3y$; $3(x + y)$

**c.** $(a + b)^2$; $a^2 + 2ab + b^2$

**d.** $(a - b)^2$; $a^2 - 2ab + b^2$

**e.** $a(b + c)$; $ab + ac$

**f.** $(a + b)^3$; $a^3 + 3a^2b + 3ab^2 + b^3$

**g.** $(a - b)^3$; $a^3 - 3a^2b + 3ab^2 - b$

**h.** $x \cdot x \cdot x$; $3x$

**i.** $x \cdot x \cdot x$; $x^3$

**j.** $(-N) \cdot (-N) \cdot (-N)$; $-N^3$

**k.** $(-n) \cdot (-n) \cdot (-n)$; $(-n)^3$

**l.** $\dfrac{m}{m}$; $1$ $[m \neq 0]$

**m.** $\left|\dfrac{c}{c}\right|$; $\dfrac{|\,c\,|}{|\,c\,|}$ $[c \neq 0]$

**n.** $\dfrac{d^3}{d^2}$; $d$ $[d \neq 0]$

**o.** $\dfrac{(a + b)^2}{a + b}$; $a + b$ $[a + b \neq 0]$

**p.** $\dfrac{p^4}{p^2}$; $p^2$ $[p \neq 0]$

## 9 · Proving Expressions Equivalent

Now that you have accepted a number of principles concerning numbers, you can show that some other truths follow from these principles by logical reasoning. The process of reasoning from some accepted principles to other truths is called **proof.** The principles we have accepted serve as foundations for the proofs. They are also sometimes referred to as assumptions, axioms, or postulates.

Is the following statement true?

$$\text{For every } m, \ 2m + 3m = 5m$$

In other words, are $2m + 3m$ and $5m$ equivalent expressions?

We could replace $m$ by various numerals to produce true statements; however, it is impossible to try every replacement. So, using the principles we have assumed, we must show that $2m + 3m$ is equivalent to $5m$.

We will start with the more complicated expression $2m + 3m$ and show by justifying each step with our basic principles that $5m$ is the result. By so doing, we may conclude that, for every $m$, $2m + 3m = 5m$ is a true statement.

**Proof:** $2m + 3m = m \cdot 2 + m \cdot 3$   [Commutative Principle of Multiplication]

$m \cdot 2 + m \cdot 3 = m(2 + 3)$   [Distributive Principle]

$m(2 + 3) = m \cdot 5$   [Arithmetic Fact: $2 + 3 = 5$]

$m \cdot 5 = 5m$   [Commutative Principle of Multiplication]

Thus, we have proved that for every $m$, $2m + 3m = 5m$.

Statements like "for every $m$, $2m + 3m = 5m$," which are proved to be true on the basis of some accepted principles are called **theorems.**

Let us prove

$$\text{For every } x, y, \text{ and } z, \ (x + y)z = xz + yz$$

**Proof:** $(x + y)z = z(x + y)$   (Why?)

$= zx + zy$   (Why?)

$= xz + yz$   (Why?)

Therefore, for every $x, y,$ and $z$, $(x + y)z = xz + yz$.

This is sometimes referred to as the right distributive principle, as contrasted to "for every $x, y,$ and $z$, $z(x + y) = zx + zy$," which is called the left distributive principle.

How can we show that $(-1) \cdot x = -x$, is true for all $x$?

We know from the principle of opposites that $x + (-x) = 0$. If we could show that $x + (-1) \cdot x = 0$ it would be clear that $(-1)x$ is the opposite of $x$ also and that the expressions $(-1) \cdot x$ and $-x$ are equivalent. We are assuming that each real number has only one opposite. After we have studied a few more principles, we shall be able to prove this.

**Proof:** $x + (-1) \cdot x = 1 \cdot x + (-1) \cdot x$   [Principle of One (Multiplication)]

$= x \cdot 1 + x \cdot (-1)$   [Commutative Principle of Multiplication]

$= x[1 + (-1)]$   [Distributive Principle]

$= x \cdot (0)$   [Principle of Opposites]

$= 0$   [Principle of Zero (Multiplication)]

But $x + (-x) = 0$, so $(-1) \cdot x = -x$.

We might refer to this as the *Principle of $-1$ (Multiplication)*. It provides us with an easily remembered method for finding the opposite of a number. This principle enables us to prove that $7x - 3x$ and $4x$, for example, are equivalent expressions.

**Proof:** $7x - 3x = 7x + [-(3x)]$   [Principle of Subtraction]

$= 7x + [-1 \cdot (3x)]$   [Principle of $-1$ (Multiplication)]

$= 7x + [(-1 \cdot 3)x]$   Why?

$= 7x + (-3)x$   $[-1 \cdot 3 = -3]$

$= [7 + (-3)]x$   Why?

$= 4x$   $[7 + (-3) = 4]$

Could we also prove that $\dfrac{x}{(-1)} = -x$ is true for all values of $x$?

**Proof:** $\dfrac{x}{-1} = x \cdot \left(\dfrac{1}{-1}\right)$   [Principle of Division]

$= x \cdot (-1)$   $\left[\dfrac{1}{-1} = -1\right]$

$= (-1) \cdot x$   [Commutative Principle (Multiplication)]

$= -x$   [Principle of $-1$ (Multiplication)]

This is frequently referred to as the *Principle of $-1$ (Division)* and it also provides us with another easily remembered method of obtaining the opposite of a number.

Observe the following expressions:

$$2 - 3 = -1 \qquad \leftrightarrow \qquad 3 - 2 = 1$$
$$5 - 2 = 3 \qquad \leftrightarrow \qquad 2 - 5 = -3$$
$$6 - 3 = 3 \qquad \leftrightarrow \qquad 3 - 6 = -3$$
$$2 - (-1) = 3 \qquad \leftrightarrow \qquad -1 - 2 = -3$$
$$-5 - 1 = -6 \qquad \leftrightarrow \qquad 1 - (-5) = 6$$
$$-4 - (-7) = 3 \qquad \leftrightarrow \qquad -7 - (-4) = -3$$

It appears that replacements in $x - y$ and $y - x$ yield opposites. We can establish the truth of this by proving that for every replacement of $x$ and $y$, $(y - x) + (x - y) = 0$.

$(y - x) + (x - y)$
$= [y + (-x)] + [x + (-y)]$    Principle of Subtraction
$= [x + (-y)] + [y + (-x)]$    Commutative Principle (Addition)
$= x + [(-y) + y] + (-x)$      Associative Principle (Addition)
$= x + 0 + (-x)$             Principle of Opposites
$= x + (-x)$               Principle of Zero (Addition)
$= 0$                     Principle of Opposites

We may conclude that

$$-(x - y) = y - x \text{ or } (x - y) = -(y - x) \text{ for every } x \text{ and } y$$

Can you show that $(x + y)$ and $(-x) + (-y)$ will yield opposites for every $x$ and $y$? Try it.

We recall the following true statements from our work with directed numbers.

$$(-2)(3) = -6 \qquad \leftrightarrow \qquad -[(2)(3)] = -6$$
$$(-4)(5) = -20 \qquad \leftrightarrow \qquad -[(4)(5)] = -20$$
$$(-\tfrac{1}{3})(\tfrac{2}{5}) = -\tfrac{2}{15} \qquad \leftrightarrow \qquad -[(\tfrac{1}{3})(\tfrac{2}{5})] = -\tfrac{2}{15}$$
$$(-5)(\tfrac{3}{5}) = -3 \qquad \leftrightarrow \qquad -[(5)(\tfrac{3}{5})] = -3$$

This leads us to feel that $(-x)y$ and $-(xy)$ are equivalent expressions.

$(-x) \cdot y = (-1 \cdot x) \cdot y$    Principle of $-1$ (Multiplication)
$= (-1)(xy)$       Associative Principle (Multiplication)
$= -(xy)$          Principle of $-1$ (Multiplication)

Thus, for all numbers $x$ and $y$, $(-x)y = -(xy)$.

Can you prove that $x(-y) = -(xy)$ by the same method? Try it.

Let us now prove that $4x + 6y - 3x - 4y$ and $x + 2y$ are equivalent expressions.

**Proof:** $4x + 6y - 3x - 4y$

$$= 4x + 6y + [-(3x)] + [-(4y)]$$
$$= 4x + 6y + (-3)x + (-4)y \qquad \text{[Proved above: For all } x \text{ and}$$
$$\qquad\qquad\qquad\qquad\qquad\qquad\qquad y, \ -(xy) = (-x)y]$$
$$= 4x + [6y + (-3)x] + (-4)y \qquad \text{Why?}$$
$$= 4x + [(-3)x + 6y] + (-4)y \qquad \text{Why?}$$
$$= [4x + (-3)x] + [6y + (-4)y] \qquad \text{Why?}$$
$$= [4 + (-3)]x + [6 + (-4)]y \qquad \text{Why?}$$
$$= 1 \cdot x + 2 \cdot y \qquad \text{Why?}$$
$$= x \cdot 1 + 2y \qquad \text{Why?}$$
$$= x + 2y \qquad \text{Why?}$$

Frequently the phrase "for every $x$" or "for all $x$" is abbreviated $\forall_x$. We shall employ this shorter symbolism on many occasions as a space saver.

# EXERCISES

1. Prove each of the following:

   **a.** $\forall_x,\ 3x + 15x = 18x$

   **b.** $\forall_a,\ a + 3a = 4a$

   **c.** $\forall_y,\ y + y = 2y$

   **d.** $\forall_z,\ \frac{1}{2}z + \frac{1}{2}z = z$

   **e.** $\forall_p,\ 7p - 2p = 5p$

   **f.** $\forall_c,\ 3c - 7c = -4c$

   **g.** $\forall_u,\ \frac{1}{2}u - \frac{3}{4}u = -\frac{1}{4}u$

   **h.** $\forall_w,\ w - w = 0$

   **i.** $\forall_{x,y},\ 6.7x + 4.6y - 4.3x - 2.4y = 2.4x + 2.2y$

   **j.** $\forall_{x,y},\ 4xy - 2xy + 6xy = 8xy$

   **k.** $\forall_{x,y,r,s},\ 10xy - 5rs - 3xy + 9rs - xy = 4rs + 6xy$

   **l.** $\forall_{x,y},\ 6 - 3x + 5y - 9 + 6x - 7y = 3x - 2y - 3$

   **m.** $\forall_{y,r,s},\ 4 + 3y - 2rs + (-4) + 7rs - 4y = 5rs - y$

   **n.** $\forall_{u,v},\ 5uv + 7uv - 9uv = 3uv$

2. Find simpler equivalent expressions for the following:

   **a.** $c - 3d - c + 4$

   **b.** $3r + 5s - 6 - 7r + 4s + 4$

   **c.** $-u + 3t + 2w - 5 - 3t$

   **d.** $-x - 3x - 5x + 7x - 2x$

   **e.** $3x - 4y - 5x + 7y$

   **f.** $1.7r + 3.2v - 4.5 + 2.5r$

   **g.** $\frac{4}{3}x - 7 + \frac{2}{5}y - \frac{3}{4}x + 5$

   **h.** $-4.9r - 6.7r + .2s - 5.8r$

   **i.** $4st + 5xy - 7st - 3xy + 4$

   **j.** $3am - 11am + 3c - 17c$

3. Study the following derivations and supply the missing reasons.

(a) Our work with signed numbers would tell us that the following statements are true:

$$(2)(3) = 6 \quad \leftrightarrow \quad -[(-2)(3)] = 6$$
$$(3)(4) = 12 \quad \leftrightarrow \quad -[(-3)(4)] = 12$$
$$(6)(5) = 30 \quad \leftrightarrow \quad -[(-6)(5)] = 30$$

Thus, we are led to believe that $xy$ and $-(-x)y$ are equivalent expressions.

We know from the Principle of Opposites that $xy + [-xy] = 0$. If we could show $xy + [-(xy)] = 0$ it would be clear that $xy$ would be equal to the opposite of $(-x)y$.

**Proof:** $xy + [-(xy)] = [x + (-x)]y$    Reason?

$\qquad\qquad\qquad = y[x + (-x)]$    Reason?

$\qquad\qquad\qquad = y(0)$           Reason?

$\qquad\qquad\qquad = 0$             Reason?

Thus, $\forall_{x,y}, \; xy = -(-x)y$.

(b) We know from our work with directed numbers that the following statements are true:

$$(4)(3) = 12 \quad \leftrightarrow \quad (-4)(-3) = 12$$
$$(2)(3) = 6 \quad \leftrightarrow \quad (-2)(-3) = 6$$
$$(5)(7) = 35 \quad \leftrightarrow \quad (-5)(-7) = 35$$

Thus, we are led to believe that $xy$ and $(-x)(-y)$ are equivalent. Can we prove this?

We know from the Principle of Opposites that $xy + [-(xy)] = 0$ is a true statement for all $x$ and $y$. If we could show that $(-x)(-y) + [-(xy)] = 0$ is also a true statement, our purpose will be accomplished.

**Proof:** $(-x)(-y) + [-(xy)]$

$\qquad = (-x)(-y) + (-x)(y)$   [Proved, for all $x, y, (-x)(y) = -(xy)$]

$\qquad = (-x)\,[(-y) + y]$       ?

$\qquad = (-x)\,[y + (-y)]$       ?

$\qquad = (-x)(0)$              ?

$\qquad = 0$

Thus, $\forall_{x,y}, \; (-x)(-y) = xy$.

(c) Prove: $\forall_x, \; -(-x) = x$

(d) Justify each step:

$$x \cdot (-y) = (-y) \cdot x \qquad \text{Reason?}$$
$$= [(-1)(y)]x \qquad \text{Reason?}$$
$$= (-1)(yx) \qquad \text{Reason?}$$
$$= -(yx) \qquad \text{Reason?}$$
$$= -(xy) \qquad \text{Reason?}$$

Hence, $\forall_{x,y},\ x(-y) = -(xy)$.

4. Give simpler equivalent expressions for each of the following:

a. $(-3)(8x)$

b. $(-6)(-1)(r)$

c. $5(s)(-3)$

d. $-6.2(-3x)$

e. $-(-5x)(3y)$

f. $(-x)(-3y)(-4)$

g. $(1.4y)(-3x)$

h. $(-6.3x)(-y)(5)$

i. $-1.5(-3r)$

j. $(-2)(-s)(-5)$

5. Tell whether or not the following are true for all replacements of the variables:

a. $(x - y)(r - s) = -(y - x)(r - s)$

b. $-y = -(-y)$

c. $-[(-x) + y] = x - y$

d. $(r - s)(x - y) = (s - r)(y - x)$

e. $-(x - y) = -x - y$

f. $-y - x = -x - y$

g. $x - y = -y + x$

h. $-[(-x) + (-y)] = x + y$

i. $x + (-y) = -[y + (-x)]$

j. $-[-(-x)] = -x$

k. $-[-(x)] + (-x) = 0$

l. $-[(-x) + x] = x$

m. $(-x)yz = -[(-x)yz]$

n. $xy(-z) = -xyz$

o. $(r - s)(x - y)(w - v) = -(s - r)(x - y)(w - v)$

p. Choose any *four* of the above which appeared to be true for all replacements of the variable and *prove* them.

6. a. Is $r + s - (x + y) = r + s - x - y$ true for all $r$, $s$, $x$, and $y$? Justify each step in the proof.

**Proof:** $r + s - (x + y)$

$$= r + s + [-(x + y)] \qquad \text{Principle of Subtraction}$$
$$= r + s + [(-1)(x + y)] \qquad \text{Reason?}$$
$$= r + s + [(-x) + (-y)] \qquad \text{Reason?}$$
$$= r + s - x - y \qquad \text{Reason?}$$

**b.** Is $s - (x - y) = s - x + y$ true for all $s$, $x$, and $y$? Justify each step in the proof.

**Proof:** $s - (x - y) = s + [-(x - y)]$
$$= s + [(-1)(x - y)]$$
$$= s + [(-1)x - (-1)y]$$
$$= s + [(-x) - (-y)]$$
$$= s + (-x) + y$$
$$= s - x + y$$

Thus, $s - (x - y)$ and $s - x + y$ are equivalent expressions.

**c.** Justify each step in the following development:

$x + y - (-x + y) = x + y + [-(-x + y)]$ p. of sub.
$= x + y + [(-1)(-x + y)]$ p. of minus 1 mult.
$= x + y + [(-1)(-x) + (-1)y]$ Dist.
$= x + y + [x + (-y)]$ prin. of minus 1 mult.
$= x + y + [(-y) + x]$ Commutative of add.
$= x + [y + (-y)] + x$ Associat of add.
$= (x + 0) + x$ prin of opposites
$= x + x$ prin of addit of 0.
$= 1 \cdot x + 1 \cdot x$ prin of mult by 1
$= (1 + 1)x$ distributive.
$= 2x$ arithmetic.

**7.** Tell whether or not the following are true for all replacements of the variables:

**a.** $x - y - (x + y) = 0$      **c.** $7x - (3x + y) - (2x - 2y) = 2x$

**b.** $2r + 3s - (2r - 4s) = 7s$      **d.** $12x - 2(3x + 4) = 6x + 8$

**e.** $4.3r - 6(1.8r - .3) = 6.5r + 1.8$

**f.** $3s - (4s + t) - 2(3s - t) = -7s + t$

**g.** $3x - [13x - (4x + 5)] = -6x + 5$

**h.** $3y - 2[3x + 5 - (2x + 4y - 5)] = -2x + 11y - 20$

**i.** $5x - 3[2x - 2y - (3x + 4y)] = 8x - 18y$

**j.** $5(3x - 2y) - 2(2x + y) = 11x - 12y$

**k.** Choose any two of the above that you judged to be true, and *prove* that each statement is true.

## 10 · Equivalent Expressions and Rational Numbers

In arithmetic you learned various rules for operations with natural numbers. All of these rules have their foundations in the basic principles of numbers and their operations. We are going to combine our new knowledge of a variable with our basic principles of numbers and operations to justify some of these rules for operations with fractional numbers.

We know that the following statements are true.

$$\frac{2 \cdot 3}{7} = \frac{6}{7} \qquad\qquad \frac{7 \cdot 3}{11} = \frac{21}{11}$$

$$\left(\frac{2}{7}\right) \cdot 3 = \frac{6}{7} \qquad\qquad \left(\frac{7}{11}\right) \cdot 3 = \frac{21}{11}$$

$$2 \cdot \left(\frac{3}{7}\right) = \frac{6}{7} \qquad\qquad 7 \cdot \left(\frac{3}{11}\right) = \frac{21}{11}$$

$$\frac{1}{7} \cdot (2 \cdot 3) = \frac{6}{7} \qquad\qquad \frac{1}{11} \cdot (7 \cdot 3) = \frac{21}{11}$$

This leads us to surmise that

$$\frac{xz}{y} \text{ and } \left(\frac{x}{y}\right) \cdot z \text{ and } x \cdot \left(\frac{z}{y}\right) \text{ and } \frac{1}{y}(xz)$$

are all equivalent expressions. Is this true for all directed numbers $x$, $z$, and $y$, $(y \neq 0)$?

Starting with one of the expressions, we will justify each step in going to an equivalent expression by the basic properties of numbers and their operations.

$$\frac{xz}{y} = xz\left(\frac{1}{y}\right) \qquad \text{Principle of Division}$$

$$= x\left[z\left(\frac{1}{y}\right)\right] \qquad \text{Associative Principle (Multiplication)}$$

$$= x\left[\left(\frac{1}{y}\right) \cdot z\right] \qquad \text{Why?}$$

$$= \left[x\left(\frac{1}{y}\right)\right] \cdot z \qquad \text{Why?}$$

$$= \left(\frac{x}{y}\right) \cdot z \qquad \text{Principle of Division}$$

Thus, we've shown that $\frac{xz}{y} = \left(\frac{x}{y}\right)z$ is true for all $x$, $z$, and $y$, $(y \neq 0)$; that is, they are equivalent expressions.

$$\frac{xz}{y} = (xz)\frac{1}{y} \qquad \text{Principle of Division}$$

$$= x\left[z\left(\frac{1}{y}\right)\right] \quad \text{Why?}$$

$$= x\left(\frac{z}{y}\right) \qquad \text{Why?}$$

Thus, $\dfrac{xz}{y} = x\left(\dfrac{z}{y}\right)$, for every $x$, $z$, and $y$, $(y \neq 0)$.

Lastly,

$$\frac{xz}{y} = xz\left(\frac{1}{y}\right) \quad \text{Why?}$$

$$= \frac{1}{y}(xz) \qquad \text{Why?}$$

Hence, $\dfrac{xz}{y} = \dfrac{1}{y}(xz)$, for every $x$, $z$, and $y$, $(y \neq 0)$.

We can summarize these findings as follows:

For every $x$, $z$, and $y$, $(y \neq 0)$,
$$\frac{xz}{y} = \left(\frac{x}{y}\right) \cdot z = x\left(\frac{z}{y}\right) = \frac{1}{y}(xz)$$

You know from working with fractions that the following statements are true.

$$\frac{1}{2} \cdot \frac{1}{3} = \frac{1}{6}$$

$$\frac{1}{5} \cdot \frac{1}{4} = \frac{1}{20}$$

$$\frac{1}{6} \cdot \frac{1}{3} = \frac{1}{18}$$

We are led to guess that $\left(\dfrac{1}{x}\right)\left(\dfrac{1}{y}\right)$ and $\dfrac{1}{xy}$ might be equivalent expressions.

We know, for all $x$ and $y$, $(x \neq 0, y \neq 0)$,
$$\left(\frac{1}{xy}\right) \cdot xy = 1$$
from the Principle of Reciprocals.

If we could show that, for all $x$ and $y$, $(x \neq 0, y \neq 0)$, $\left[\left(\dfrac{1}{x}\right)\left(\dfrac{1}{y}\right)\right] \cdot xy = 1$

is a true statement, we would agree that $\left(\frac{1}{x}\right)\left(\frac{1}{y}\right)$ and $\frac{1}{xy}$ are equivalent expressions. We are assuming that every real number except zero has a unique reciprocal. Later we shall prove this.

**Proof:** $\left[\left(\frac{1}{x}\right) \cdot \left(\frac{1}{y}\right)\right]xy$

$= \left[\left(\frac{1}{x}\right)\left(\frac{1}{y}\right)x\right]y$      Associative Principle (Multiplication)

$= \left[\left(\frac{1}{x}\right) \cdot x \cdot \left(\frac{1}{y}\right)\right]y$      Commutative Principle (Multiplication)

$= \left[\left(\frac{1}{x}\right)x\right]\left[\left(\frac{1}{y}\right) \cdot y\right]$      Associative Principle (Multiplication)

$= \left[x\left(\frac{1}{x}\right)\right]\left[y \cdot \left(\frac{1}{y}\right)\right]$      Commutative Principle (Multiplication)

$= (1) \cdot (1)$      Principle of Reciprocals

$= 1$      Principle of Multiplication by One

Therefore, for all $x$ and $y$, $(x \neq 0, y \neq 0)$,

$$\left(\frac{1}{x}\right)\left(\frac{1}{y}\right) = \frac{1}{xy}.$$

Is $\left(\frac{x}{y}\right) \cdot \left(\frac{r}{s}\right) = \frac{xr}{ys}$, $(y \neq 0, s \neq 0)$ a true statement for all values of $x$, $y$, $r$, and $s$?

**Proof:** $\left(\frac{x}{y}\right)\left(\frac{r}{s}\right) = \left[x\left(\frac{1}{y}\right)\right]\left[r\left(\frac{1}{s}\right)\right]$      Principle of Division

$= x\left[\left(\frac{1}{y}\right) \cdot r\right]\left(\frac{1}{s}\right)$      Why?

$= x\left[r \cdot \left(\frac{1}{y}\right)\right]\left(\frac{1}{s}\right)$      Why?

$= (xr)\left(\frac{1}{y} \cdot \frac{1}{s}\right)$      Why?

$= (xr)\left(\frac{1}{ys}\right)$      Why?

$= \frac{xr}{ys}$      Why?

Hence, for all $x$, $y$, $r$, $s$, $(y \neq 0, s \neq 0)$,

$$\left(\frac{x}{y}\right)\left(\frac{r}{s}\right) = \frac{xr}{ys}$$

We know from working with fractions in arithmetic that the following statements are true:

$$\frac{2}{4} = \frac{1}{2}$$          $$\frac{1 \cdot 2}{2 \cdot 2} = \frac{2}{4}$$

$$\frac{3}{9} = \frac{1}{3}$$          $$\frac{1 \cdot 3}{3 \cdot 3} = \frac{3}{9}$$

$$\frac{5}{25} = \frac{1}{5}$$          $$\frac{1 \cdot 5}{5 \cdot 5} = \frac{5}{25}$$

$$\frac{4}{8} = \frac{1}{2}$$          $$\frac{1 \cdot 4}{2 \cdot 4} = \frac{4}{8}$$

We are led to think that $\dfrac{xr}{yr}$ and $\dfrac{x}{y}$ may be equivalent expressions. Let's see whether or not this is the case.

$$\frac{xr}{yr} = \left(\frac{x}{y}\right)\left(\frac{r}{r}\right) \qquad \text{just proved}$$

$$= \frac{x}{y} \cdot \left[r\left(\frac{1}{r}\right)\right] \qquad \text{Principle of Division}$$

$$= \frac{x}{y} \cdot (1) \qquad \text{Principle of Reciprocals}$$

$$= \frac{x}{y} \qquad \text{Principle of Multiplication by One}$$

Thus, for all $x$, $y$, and $r$, $(y \neq 0, r \neq 0)$,

$$\frac{xr}{yr} = \frac{x}{y}.$$

We recall from working with fractions in arithmetic that the following statements are true:

$$\frac{1}{4} + \frac{2}{5} = \frac{1 \times 5}{4 \times 5} + \frac{2 \times 4}{5 \times 4} = \frac{5}{20} + \frac{8}{20} = \frac{5 + 8}{20} = \frac{13}{20}$$

$$\frac{2}{3} + \frac{5}{7} = \frac{2 \times 7}{3 \times 7} + \frac{5 \times 3}{7 \times 3} = \frac{14}{21} + \frac{15}{21} = \frac{14 + 15}{21} = \frac{29}{21}$$

$$\frac{1}{3} + \frac{1}{2} = \frac{1 \times 2}{3 \times 2} + \frac{1 \times 3}{2 \times 3} = \frac{2}{6} + \frac{3}{6} = \frac{2 + 3}{6} = \frac{5}{6}$$

$$\frac{1}{4} + \frac{1}{5} = \frac{1 \times 5}{4 \times 5} + \frac{1 \times 4}{5 \times 4} = \frac{5}{20} + \frac{4}{20} = \frac{5 + 4}{20} = \frac{9}{20}$$

We are led to believe that $\dfrac{x}{y} + \dfrac{r}{s}$ and $\dfrac{xs}{ys} + \dfrac{ry}{sy}$ and $\dfrac{xs + ry}{ys}$ are equivalent expressions $y \neq 0$, $s \neq 0$.

$$\dfrac{x}{y} + \dfrac{r}{s} = \dfrac{xs}{ys} + \dfrac{ry}{sy} \qquad \left( \text{Proved earlier that } \dfrac{xr}{yr} = \dfrac{x}{y} \right)$$

$$= \dfrac{xs}{ys} + \dfrac{ry}{ys} \qquad \text{Commutative Principle (Multiplication)}$$

$$= (xs)\left(\dfrac{1}{ys}\right) + (ry)\left(\dfrac{1}{ys}\right) \quad \text{Principle of Division}$$

$$= (xs + ry)\left(\dfrac{1}{ys}\right) \qquad \text{Distributive Principle}$$

$$= \dfrac{xs + ry}{ys} \qquad \text{Principle of Division}$$

Thus, for all $x$, $y$, $r$, and $s$, $(y \neq 0,\ s \neq 0)$, $\dfrac{x}{y} + \dfrac{r}{s} = \dfrac{xs + ry}{ys}$ is a true statement.

Recall that division is the inverse of multiplication. Thus, $\dfrac{\frac{1}{2}}{\frac{3}{5}}$ is equivalent to $\dfrac{1}{2} \times \dfrac{5}{3}$ and $\dfrac{\frac{6}{7}}{\frac{4}{5}}$ is equivalent to $\dfrac{6}{7} \times \dfrac{5}{4}$.

We are led to expect that, for all $x$, $y$, $r$, and $s$, $(y \neq 0,\ r \neq 0,\ s \neq 0)$,

$$\dfrac{\frac{x}{y}}{\frac{r}{s}} = \dfrac{x}{y} \times \dfrac{s}{r}.$$

**Proof:** $\dfrac{\frac{x}{y}}{\frac{r}{s}} = \dfrac{\frac{x}{y} \cdot \left(\frac{s}{r}\right)}{\frac{r}{s} \cdot \left(\frac{s}{r}\right)} \quad \left( \text{For all } x,\ y,\ \text{and } r,\ (y \neq 0,\ r \neq 0),\ \dfrac{xr}{yr} = \dfrac{x}{y} \right)$

$$= \dfrac{\frac{x}{y} \cdot \left(\frac{s}{r}\right)}{1} \qquad \text{Principle of Reciprocals}$$

$$= \dfrac{x}{y} \cdot \dfrac{s}{r} \qquad \text{Principle of Division}$$

Thus, $\dfrac{\dfrac{x}{y}}{\dfrac{r}{s}} = \dfrac{x}{y} \cdot \dfrac{s}{r}$ holds true for all $x$, $y$, $r$, $s$, $(y \neq 0, r \neq 0, s \neq 0)$.

We have shown thus that the rules of operations for rational numbers are well grounded in the basic principles which underlie all of algebra. We will ask you to justify more of these rules in some of the exercises to follow.

You will recall from working with directed numbers that the following statements are true.

$$-\left(\frac{-2}{3}\right) = \frac{2}{3} \quad \leftrightarrow \quad -\left(\frac{2}{-3}\right) = \frac{2}{3}$$

$$-\left(\frac{-5}{8}\right) = \frac{5}{8} \quad \leftrightarrow \quad -\left(\frac{5}{-8}\right) = \frac{5}{8}$$

$$-\left(\frac{-6}{11}\right) = \frac{6}{11} \quad \leftrightarrow \quad -\left(\frac{6}{-11}\right) = \frac{6}{11}$$

Thus, we are led to believe that $-\left(\dfrac{-x}{y}\right)$ and $-\left(\dfrac{x}{-y}\right)$ and $\dfrac{x}{y}$ are equivalent expressions. (We, of course, rule out the replacement of $y$ by 0. Why?)

**Proof:** $-\left(\dfrac{x}{-y}\right) = (-1)\left[\dfrac{x}{-y}\right]$  Principle of $-1$ (Multiplication)

$\qquad\qquad = \dfrac{(-1) \cdot x}{(-y)}$  Proved previously
$\qquad\qquad\qquad\qquad$ $\left(\text{For all } x, z, \text{ and } y, y \neq 0, x\left(\dfrac{z}{y}\right) = \dfrac{xz}{y}\right)$

$\qquad\qquad = \dfrac{(-1) \cdot x}{(-1) \cdot y}$  Principle of $-1$ (Multiplication) and the commutative principle (multiplication).

$\qquad\qquad = \dfrac{x}{y}$  For every $x$, $y$, and $r$, $y \neq 0$, $r \neq 0$,
$\qquad\qquad\qquad\qquad$ $\dfrac{xr}{yr} = \dfrac{x}{y}$

Thus, the expressions $\dfrac{x}{y}$ and $-\left(\dfrac{x}{-y}\right)$ are equivalent.

Could you use a similar approach to show that $\dfrac{x}{y}$ and $-\left(\dfrac{-x}{y}\right)$ are equivalent? Try it.

Can you show that $\dfrac{x}{y}$ and $\dfrac{-x}{-y}$ are equivalent expressions? Try it.

## EXERCISES

1. Give three different expressions equivalent to the following:

**EXAMPLE**     $\dfrac{3(6)}{5}$

**SOLUTION**     $\left(\dfrac{3}{5}\right)(6)$;   $\dfrac{1}{5}[3(6)]$;   $3\left(\dfrac{6}{5}\right)$

a. $\dfrac{(5)(6)}{7}$

b. $\dfrac{(3)(7)}{5}$

c. $8 \cdot \left(\dfrac{7}{6}\right)$

d. $\dfrac{1}{3}(4 \times 5)$

e. $\dfrac{4}{7} \cdot (6)$

f. $9\left(\dfrac{7}{8}\right)$

g. $\dfrac{(4)(9)}{7}$

h. $\dfrac{1}{4}(3 \cdot 9)$

i. $5\left(\dfrac{7}{6}\right)$

2. State reasons for each step in the following proofs:

a. $\dfrac{-x}{-y} = \dfrac{(-1)x}{(-1)y}$

$= \dfrac{x(-1)}{y(-1)}$

$= \dfrac{x}{y}$

Thus, $\dfrac{-x}{-y} = \dfrac{x}{y}$ for all $x$ and $y$, $(y \neq 0)$.

b. $\dfrac{x(-y)}{r(-s)} = \dfrac{-xy}{-rs}$

$= \dfrac{(-1)(xy)}{(-1)(rs)}$

$= \dfrac{xy}{rs}$

Thus, for all $x$, $y$, $r$, and $s$, $(r \neq 0, s \neq 0)$, $\dfrac{x(-y)}{r(-s)} = \dfrac{xy}{rs}$.

c. $\dfrac{a - b}{b - a} = \dfrac{1 \cdot (a - b)}{-(a - b)}$

$= \dfrac{1 \cdot (a - b)}{-1 \cdot (a - b)}$

$= \dfrac{1}{-1} = -1$ (for all $a$ and $b$, $a \neq b$)

**d.** $-\dfrac{(x)(-y)}{rs} = -\dfrac{-xy}{rs}$

$\qquad\qquad = \dfrac{xy}{rs}$

Thus, $-\dfrac{(x)(-y)}{rs} = \dfrac{xy}{rs}$ for all $x$, $y$, $r$, and $s$, $(r \neq 0, s \neq 0)$.

**e.** Could we show $-\dfrac{x-y}{r-s}$ and $\dfrac{y-x}{r-s}$ to be equivalent? Supply the reasons.

$-\dfrac{(x-y)}{r-s} = \dfrac{-(x-y)}{r-s}$

$\qquad\qquad = \dfrac{(-1)(x-y)}{r-s}$

$\qquad\qquad = \dfrac{(-1)(x)-(-1)(y)}{r-s}$

$\qquad\qquad = \dfrac{(-x)-(-y)}{r-s}$

$\qquad\qquad = \dfrac{(-x)+y}{r-s}$

$\qquad\qquad = \dfrac{y+(-x)}{r-s}$

$\qquad\qquad = \dfrac{y-x}{r-s}$

**3.** Are $\dfrac{(-x)(-y)}{rs}$ and $\dfrac{xy}{rs}$ equivalent expressions? Prove your answer.

**4.** Prove that $\dfrac{(-x)(-y)}{(-r)(-s)}$ and $\dfrac{xy}{rs}$ are equivalent expressions. (Remember, once we have proved a statement, we may use it whenever needed in later proofs.)

**5.** Supply the reasons.

$(2a)(3b) = [(2a)3]b$

$\qquad\quad = [3(2a)]b$

$\qquad\quad = [3 \cdot 2a]b$

$\qquad\quad = 6ab$

**6.** Supply the reasons:

$$\frac{10r}{2rs} = 10r \times \frac{1}{2rs}$$

$$= 10r \times \frac{1}{2} \times \frac{1}{rs}$$

$$= 10r \times \frac{1}{2} \times \frac{1}{r} \times \frac{1}{s}$$

$$= 10r \times \left(\frac{1}{2} \times \frac{1}{r}\right) \times \frac{1}{s}$$

$$= 10 \cdot r \times \left(\frac{1}{r} \times \frac{1}{2}\right) \times \frac{1}{s}$$

$$= \left[10\left(r \times \frac{1}{r}\right)\right] \times \frac{1}{2} \times \frac{1}{s}$$

$$= [10 \cdot 1] \times \frac{1}{2} \times \frac{1}{s}$$

$$= 10 \times \frac{1}{2} \times \frac{1}{s}$$

$$= 5 \times \frac{1}{s}$$

$$= \frac{5}{s}$$

Thus, $\dfrac{10r}{2rs} = \dfrac{5}{s}$.

It is not necessary to go through all of these steps in ordinary practice, for many of the steps may be omitted to economize the effort. However, if you do shorten your proofs, be careful not to omit any essential steps.

**7.** Indicate whether or not the following are true for all replacements of the variables:

**a.** $\dfrac{-3x}{2y} = -\dfrac{3x}{2y}, \ (y \neq 0)$

**e.** $-\dfrac{(-x)(3)}{(y)(-7)} = \dfrac{(x)(3)}{(y)(7)}, \ (y \neq 0)$

**b.** $-\dfrac{-5x}{-3x} = \dfrac{5x}{3x}, \ (x \neq 0)$

**f.** $\dfrac{t}{-y} = \dfrac{-t}{y}, \ (y \neq 0)$

**c.** $-\dfrac{-w}{r} = \dfrac{-w}{-r}, \ (r \neq 0)$

**g.** $-\dfrac{-s}{x} = -\dfrac{s}{x}, \ (x \neq 0)$

**d.** $-\dfrac{s}{-t} = \dfrac{s}{t}, \ (t \neq 0)$

**h.** $-\dfrac{1}{r-s} = \dfrac{1}{s-r}, \ (r. \neq s)$

**i.** $-\dfrac{1}{(x+y)} = \dfrac{1}{-x-y}$, $(x+y \neq 0;\; -x-y \neq 0)$

**j.** $-\dfrac{-(r-s)}{(x-y)} = \dfrac{r-s}{x-y}$, $(x \neq y)$

**k.** $-\dfrac{1}{-(y-x)} = \dfrac{(-1)}{y-x}$, $(x \neq y)$

**l.** $-\dfrac{(x-y)}{(r-s)} = \dfrac{xy}{s-r}$, $(s \neq r)$

**m.** $-\dfrac{-(x-y)}{(r-s)} = \dfrac{y-x}{r-s}$, $(r \neq s)$

**n.** $-\dfrac{-(x-y)}{-(r-s)} = \dfrac{x-y}{r-s}$, $(r \neq s)$

**o.** $-\dfrac{-(x-y)(r-s)}{(s-t)(x+y)} = \dfrac{(x-y)(r-s)}{(s-t)(x+y)}$, $(s \neq t;\; x+y \neq 0)$

**p.** $-\dfrac{(x-y)(r-s)}{-(s-t)(x+y)} = \dfrac{(x-y)(r-s)}{(t-s)(x+y)}$, $(t \neq s;\; x+y \neq 0)$

**8.** Justify each of the following steps:

$$\frac{x}{y} - \frac{r}{s} = \frac{xs}{ys} - \frac{ry}{sy}$$

$$= \frac{xs}{ys} + \left(-\frac{ry}{sy}\right)$$

$$= \frac{xs}{ys} + \frac{(-ry)}{sy}$$

$$= \frac{xs}{ys} + \frac{(-ry)}{ys}$$

$$= \frac{xs + (-ry)}{ys}$$

$$= \frac{xs - ry}{ys}$$

Thus, for all $x, y, r, s$, $(s \neq 0, y \neq 0)$, $\dfrac{x}{y} - \dfrac{r}{s} = \dfrac{xs - ry}{ys}$.

**9.** For each expression, write a single fractional expression equivalent to it:

**EXAMPLE** $\qquad \dfrac{y}{3} + \dfrac{x}{4}$

**SOLUTION** $\qquad \dfrac{y}{3} + \dfrac{x}{4} = \dfrac{4y + 3x}{12}$

**a.** $\dfrac{3}{r} + \dfrac{7}{s}$, $(r \neq 0; s \neq 0)$

**b.** $\dfrac{x}{3} - \dfrac{x}{4}$

**c.** $\dfrac{x}{4} \times \dfrac{y}{7}$

**d.** $\dfrac{2}{x} + \dfrac{3}{y}$, $(x \neq 0, y \neq 0)$

**e.** $\dfrac{r}{3} \times \dfrac{2}{s}$, $(s \neq 0)$

**f.** $\dfrac{y}{s} + \dfrac{x}{r}$, $(r \neq 0; s \neq 0)$

**g.** $\dfrac{3}{x} - \dfrac{1}{s}$, $(x \neq 0; s \neq 0)$

**h.** $\dfrac{6}{r} \div \dfrac{7}{s}$, $(r \neq 0; s \neq 0)$

**i.** $\dfrac{x}{r} - \dfrac{y}{s}$, $(r \neq 0, s \neq 0)$

**j.** $\dfrac{5}{x} \times \dfrac{(-3)}{y}$, $(x \neq 0; y \neq 0)$

**k.** $\dfrac{4}{(-x)} \div \dfrac{r}{s}$, $(x \neq 0; r \neq 0; s \neq 0)$

**l.** $\dfrac{x}{3} + \dfrac{x}{2} + \dfrac{x}{5}$

**m.** $\dfrac{1}{rs} + \dfrac{3}{xy}$, $(r \neq 0; s \neq 0; x \neq 0; y \neq 0)$

**n.** $\dfrac{y}{x} \div \dfrac{5}{6}$, $(x \neq 0)$

**o.** $\dfrac{s}{y} \times \dfrac{x}{5}$, $(y \neq 0)$

**p.** $\dfrac{r}{t} - \dfrac{x}{y}$, $(t \neq 0; y \neq 0)$

**q.** $\dfrac{(1-x)}{t} + \dfrac{y}{r}$, $(t \neq 0; r \neq 0)$

**r.** $\dfrac{(-2)}{y} \times \dfrac{x}{(-3)}$, $(y \neq 0)$

**s.** $\dfrac{3}{y} \div \dfrac{r}{s}$, $(y \neq 0; s \neq 0; r \neq 0)$

**t.** $\dfrac{3}{x} - \dfrac{5}{r} + \dfrac{2}{s}$, $(x \neq 0; r \neq 0; s \neq 0)$

**10.** For each expression, give a simpler expression equivalent to it:

**EXAMPLE** $\qquad -25 \cdot \dfrac{1}{5}\left(\dfrac{1}{2}x\right)$

**SOLUTION** $\qquad -25 \cdot \dfrac{1}{5}\left(\dfrac{1}{2}x\right)$

$$= -5\left(\dfrac{1}{2}x\right)$$

$$= -\dfrac{5}{2}x$$

**a.** $12\left(\dfrac{1}{3}x\right)$

**b.** $(-18r)\left(-\dfrac{1}{9}\right)$

**c.** $-\left(\dfrac{1}{2}\right)(-28x)$

**d.** $\left(-\dfrac{1}{3}\right)\left(\dfrac{5}{7}x\right)\left(-\dfrac{6}{11}t\right)$

**e.** $\left(-\dfrac{3}{7}x\right)\left(\dfrac{4}{5}y\right)$

**f.** $\dfrac{16xr}{2r}$

**g.** $25r \div \dfrac{1}{5}$

**h.** $\dfrac{(-27)x}{9}$

**i.** $\dfrac{4xy}{8y}$

**j.** $-26y \div \left[\dfrac{1}{2}(-x)\right]$

**k.** $\dfrac{-15xrs}{-3xs}$

**l.** $\dfrac{5x}{-15rt}$

**m.** $\left(\dfrac{1}{5}x\right)\left[\dfrac{1}{3}(-y)\right]$

**n.** $-39xy \div \left(\dfrac{1}{3}y\right)$

**o.** $\dfrac{(-7)xrt}{49r}$

**p.** $-\dfrac{-16xyt}{4yt}$

**q.** $-\dfrac{-32xt}{-4t}$

**11.** Tell whether or not each of the following is true for all replacements of the variables:

**a.** $(6r - 12s) \div 6 = r - 2s$

**b.** $\dfrac{1}{3}(4x - 5y) = \dfrac{4}{3}x - \dfrac{5}{3}y$

**c.** $(35x - 28y)\dfrac{1}{7} = 5x - 4y$

**d.** $\dfrac{18x - 21t}{(-3)} = -6x - 7t$

**e.** $\dfrac{-(2r + 5s)}{2} = -r + \dfrac{5}{2}s$

**f.** $(x + 5) \div (-5) = -\dfrac{x}{5} - 1$

**g.** $\dfrac{r - 2y}{3} = \dfrac{r}{3} - \dfrac{2}{3}y$

**h.** $\dfrac{5}{6}(24x - 3y) = 20x - \dfrac{5}{2}y$

**i.** $(3x - 7y) \div \dfrac{1}{3} = x - \dfrac{7}{3}y$

**j.** $\dfrac{3xy - 8xr}{2x} = \dfrac{3}{2}y - 4r$

**k.** $\dfrac{1}{3}(6x - 4y) + \dfrac{1}{4}(8x + 3y) = 4x - \dfrac{7}{12}y$

**l.** $\dfrac{1}{5}(x - y) - \dfrac{1}{3}(y - x) = \dfrac{8}{15}x + \dfrac{2}{15}y$

**m.** $\dfrac{4r - 3s}{5} - \dfrac{2r + 5s}{7} = \dfrac{18}{35}r - \dfrac{8}{7}s$

**n.** $\dfrac{2}{7}(4x - 7) + \dfrac{1}{7}(3x + 8) = \dfrac{11}{7}x + \dfrac{6}{7}$

**o.** $\dfrac{-5x - 11y}{5} - \dfrac{4x + 3y}{7} = -\dfrac{11}{7}x - \dfrac{92}{35}y$

**p.** $\dfrac{2}{3}r \div \dfrac{4}{5}s = \dfrac{5r}{6s}; \ (s \neq 0)$

**q.** $\dfrac{\frac{3}{5}x}{\frac{2}{8}t} = \dfrac{12x}{5t}; \ (t \neq 0)$

**r.** $\dfrac{3(x - y)}{2(y - x)} = \dfrac{3}{2}; \ (x \neq y)$

**s.** $\dfrac{6}{5}r \div \dfrac{5}{3}s = 2\dfrac{r}{s}; \ (s \neq 0)$

**12.** For each expression, give a simpler equivalent expression:

**a.** $\dfrac{1}{2}(3r - 7s) - \dfrac{4}{3}(r + 5s)$

**b.** $\dfrac{3}{8}(5x - 4y) - \dfrac{5}{3}x$

**c.** $\dfrac{2}{3}(2x + 4y - 5r) - \dfrac{5}{6}r$

**d.** $\dfrac{2}{3}\left(\dfrac{5}{8}r - \dfrac{15}{7}s\right) + \dfrac{2}{9}(r + 2s)$

**e.** $\left(5x - \dfrac{3}{7}y\right) \div \dfrac{4}{3}$

**f.** $\dfrac{\dfrac{5}{8}x}{\dfrac{3}{4}y}$

**g.** $\dfrac{\dfrac{7}{9}r}{\dfrac{3}{11}}$

**h.** $\dfrac{4}{5}(3x - 2y) \div 5$

**i.** $\dfrac{\dfrac{7}{3}(y - r) + \dfrac{1}{3}y}{5}$

## 11 · Complex Fractions

Below are several examples of what are commonly called "complex fractions."

$$\dfrac{\dfrac{2}{3}}{\dfrac{1}{2}} ; \quad \dfrac{\dfrac{x}{8}}{7} ; \quad \dfrac{\dfrac{x}{y}}{3} ; \quad \dfrac{\dfrac{a}{b}}{\dfrac{c}{d}} ; \quad \dfrac{6}{\dfrac{7}{11}} ; \quad \dfrac{x + \dfrac{y}{2}}{3x - \dfrac{7}{3}} ; \quad \dfrac{\dfrac{a}{b} + 2}{\dfrac{c}{4}} ;$$

$$\dfrac{\dfrac{2x + 3}{2}}{\dfrac{x + y}{z}} ; \quad \dfrac{\dfrac{x + y}{x - y}}{\dfrac{a}{b}} ; \quad \dfrac{\dfrac{a}{b} + \dfrac{c}{d}}{\dfrac{x}{y} + \dfrac{r}{s}}$$

We would like to find an expression equivalent to each of those above which is not as complicated. To do this, we recall that any number multiplied by the number one is the same number.

**EXAMPLE 1**   Simplify: $\dfrac{\dfrac{2}{3}}{\dfrac{1}{2}}$

**SOLUTION**

$$\dfrac{\dfrac{2}{3}}{\dfrac{1}{2}} \cdot \dfrac{6}{6} = \dfrac{\dfrac{2}{3} \cdot 6}{\dfrac{1}{2} \cdot 6}$$

$$= \dfrac{4}{3}, \text{ and we have accomplished our purpose.}$$

Study the following examples carefully, and see whether you can justify each step by familiar principles.

**EXAMPLE 2**
$$\frac{\dfrac{x}{8}}{7} = \frac{\dfrac{x}{8}}{7} \cdot \frac{8}{8} = \frac{\dfrac{x}{8} \cdot 8}{7 \cdot 8} = \frac{x}{56}$$

**EXAMPLE 3**
$$\frac{\dfrac{x}{y}}{3} = \frac{\dfrac{x}{y}}{3} \cdot \frac{y}{y} = \frac{\dfrac{x}{y} \cdot y}{3 \cdot y} = \frac{x}{3y}, \ (y \neq 0)$$

**EXAMPLE 4**
$$\frac{\dfrac{a}{b}}{\dfrac{c}{d}} = \frac{\dfrac{a}{b}}{\dfrac{c}{d}} \cdot \frac{bd}{bd} = \frac{\dfrac{a}{b} \cdot bd}{\dfrac{c}{d} \cdot bd} = \frac{ad}{bc}, \ (b \neq 0, \ c \neq 0, \ d \neq 0)$$

Do you see that $\dfrac{bd}{bd} = 1$ for every $b$ and $d$, $(b \neq 0, \ d \neq 0)$?

**EXAMPLE 5**
$$\frac{6}{\dfrac{7}{11}} = \frac{6}{\dfrac{7}{11}} \cdot \frac{11}{11} = \frac{6 \cdot 11}{\dfrac{7}{11} \cdot 11} = \frac{66}{7}$$

**EXAMPLE 6**
$$\frac{x + \dfrac{y}{2}}{3x - \dfrac{7}{3}} = \frac{x + \dfrac{y}{2}}{3x - \dfrac{7}{3}} \cdot \frac{6}{6}$$

$$= \frac{\left(x + \dfrac{y}{2}\right) \cdot 6}{\left(3x - \dfrac{7}{3}\right) \cdot 6}$$

$$= \frac{6x + 3y}{18x - 14}, (18x - 14 \neq 0)$$

**EXAMPLE 7**
$$\frac{\dfrac{a}{b+2}}{\dfrac{c}{4}} = \frac{\dfrac{a}{b+2}}{\dfrac{c}{4}} \cdot \frac{4(b+2)}{4(b+2)} = \frac{\dfrac{a}{b+2} \cdot 4(b+2)}{\dfrac{c}{4} \cdot 4(b+2)}$$

$$= \frac{4a}{c(b+2)}, \ (c \neq 0, \ b + 2 \neq 0)$$

**EXAMPLE 8**
$$\frac{\dfrac{2x+3}{2}}{\dfrac{x+y}{z}} = \frac{\dfrac{2x+3}{2}}{\dfrac{x+y}{z}} \cdot \frac{2z}{2z} = \frac{\dfrac{2x+3}{2} \cdot 2z}{\dfrac{x+y}{z} \cdot 2z} = \frac{(2x+3)z}{(x+y)2}$$

$$= \frac{z(2x+3)}{2(x+y)}, \ (x + y \neq 0, \ z \neq 0)$$

Now examine all of the preceding examples to see whether you can save yourself a few steps. Do you see that the following principle holds?

$$\forall_{a,b,c,d},\ \frac{\dfrac{a}{b}}{\dfrac{c}{d}} = \frac{ad}{bc},\ (b \neq 0,\ c \neq 0,\ d \neq 0)$$

Why is zero a permissible replacement for $a$? Why cannot $b$ be replaced by 0?

**EXAMPLE 9**
$$\frac{\dfrac{x + y}{x - y}}{\dfrac{a}{b}} = \frac{b(x + y)}{a(x - y)}$$
State the limitations on the replacements of the variables.

**EXAMPLE 10**
$$\frac{\dfrac{a}{b} + \dfrac{c}{d}}{\dfrac{x}{y} + \dfrac{r}{s}} = \frac{\dfrac{ad + bc}{bd}}{\dfrac{xs + ry}{sy}} = \frac{sy(ad + bc)}{bd(xs + ry)}$$

$$(b \neq 0,\ d \neq 0,\ y \neq 0,\ s \neq 0,\ xs + ry \neq 0)$$

# EXERCISES

For each of the following, find a less complicated equivalent expression:

**1.** $\dfrac{\dfrac{1}{2}}{\dfrac{2}{3}}$

**2.** $\dfrac{\dfrac{3}{7}}{\dfrac{4}{5}}$

**3.** $\dfrac{\dfrac{7}{a}}{9}$

**4.** $\dfrac{13}{\dfrac{x}{3}}$

**5.** $\dfrac{\dfrac{a - b}{3}}{\dfrac{x}{y}}$

**6.** $\dfrac{6 - \dfrac{7}{r}}{3 + \dfrac{2}{r}}$

**7.** $\dfrac{\dfrac{6x - y}{3}}{y}$

**8.** $\dfrac{\dfrac{3}{x} - 4}{x + 2}$

9. $\dfrac{\dfrac{1}{x}}{\dfrac{x}{y}}$

10. $\dfrac{2 - \dfrac{7}{s}}{s - \dfrac{3}{2}}$

11. $\dfrac{x - \dfrac{3 - y}{x}}{2x - 3}$

12. $\dfrac{\dfrac{-x}{y}}{\dfrac{r}{t}}$

13. $\dfrac{r + \dfrac{s}{t}}{r - \dfrac{s}{t}}$

14. $\dfrac{2x - y}{\dfrac{3}{2} - \dfrac{x}{3}}$

15. $\dfrac{3 + \dfrac{r}{5}}{r - \dfrac{6}{7}}$

16. $\dfrac{3 + \dfrac{5}{x + y}}{7 + \dfrac{3}{x + y}}$

17. $\dfrac{7 - \dfrac{1}{2x}}{6 + \dfrac{1}{x^2}}$

18. $\dfrac{r - \dfrac{7}{9}}{\dfrac{2}{r} - 3}$

19. $\dfrac{\dfrac{a - b}{a + b}}{\dfrac{a + b}{a - b}}$

20. $\dfrac{\dfrac{x^2 - y^2}{x + y}}{\dfrac{x - y}{x + y}}$

# VOCABULARY

additive identity (107)
assumption (121)
closure (106)
complex fractions (140)
equivalent expressions (118)
expression (117)
finite system (109)
left distributive principle (121)
multiplicative identity (107)
number field (108)
numerical variable (114)
open sentence (94)
postulate (121)

Principle of −1 (Division) (122)
Principle of −1 (Multiplication) (122)
Principle of Opposites (108)
Principle of Reciprocals (108)
Principle of Subtraction (108)
proof (121)
reciprocal (107)
replacement set (114)
right distributive principle (121)
term (117)
theorem (121)
value (117)
variable (99)

# REVIEW EXERCISES

1. Label each statement as true or false:

**a.** $.01\% = \dfrac{1}{10,000}$

**f.** $-6$ is the reciprocal of $-\dfrac{1}{6}$.

**b.** $|-4| \neq |+4|$

**g.** $-6$ is the opposite of $-[-6]$.

**c.** $|-4+(-6)| = |6-(-4)|$

**h.** $\left|-\dfrac{3}{7}\right| = \left|\dfrac{-3}{-7}\right|$

**d.** $5 \geq 2$

**e.** $-3 \leq -3$

**i.** $\left|\dfrac{3-7}{2}\right| = \left|\dfrac{7-3}{2}\right|$

2. In each sentence, replace the variables by a numeral which will yield a true statement and also by one that will yield a false statement:

**a.** $-4 + z \geq 14$

**i.** $t - (y - x) = t - x + y$

**b.** $3 \cdot v = 31$

**j.** $\dfrac{1}{(y-x)} = \dfrac{-1}{x-y}, \ (x \neq y)$

**c.** $-3 + 2w \leq -14$

**d.** $\dfrac{-6}{x} + 3 > 5$

**k.** $\dfrac{3}{x} - \dfrac{1}{s} = \dfrac{2}{xs}, \ (x \neq 0; s \neq 0)$

**e.** $\dfrac{-17}{z} \neq 14$

**l.** $\dfrac{3}{y} \div \dfrac{r}{s} = \dfrac{3s}{yr}, \ (y \neq 0; r \neq 0;$
$s \neq 0)$

**f.** $\dfrac{|w|}{3} < 5$

**m.** $\dfrac{y}{3} + \dfrac{x}{4} = \dfrac{4y + 3x}{12}$

**g.** $-x = -[(-x)]$

**h.** $(r-s)(t-w) = -(s-r)(w-t)$

**n.** $\dfrac{-18x + 14y}{-2} = 9x + 7y$

3. Tell whether each of the following is true for all replacements of the variable:

**a.** $\dfrac{4z}{2z} = 2; \ (z \neq 0)$

**b.** $|x - y| = |y - x|$

**c.** $|xy| = |x| \cdot |y|$

**d.** $-|xx| = x \cdot (-x)$

**e.** $|x| \geq x$

**f.** $|x + y| = |-x| + |-y|$

4. Is the set of all integers closed under the operation of addition? Explain.

5. In the set of rational numbers
   a. Identify the additive identity.
   b. Identify the multiplicative identity.
   c. Is the set of rational numbers a number field? Why?

6. For each open sentence, there is a specified replacement set for the variable. Make one replacement resulting in a true statement and one replacement making the statement false.
   a. $|3 - x| \geq 5$; the set of integers
   b. $\dfrac{3}{4}x - \dfrac{1}{8} > 1\dfrac{1}{2}$; the set of rational numbers
   c. $\dfrac{3 + |z|}{4} \not> 7$; the set of real numbers

7. Find the value of each expression when the variables are replaced as directed:
   a. $\dfrac{|x| - y}{|y - x|}$; $-3$ for $x$, $-7$ for $y$
   b. $\dfrac{3 - 7 \cdot |x|}{x^2 y}$; $-6$ for $x$, $4$ for $y$

8. State a reason for each step.
   a. $6z - 3z \overset{(1)}{=} 6z + [-(3z)]$
   $$\overset{(2)}{=} 6z + [-1 \cdot (3z)]$$
   $$\overset{(3)}{=} 6z + [(-1 \cdot 3) \cdot z]$$
   $$\overset{(4)}{=} 6z + (-3)z$$
   $$\overset{(5)}{=} [6 + (-3)]z$$
   $$\overset{(6)}{=} 3z$$
   b. $\dfrac{x}{-1} \overset{(1)}{=} x \cdot \dfrac{1}{-1}$
   $$\overset{(2)}{=} x \cdot (-1)$$
   $$\overset{(3)}{=} (-1) \cdot x$$
   $$\overset{(4)}{=} -x$$
   c. $xy + (-x)y \overset{(1)}{=} [x + (-x)]y$
   $$\overset{(2)}{=} y[x + (-x)]$$
   $$\overset{(3)}{=} y(0)$$
   $$\overset{(4)}{=} 0$$

d. $\dfrac{\dfrac{x}{y} + 7}{\dfrac{1}{y}} \overset{(1)}{=} \dfrac{y\left(\dfrac{x}{y} + 7\right)}{y\left(\dfrac{1}{y}\right)}$

$\qquad\qquad \overset{(2)}{=} \dfrac{x + 7y}{1}$

$\qquad\qquad \overset{(3)}{=} x + 7y$

e. $xy + (-x)y \overset{(1)}{=} [x + (-x)]y$

$\qquad\qquad\quad \overset{(2)}{=} y[x + (-x)]$

$\qquad\qquad\quad \overset{(3)}{=} y \cdot 0$

$\qquad\qquad\quad \overset{(4)}{=} 0$

f. $3a \cdot 5b \cdot (-2c) \overset{(1)}{=} 3 \cdot 5ab \cdot (-2c)$

$\qquad\qquad\qquad \overset{(2)}{=} 15 \cdot (-2) \cdot abc$

$\qquad\qquad\qquad \overset{(3)}{=} -30abc$

g. $r + t - (w + v) \overset{(1)}{=} r + t + [-(w + v)]$

$\qquad\qquad\qquad \overset{(2)}{=} r + t + [-1(w + v)]$

$\qquad\qquad\qquad \overset{(3)}{=} r + t + [(-w) + (-v)]$

$\qquad\qquad\qquad \overset{(4)}{=} r + t - w - v$

9. Write a simpler equivalent expression for each of the following:

a. $\dfrac{3}{2}x + 4 - \dfrac{5}{2}y + \dfrac{3}{2}x + 2 + \left(-\dfrac{3}{2}y\right)$

b. $3x - 5x + \left(-2\dfrac{1}{3}x\right) - 5\dfrac{2}{3}x + 9x$

c. $(-3)(-x)\left(-\dfrac{1}{3}\right)$

d. $\left(7x - \dfrac{2}{7}x\right) \div \dfrac{3}{4}$

10. For each of the following expressions, write a single fractional expression equivalent to it:

    a. $\dfrac{2}{r} + \dfrac{3}{t}$  $(r \neq 0,\ t \neq 0)$

    b. $\dfrac{6}{r} \div \dfrac{11}{t}$  $(r \neq 0,\ t \neq 0)$

    c. $\dfrac{5}{t} \times \dfrac{r}{-6}$  $(t \neq 0)$

    d. $\dfrac{3}{y} - \dfrac{4}{t}$  $(y \neq 0,\ t \neq 0)$

11. For each of the following find a simpler equivalent expression:

    a. $\dfrac{\frac{3}{4}}{\frac{7}{8}}$

    b. $\dfrac{\frac{2}{7}}{\frac{7}{2}}$

    c. $\dfrac{x - \frac{1}{2}}{x + \frac{3}{4}}$

    d. $\dfrac{\frac{2a - b}{3}}{\frac{a + b}{2}}$

    e. $\dfrac{1 - \frac{a}{b}}{1 - \frac{c}{d}}$

    f. $\dfrac{3 - \frac{1}{x}}{4 - \frac{1}{y}}$

    g. $\dfrac{5a - \frac{1}{2}}{3a + \frac{1}{2}}$

    h. $\dfrac{\frac{a}{b} + \frac{c}{d}}{\frac{x}{y}}$

# CHAPTER TEST

1. Label each statement as true or false:

    a. $|-3 - 5| = |3 - (-5)|$

    b. $4 \geq 4$

    c. $-3 < 1$

    d. $.2\% \neq .002$

    e. $\dfrac{3}{8} \neq .3751$

    f. $-\dfrac{2}{11} < -\dfrac{3}{13}$

    g. $\dfrac{2}{7} \geq \dfrac{3}{8}$

    h. $\forall_{x,y},\ |x + y| \geq |x| - |y|$

    i. $\forall_{x,y},\ |xy| = |x| \cdot |y|$

    j. $\forall_{x,y},\ xy = |x| \cdot |y|$

2. In each of the following, replace the variable with a numeral which will make the sentence true and a numeral which will make it false. Use the set of real numbers as the replacement set.

a. $\dfrac{-3r + 7}{-7} = 2$

d. $-6s + 7 \geq 14$

b. $-\dfrac{2}{3} = \dfrac{-7}{t}$

e. $\dfrac{t}{t} < 2$

c. $\dfrac{y}{-11} \neq 15$

3. At each step identify the principle used:

a. $(5x)(11z) \overset{(1)}{=} [(5x) \cdot 11] \cdot z$
$\overset{(2)}{=} [5 \cdot (x \cdot 11)] \cdot z$
$\overset{(3)}{=} [5(11 \cdot x)] \cdot z$
$\overset{(4)}{=} [(5 \cdot 11) \cdot x] \cdot z$
$\overset{(5)}{=} [55x] \cdot z$
$\overset{(6)}{=} 55(xz)$

b. $-13x + 7x \overset{(1)}{=} x \cdot (-13) + x \cdot 7$
$\overset{(2)}{=} x(-13 + 7)$
$\overset{(3)}{=} x \cdot (-6)$
$\overset{(4)}{=} -6x$

c. $\dfrac{xr}{yr} \overset{(1)}{=} \left(\dfrac{x}{y}\right)\left(\dfrac{r}{r}\right)$
$\overset{(2)}{=} \dfrac{x}{y} \cdot \left[ r \cdot \left(\dfrac{1}{r}\right) \right]$
$\overset{(3)}{=} \dfrac{x}{y} \cdot 1$
$\overset{(4)}{=} \dfrac{x}{y}$

d. $x \cdot (-y) \overset{(1)}{=} (-y) \cdot x$
$\overset{(2)}{=} [(-1)(y)] \cdot x$
$\overset{(3)}{=} (-1)(yx)$
$\overset{(4)}{=} (-1)(xy)$
$\overset{(5)}{=} -(xy)$

4. For each open sentence, the replacement set of the variable is specified. Make one replacement of the variable resulting in a true statement and one replacement resulting in a false statement.

   a. $|z| + 3 > 5$; the set of integers.

   b. $5 + \dfrac{y}{3} < 4$; the set of integers.

   c. $6 + |7 - 3x| > 9$; the set of real numbers.

5. Find the value of each of the following expressions, for the designated replacements of the variables:

   a. $\dfrac{x + 3y}{y - (-5y)}$; $-3$ for $x$, $5$ for $y$.

   b. $3x(y - x)$; $-4$ for $x$, $-2$ for $y$.

6. Tell whether each of the following is true for all replacements of the variables. The replacement set is the set of real numbers.

   a. $-(y - x) = -x - y$

   b. $(s - t)(x - y) = -(t - s)(x - y)$

   c. $-[-x] + (-x) = 0$

   d. $(xy)(-z) = -x(yz)$

   e. $15x - [16x - (11x + 3)] = 10x - 3$

   f. $-\dfrac{-t}{s} = \dfrac{t}{s}$  $(s \neq 0)$

   h. $\dfrac{r + 5t}{-2} = -\dfrac{r}{2} - \dfrac{5}{2}t$

   g. $\dfrac{t}{-y} = \dfrac{-t}{y}$  $(y \neq 0)$

   i. $\dfrac{4}{3}(5x - 6) = \dfrac{20}{3}x - 8$

7. a. Is the set of odd positive integers closed under the operation of addition?

   b. Give the simplest numeral for the opposite of $-[-(-3)]$.

8. For the set of numbers on a 12-hour clock, answer the following questions:

   a. $10 + 4 = \square$

   b. $4 \cdot 4 = \square$

   c. What is the additive identity in this set of numbers?

   d. What is the reciprocal of 3 in this set of numbers?

   e. Is this set of numbers (operations: addition and multiplication) a number field? Why or why not?

# CUMULATIVE REVIEW

**1.** For each number, tell whether it is rational or irrational:

**a.** $3.65165165\overset{...}{1}$

**e.** $3 + \sqrt{2}$

**b.** $-4.314679$

**f.** $-3\frac{8}{11}$

**c.** $-11.125$

**g.** $2.111\overset{.}{1}$

**d.** $\sqrt{81}$

**2.** Does every point of the number line have as its coordinate a number whose name is of the form $\frac{\square}{\triangle}$ or $-\frac{\square}{\triangle}$ (where replacements for $\triangle$ and $\square$ are chosen from the counting numbers)?

**3.** Write the simplest numeral for the following:

**a.** $\dfrac{\left(\dfrac{5}{13} + \dfrac{7}{13}\right) \cdot 6}{\dfrac{4}{11}}$

**b.** $8\left[\dfrac{1}{5}(7 + 8 \times 3)\right] - 7$

**c.** $\dfrac{5}{6} \cdot \left[\dfrac{(4 - 7) + 3 \times (-5)}{4}\right]$

**4.** Let $R$ stand for the set of real numbers.
$R_a$ stand for the set of rational numbers.
$I$ stand for the set of all integers.
$I_p$ stand for the set of positive integers.
Label each statement as true or false.

**a.** $-3 \in I$

**d.** $\dfrac{-7}{3} \in R$

**b.** $\dfrac{5}{6} \in R_a$

**e.** $I_p \subset R_a$

**c.** $0 \in I_p$

**f.** $R \subset I$

★ **g.** Describe the complement of $I_p$ if the universe is $I$.

**h.** Explain what is meant by $I$ being a proper subset of $R_a$.

**i.** Is $I_p$ closed under the operations of addition, subtraction, and division?

**5. a.** Find the value of $\dfrac{2 - 3(k - r)}{3t}$ for the following replacements: 2 for $k$, $-3$ for $r$, and 4 for $t$.

**b.** Find the value of $\dfrac{(-6) \cdot (3a - 4d)}{5d}$ for the following replacements: 3 for $a$ and $-4$ for $d$.

**6.** In each of the following, make a replacement for the variable to result in a true statement, then a replacement giving a false statement:

**a.** $\dfrac{3.5}{x} = -7$

**b.** $\dfrac{r}{-6} = 4$

**c.** $-6 + x = 11$

**d.** $s - (-3) = -7$

**e.** $y + (-4) = 7$

**f.** $(-6) \cdot y = 18$

**g.** $y \times (5) = -30$

**h.** $6 \div r = \dfrac{1}{3}$

**i.** $y \div 6 = -4$

**j.** $s - 6 = -7$

**7.** True or false?

**a.** $0 \not< -2$

**b.** $-8 > -7$

**c.** $-10 < -9$

**d.** $-6 \leq 2$

**e.** $6 \geq -1$

**f.** $-2 \not> 2$

**g.** $|-3| > 2$

**h.** $-4 \neq |4|$

**i.** $-5 \leq -4$

**j.** $-3 \neq |3 - (-2)|$

**8.** Replace the frames with

    (1)   an integer name which will give a true statement.

    (2)   an integer name which will give a false statement.

**a.** $\triangle + (-7) \leq -13$

**b.** $(-7) \times \triangle \not< |2|$

**c.** $|\square| - 3 = 14$

**d.** $(-2) \cdot \bigcirc - 3 < 11$

**e.** $-11 < 3 \square + 1$

**f.** $|\triangle - 2| \not< 6$

**9.** Name the principles involved in going from one statement to another:

**a.** $7 \cdot 3 + 7 \cdot [4 + (-3)] \overset{(1)}{=} 7 \cdot \{3 + [4 + (-3)]\}$

$\overset{(2)}{=} 7 \cdot \{3 + [(-3) + 4]\}$

$\overset{(3)}{=} 7 \cdot \{[3 + (-3)] + 4\}$

$\overset{(4)}{=} 7 \cdot (0 + 4)$

$\overset{(5)}{=} 7 \cdot 4$

**b.** $[(-6) \cdot 5 + 7 \cdot (-6)] \times 1 \overset{(1)}{=} (-6) \cdot 5 + 7 \cdot (-6)$

$\overset{(2)}{=} (-6) \cdot 5 + (-6) \cdot 7$

$\overset{(3)}{=} (-6) \cdot (5 + 7)$

**c.** $(-3) \cdot [6 - 5] + (-15) \overset{(1)}{=} (-3) \cdot [6 + (-5)] + (-15)$

$\overset{(2)}{=} (-3) \cdot 6 + (-3) \cdot (-5) + (-15)$

$\overset{(3)}{=} -18 + 15 + (-15)$

$\overset{(4)}{=} -18 + [15 + (-15)]$

$\overset{(5)}{=} -18 + 0$

$\overset{(6)}{=} -18$

**10.** Is the set of integers a number field? Why?

**11.** Write a single fractional expression equivalent to each of the following:

**a.** $\dfrac{y}{t} \div \dfrac{3}{2}$ 　　　　　　　　　　　**c.** $\dfrac{x}{3} \times \dfrac{y}{5}$

**b.** $\dfrac{x}{3} + \dfrac{r}{t}$ 　　　　　　　　　　　**d.** $\dfrac{x}{t} - \dfrac{r}{s}$

**12.** State the basic principle involved in each step:

**a.** $x + (-1) \cdot x \overset{(1)}{=} 1 \cdot x + (-1) \cdot x$

$\overset{(2)}{=} x \cdot 1 + x \cdot (-1)$

$\overset{(3)}{=} x[1 + (-1)]$

$\overset{(4)}{=} x \cdot (0)$

$\overset{(5)}{=} 0$

**b.** $\dfrac{x(-y)}{r(-s)} \overset{(1)}{=} \dfrac{-(xy)}{-(rs)}$

$\overset{(2)}{=} \dfrac{(-1)(xy)}{(-1)(rs)}$

$\overset{(3)}{=} 1 \cdot \dfrac{(xy)}{(rs)}$

$\overset{(4)}{=} \dfrac{(xy)}{(rs)} \cdot 1$

$\overset{(5)}{=} \dfrac{xy}{rs}$

13. Tell which of the following are true for all replacements of the variables:

    **a.** $x + (-y) = -[y + (-x)]$

    **b.** $(r - s)(x - t) = (s - r)(t - x)$

    **c.** $-[(-x)yz] = (-x)yz$

    **d.** $4(6x - 2y) - 3(4x + y) = 12x - 11y$

    **e.** $-\dfrac{1}{r - t} = \dfrac{1}{t - r}$  $(r \neq t)$

    **f.** $(35x + 14y)\dfrac{1}{7} = 5x + \dfrac{y}{2}$

14. In the set of numbers of a "four-hour" clock, determine what replacements for the frames will produce a true sentence:

    **a.** $3 + 2 = \square$

    **b.** $1 + 4 = \square$

    **c.** What is the additive identity of this system?

15. Prove the theorem, $\forall_{a,b,c},\ a(b - c) = ab - ac$.

..................................................................................................

# BIBLIOGRAPHY

Bakst, A., *Mathematics—Its Magic and Mastery*, D. Van Nostrand, Toronto, 1952, "Simple Calculating Devices"—pages 113–124, "Rapid Calculations"—pages 125–133.

Bakst, A., *Mathematical Puzzles and Pastimes*, D. Van Nostrand, Toronto, 1954, "Fancy Number Systems"—pages 43–55.

Gardner, Martin, *Mathematical Puzzles of Sam Loyd*, Dover Publications, New York, 1959.

Johnson, D. A., and Glenn, W. A., *Number Patterns*, Webster, St. Louis, 1960.

Northrop, E. P., *Riddles in Mathematics*, D. Van Nostrand, Toronto, 1944.

School Mathematics Study Group, *Mathematics for High School: First Course in Algebra, Part 1 (Revised Edition)*, SMSG, New Haven, Connecticut, 1960, pages 77–96.

University of Illinois Committee on School Mathematics, *Unit 2, "Generalizations and Algebraic Manipulation,"* UICSM, Urbana, Illinois, 1960.

# Open Sentences, Equations,

# and Solution Sets

## I · What Is An Equation?

From your previous study, you have gained some familiarity with equations. Below are a number of equations:

$$\frac{1}{2} = \frac{4}{8} \qquad\qquad 4x = -27 \qquad\qquad a = a + 1$$

$$.5 = 50\% \qquad\qquad 1.7 = 20 \qquad\qquad 1\% = 56$$

$$\qquad\qquad\qquad |c| = -2$$

$$.07 = \frac{14}{200} \qquad\qquad \frac{1}{y} = 2 + \frac{2}{y} \qquad 16d + 4 = 20$$

$$3 + x = x + 3$$

Equations are mathematical sentences. The equations above can be classified into three basic kinds of sentences:

(1) True sentences; for example, $\frac{1}{2} = \frac{4}{8}$. Find other true sentences among the above.

(2) False sentences; for example, $1.7 = 20$. Find other false sentences among the above sentences.

(3) Sentences which are neither true nor false, that is, open sentences;

for example, $4x = -27$. Those sentences which are neither true nor false can be further classified into three types.

(3a) Sentences in which there is at least one replacement for the variable, and perhaps several, which will yield a true sentence; for example, $4x = -27$. What numeral in place of $x$ will yield a true sentence? Find other sentences of this type.

(3b) Sentences in which no replacement for the variable will yield a true sentence; for example, $a = a + 1$. Find other sentences of this type.

(3c) Sentences in which every replacement of the variable will produce a true sentence. Which sentence above is such a sentence?

In this chapter you will concentrate on the study of sentences which are neither true nor false; that is, open sentences. You will develop a method of discovering replacements for the variables which will result in true sentences. In each case you will need to know the replacement set for the variables. We shall agree that whenever the replacement set is not specified, it is the set of real numbers.

## EXERCISES

Classify each of the sentences below into one of the following categories:

(1) True sentence

(2) False sentence

(3) Sentence which is neither true nor false, (that is, an open sentence,) but in which there is at least one replacement for the variable which will result in a true sentence. Find the replacement or several replacements.

(4) Sentence which is neither true nor false and in which there is no replacement for the variable which will result in a true sentence.

(5) Sentence which is neither true nor false, and in which every replacement for the variable will result in a true sentence.

EXAMPLE 1    $\dfrac{x}{x} = 2$

SOLUTION    $\dfrac{x}{x} = 2$ is neither true nor false, that is, it is an open sentence. There is no replacement for $x$ which yields a true sentence, for we know that the quotient of every non-zero number divided by itself is 1, and $1 \neq 2$. $\left[\text{Remember } \dfrac{0}{0} \text{ is meaningless.}\right]$

EXAMPLE 2    $\dfrac{2}{3} = .66$

SOLUTION    $\dfrac{2}{3} = .66$ is a false sentence. $\dfrac{2}{3}$ and $.66$ are names of two different numbers, although $\dfrac{2}{3}$ is only a very little larger than $.66$.

EXAMPLE 3    $175\% = 1.75$

SOLUTION    $175\% = 1.75$ is a true sentence.

EXAMPLE 4    $5x + 2 = -3$

SOLUTION    $5x + 2 = -3$ is neither true nor false, that is, it is an open sentence. Replacing $x$ by $-1$ results in a true sentence:
$$5 \cdot (-1) + 2 = -3$$

EXAMPLE 5    $21u - 6u = 15u$

SOLUTION    $21u - 6u = 15u$ is neither true nor false. Every replacement of $u$ by a real number produces a true sentence.

**Proof:**  $21u - 6u = u \cdot 21 - u \cdot 6$
$$= u(21 - 6)$$
$$= u \cdot 15$$
$$= 15u$$

Re-read the instructions before attempting these questions:

**1.** $\sqrt{6.25} = 2.5$

**2.** $\left| -\dfrac{6}{2} \right| = 3$

**3.** $.01 = .1\%$

**4.** $10^4 = 10,000$

**5.** $(-1)^5 = -1$
  Hint: $[(-1)^2 = (-1)(-1);$
     $(-1)^3 = (-1)(-1)(-1)]$

**6.** $10x = \dfrac{1}{2}$

**7.** $|y - y| = 0$

**8.** $a^2 = a^3$

**9.** $12m + 3 = 0$

**10.** $p(p - 1) = 0$

**11.** $75\% = \dfrac{3}{4}$

**12.** $z^3 = -1$

**13.** $11n + 12n = 23$

**14.** $|2d| = 5$

**15.** $s^2 = 9$

**16.** $(-4)^3 = 64$

**17.** $\dfrac{2g}{g} = -2$

**18.** $17 = \dfrac{b}{2}$

**19.** $\dfrac{3}{v} = 5$

**20.** $w \cdot |w| = -16$

**21.** $x \cdot x = x^2$

**22.** $|3a - a| = |a - 3a|$

## 2 · Solving Equations

Consider the following equation:

$$2x + 3 = 1$$

It is easy to see that $-1$ in place of $x$ will result in a true sentence.

$$2 \cdot (-1) + 3 = 1$$
$$-2 + 3 = 1$$
$$1 = 1$$

The number $-1$ is called **the root** of the equation $2x + 3 = 1$. The **solution set** of this equation is $\{-1\}$; that is, a set consisting of **one** element, namely, the number $-1$. A root is said *to satisfy an equation*; thus the number $-1$ *satisfies* the equation $2x + 3 = 1$. To solve an equation means to find a number or numbers that satisfy the equation.

What is the root of each of the following equations?

(1)   $m = -7$

(2)   $t + 3 = 5$

(3)   $s + 7 = 1$

(4)   $x + 3 = 3$

(5)   $y - 4 = 2$

(6)   $c - 3 = 8$

(7)   $n - \dfrac{1}{2} = -\dfrac{1}{2}$

(8)   $5d = 10$

(9)   $3u = 1$

(10)   $-2f = 10$

You probably had no difficulty telling the roots of the equations above because they are very simple. For example, in the equation (2) above, you may ask yourself the question:

What number added to 3 gives 5? $[t + 3 = 5]$

The answer, of course, is 2. Therefore, the number 2 is the root of this equation, and $\{2\}$ is the solution set.

In equation (7) above, the question to ask yourself is:

$\frac{1}{2}$ subtracted from what number gives $-\frac{1}{2}$?

The answer, of course, is 0, because $0 - \frac{1}{2} = -\frac{1}{2}$. Thus, 0 is the root of the

equation $n - \frac{1}{2} = -\frac{1}{2}$. Its solution set is $\{0\}$.

Some equations are more complicated than these, and it may be very difficult to "guess" their roots. In such cases it helps to have some kind of a "method," or "system," by which to "compute" the roots. In the next section, you will be taught a method which will enable you to solve more complicated problems.

# EXERCISES

1. "Guess" the roots of each of the following equations:

a. $m + 3 = 7$

b. $n + 8 = 1$

c. $x + 2 = 0$

d. $a - 5 = 2$

e. $s - 10 = 15$

f. $t - 13 = 0$

g. $2 - b = 0$

h. $22 - v = 7$

i. $15 - c = 20$

j. $6 - h = -5$

k. $3y = 12$

l. $5z = -60$

m. $4d = \frac{1}{2}$

n. $\frac{1}{3}w = 10$

o. $\frac{1}{5}p = -5$

p. $\frac{s}{6} = 10$

q. $\frac{2}{j} = 2$

r. $\frac{5}{k} = -2.5$

s. $\frac{-10}{z} = -100$

t. $3x - 5 = -23$

u. $|x| = 9$

v. $\frac{3 \cdot |r|}{2} = 6$

w. $|t - 3| = 5$

x. $5 \cdot |x + 4| = 30$

y. $7 - \left|\frac{v}{2}\right| = 3$

z. $\frac{9 + |2r + 1|}{5} = 4$

**2.** Determine the root of each of the following equations. It may take several trials to find what replacement for the variable produces a true statement.

**EXAMPLE 1**   $5x + 11 = 36$

**SOLUTION**   If we replace $x$ with 4, we have

$$5(4) + 11 = 36$$
$$20 + 11 = 36$$
$$31 = 36$$

Since this is not a true statement, 4 is not a root of the equation.

If we replace $x$ with 6, we have

$$5(6) + 11 = 36$$
$$30 + 11 = 36$$
$$41 = 36$$

Since this is not a true statement, 6 is not a root of the equation. It appears as though the root must be between 4 and 6.

If we replace $x$ with 5, we have

$$5(5) + 11 = 36$$
$$25 + 11 = 36$$
$$36 = 36$$

Since this is a true statement, 5 is the root of the equation.

**EXAMPLE 2**   $11 - 3c = 2$

**SOLUTION**   If we replace $3c$ by $\triangle$, we have

$$11 - \triangle = 2$$

Since we know that $11 - 9 = 2$, $\triangle$ must be another name for 9. This means that $3c$ must be another name for 9. Then

$$3c = 9$$
$$c = 3$$

If we now replace $c$ by 3 in the equation, we get

$$11 - 3 \cdot 3 = 2$$
$$11 - 9 = 2$$
$$2 = 2$$

Since this is a true statement, 3 is the root of the equation.

Determine the roots of these equations by the trial method:

**a.** $-11 + z = -15$

**b.** $-14 - x = 5$

**c.** $\frac{1}{7}y = 5$

**d.** $7.5k = -15$

**e.** $\frac{-6.2}{x} = 3.1$

**f.** $13 + 2x = 3.9$

**g.** $r + (-7.3) = 8.9$

**h.** $\frac{4}{5} - x = \frac{4}{5}$

**i.** $\frac{4}{3}x = -8$

**j.** $2.5y + 4.5 = 17$

**k.** $-13.3 = s + 5$

**l.** $-4 = x - (-7)$

**m.** $\frac{2}{3}y = 12$

**n.** $17 + 3x = 29$

**o.** $6 + (-z) = 7$

**p.** $y - (-4) = -3$

**q.** $\frac{5}{3}r - 3 = 7$

**r.** $x + (-13) = 14$

**s.** $y - 7 = -14$

**t.** $\frac{3}{2}s = -15$

**u.** $\frac{4}{7}x - 11 = -3$

**v.** $\frac{2 \cdot |r| - 3}{3} = 3$

**w.** $2 = \frac{4 - |s|}{2}$

**x.** $7 \cdot |t - 3| = 70$

**y.** $\left|\frac{u + 2}{u - 2}\right| = 3$

**z.** $|x| - x = 1$

## 3 · Equation Principles

You have already learned that principles are a part of the foundation upon which mathematical proofs rest. We shall state two principles which will enable us to prove that a certain number is a root of a given equation. Furthermore, we shall be able to prove that that number is the only root of the given equation. You may already have formulated these principles in your own mind as a result of the exercises in the preceding section.

Before we state the two principles, we need to examine the meaning of the phrase "if and only if" which is commonly used in mathematics. Consider, for example, the following sentence:

> A triangle is an equilateral triangle **if and only if** it has three equal sides.

This sentence means the same as the two following sentences combined:

> If a triangle is an equilateral triangle, then it has three equal sides
>
> and
>
> If a triangle has three equal sides, then it is an equilateral triangle.

Now we shall state the first of the two *equation principles*. We shall call it **"the Equation Principle for Addition."**

### Equation Principle For Addition

For every $x$, $y$, and $z$, $x = y$ if and only if $x + z = y + z$. This principle, restated as two sentences, is:

For every $x$, $y$, and $z$, if $x = y$, then $x + z = y + z$

and

For every $x$, $y$, and $z$, if $x + z = y + z$, then $x = y$

Let us see how we can use this principle in finding a root of an equation and then proving that it is the only root of the given equation. Consider the following equation:

$$r + 7 = 12$$

This equation is of the form $x = y$, where $x$ is replaced by $r + 7$ and $y$ by 12. Now, we use the **Equation Principle for Addition** and replace $y$ by $-7$.

If $r + 7 = 12$, then $r + 7 + (-7) = 12 + (-7)$

Simplifying;
$$r + 0 = 5$$
$$r = 5$$

Can you guess why we replaced $z$ by $-7$ and not by some other number name?

We can easily see that 5 satisfies the equation $r + 7 = 12$ because $5 + 7 = 12$ is true. Thus the root of the equation $r = 5$ is the number 5.

In order to prove that 5 is the only root of the given equation, we must prove that the following statement:

$$r + 7 = 12 \text{ if and only if } r = 5.$$

This is equivalent to proving the following:

(1)   If $r + 7 = 12$, then $r = 5$

and

(2)   If $r = 5$, then $r + 7 = 12$

**Proof(** (1)   If $r + 7 = 12$                          [by the **Equation**
then $(r + 7) + (-7) = 12 + (-7)$   **Principle for Addition**]
$r + [7 + (-7)] = 12 + (-7)$      [Associative Principle]
$r + 0 = 5$                       [Arithmetic]
$r = 5$                          [Principle of 0]

(2)   If $r = 5$,
then $r + 7 = 5 + 7$   **[by the Equation Principle for Addition]**
or $r + 7 = 12$        [by the fact of arithmetic:
$5 + 7 = 12$]

Thus, 5 is the only root of the equation $r + 7 = 12$ and so $\{5\}$ is the solution set of this equation.

From the previous chapter, you already know that every real number has an opposite. The Equation Principle of Addition enables us to prove that every real number has *exactly one opposite*. We shall prove this, by assuming first that for a real number $m$, there are two opposites, say $x$ and $y$. Then it is true that

$$m + x = 0$$
$$\text{and}$$
$$m + y = 0$$

But, if $m + x = 0$ and $m + y = 0$, then

$$m + x = m + y$$
$$-m + m + x = -m + m + y$$
$$0 + x = 0 + y$$
$$x = y$$

This proves that $x$ and $y$ are the same number. Thus, $m$ has exactly one opposite.

## EXERCISES

Find the root, then prove that it is the only root, of each of the following equations:

1. $m + 3 = 4$
2. $p + 1 = 0$
3. $t + 6 = 2$
4. $x + (-2) = 7$
5. $y + (-5) = -2$
6. $s + (-1) = -1$

Using EPA, find the root of each of the following equations; then check.

**EXAMPLE 1**     $x - 2 = -13$

**SOLUTION**

$$x - 2 = -13$$
$$x + (-2) = -13$$
$$x + (-2) + 2 = (-13) + 2$$
$$x + 0 = -11$$
$$x = -11$$

*Check:* If $x = -11$, $x - 2 = -11 - 2$
$$= -13$$
$-11$ is the root of the equation $x - 2 = -13$.

**EXAMPLE 2**    $3 - x = 17$

**SOLUTION**    $3 - x = 17$

$$(3 - x) + x = 17 + x$$
$$3 + (-x + x) = 17 + x$$
$$3 + 0 = 17 + x$$
$$3 = 17 + x$$
$$3 + (-17) = (17 + x) + (-17)$$
$$3 + (-17) = x + [17 + (-17)]$$
$$3 + (-17) = x + 0$$
$$3 + (-17) = x$$
$$-14 = x$$

*Check:* If $x = -14$, $3 - x = 3 - (-14)$
$$= 3 + 14$$
$$= 17. \text{The root is } -14.$$

Find the root of each of the following equations; then check:

**1.** $y + 6 = 21$

**2.** $a + 5 = 17$

**3.** $c + \dfrac{1}{3} = \dfrac{1}{2}$

**4.** $.7 + x = 0$

**5.** $d - 3 = 9$

**6.** $z - 7 = 1$

**7.** $b - 1 = -3$

**8.** $m - 15 = -8$

**9.** $r - .63 = \dfrac{1}{2}$

**10.** $s - 16 = 0$

**11.** $f - \dfrac{2}{7} = -\dfrac{1}{3}$

**12.** $t + \dfrac{3}{11} = -\dfrac{1}{2}$

**13.** $u + \dfrac{4}{7} = -\dfrac{8}{9}$

**14.** $w - \dfrac{3}{2} = -\dfrac{5}{7}$

**15.** $-7 + r = -8$

**16.** $-11 = x + 7$

**17.** $s + (-3.1) = 4.7$

**18.** $x - (-11) = 14$

**19.** $(-3.5) - y = 7.5$

**20.** $14.1 = z - 7.9$

**21.** $x - \dfrac{4}{3} = -\dfrac{5}{3}$

**22.** $t + (-2.2) = -5.3$

**23.** $-4\dfrac{1}{4} = s - \dfrac{3}{4}$

**24.** $1.4 - x = 7.2$

**25.** $w + \dfrac{4}{9} = \dfrac{5}{7}$

**26.** $-1.9 + v = -41.7$

**27.** $-4.3 = 7.2 + k$

**28.** $y + \left(-\frac{5}{3}\right) = -\frac{4}{9}$

**29.** $-1.6 - x = 14.1$

**30.** $-7.9 = 1.3 - y$

**31.** $4\frac{7}{8} + x = -17\frac{1}{8}$

**32.** $-\frac{7}{5} + z = \frac{4}{3}$

**33.** $v - \frac{5}{3} = -\frac{9}{4}$

**34.** $-5.9 = x + (-3.4)$

**35.** $l - 3\frac{1}{2} = 6\frac{3}{4}$

**36.** $-x + 7 = 19$

**37.** $(-4) - y = 13$

**38.** $-5.9 = y - 7.1$

**39.** $\frac{4}{3} + r = -\frac{7}{8}$

**40.** $t + \frac{7}{8} = -\frac{5}{9}$

**41.** $-y + \frac{4}{3} = -\frac{7}{5}$

**42.** $-\frac{7}{5} = \frac{5}{9} + (-z)$

**43.** $\frac{5}{11} - x = \frac{6}{7}$

**44.** $6.23 + y = -7.96$

**45.** $6\frac{3}{8} = z - 4\frac{1}{9}$

**46.** $-21.8 = x + 7.3$

**47.** $-3.9 - y = -5.9$

## 4 · The Multiplication Principle

We now state the second equation principle, which we call the **"Equation Principle for Multiplication"**.

### Equation Principle For Multiplication

For every $x$, $y$, and $z$ ($z \neq 0$), $x = y$ if and only if $x \cdot z = y \cdot z$. This principle, stated as two sentences, is

For every $x$, $y$, and $z$ if $x = y$, then $x \cdot z = y \cdot z$

and

For every $x$, $y$, and $z$ ($z \neq 0$), if $x \cdot z = y \cdot z$, then $x = y$.

Let us use the **Equation Principle for Multiplication** to find the root and prove that it is the only root of this equation.

$$-2r = -78$$

This equation is of the form $x = y$, where $x$ is replaced by $-2r$ and $y$ is replaced by $-78$. Now, let us replace $z$ by $-\frac{1}{2}$:

$$-2r \cdot (-\tfrac{1}{2}) = -78 \cdot (-\tfrac{1}{2})$$
$$-2 \cdot (-\tfrac{1}{2}) \cdot r = 39 \quad \text{[Why?]}$$
$$r = 39 \quad \text{[Why?]}$$

The root of the last equation is 39. Let us check the number 39 in the original equation:

$$\text{If } r = 39,\ -2r = -2 \cdot 39$$
$$= -78$$

Thus, 39 is the root of the equation.

In order to prove that 39 is the only root, we must prove the statement:

(1) If $-2r = -78$, then $r = 39$

and

(2) If $r = 39$, then $-2r = -78$.

Prove this using the **Equation Principle for Multiplication.**

## EXERCISES

Find the root, then prove that it is the only root, of each of the following equations:

**1.** $5x = 40$

**2.** $-10y = 20$

**3.** $\frac{2}{3}d = -5$

**4.** $-\frac{4}{5}m = -\frac{2}{3}$

**5.** $1.6t = -3.8$

Find the root of each of the following equations, then check:

**EXAMPLE** $\qquad \frac{7}{8}n = -\frac{1}{2}$

**SOLUTION**

$$\frac{7}{8}n = -\frac{1}{2}$$

$$\frac{7}{8}n \cdot \frac{8}{7} = -\frac{1}{2} \cdot \frac{8}{7}$$

$$\frac{7}{8} \cdot \frac{8}{7} \cdot n = -\frac{8}{14}$$

$$n = -\frac{4}{7}$$

$Check:$ If $n = -\frac{4}{7}$, $\frac{7}{8} \cdot \left(-\frac{4}{7}\right) = -\frac{28}{56}$

$$= -\frac{1}{2}$$

The root is $-\frac{4}{7}$.

**6.** $4s = 36$

**7.** $3a = 17$

**8.** $16x = 3$

**9.** $-96y = -16$

**10.** $100z = 1$

**11.** $-.01p = -2$

**12.** $-\frac{4}{7}t = 95$

**13.** $\frac{1}{4}u = -\frac{3}{2}$

**14.** $67r = -67$

**15.** $\frac{9}{2}c = -\frac{3}{11}$

**16.** $-\frac{1}{3}r = \frac{1}{3}$

**17.** $-\frac{10}{3}h = -\frac{7}{12}$

**18.** $-70 = 3.5r$

**19.** $\frac{5}{7}x = -\frac{7}{8}$

**20.** $-\frac{4.7}{y} = 9.4$

**21.** $.07y = 8.4$

**22.** $-\frac{1}{5} = \frac{1}{7}y$

**23.** $-\frac{2}{3}x = \frac{2}{3}$

**24.** $\frac{4}{7}r = \frac{7}{4}$

**25.** $-\frac{5}{2} = \frac{6}{y}$

**26.** $\frac{2}{3} = \frac{w}{7}$

**27.** $-\frac{4.2}{x} = 2.1$

**28.** $2\frac{1}{3}y = -\frac{7}{8}$

**29.** $-3.9 = \frac{1.3}{x}$

**30.** $-2.1 = .7r$

**31.** $-\frac{4}{9} = \frac{3}{11}x$

**32.** $-\frac{7}{12}y = -\frac{5}{3}$

**33.** $\frac{y}{2.5} = -6.25$

**34.** $.36 = -\frac{7.2}{x}$

**35.** $-3.9 = -\frac{r}{1.9}$

**36.** $\frac{6}{7}t = -1.2$

**37.** $7.8w = 1.2$

**38.** $-\frac{5}{7}v = -\frac{4}{9}$

**39.** $-\frac{9}{8} = \frac{7}{17}x$

**40.** $-\frac{3}{19}x = \frac{4}{7}$

**41.** $\frac{8}{13}y = -\frac{5}{7}$

**42.** $\frac{-1.3}{t} = -3.9$

Study these examples carefully.

**EXAMPLE 1**     $5a + 1 - 3a = 4a - 2$

**SOLUTION**
$$5a + 1 - 3a = 4a - 2$$
$$5a - 3a + 1 = 4a - 2$$
$$2a + 1 = 4a - 2$$
$$2a + 1 - 2a = 4a - 2 - 2a$$
$$2a - 2a + 1 = 4a - 2a - 2$$
$$1 = 2a - 2$$
$$1 + 2 = 2a - 2 + 2$$
$$3 = 2a$$
$$a = \frac{3}{2}$$

*Check:* If $a = \frac{3}{2}$, $5a + 1 - 3a$ | If $a = \frac{3}{2}$, $4a - 2$

$$= 5 \cdot \frac{3}{2} + 1 - 3 \cdot \frac{3}{2} \qquad\qquad = 4 \cdot \frac{3}{2} - 2$$

$$= \frac{15}{2} + 1 - \frac{9}{2} \qquad\qquad = \frac{12}{2} - 2$$

$$= 7\frac{1}{2} + 1 - 4\frac{1}{2} \qquad\qquad = 6 - 2$$

$$= 8\frac{1}{2} - 4\frac{1}{2} \qquad\qquad = 4$$

$$= 4$$

The solution set of the equation is $\left\{\frac{3}{2}\right\}$.

The root is $\frac{3}{2}$ or $1\frac{1}{2}$.

**EXAMPLE 2**     $2 - \frac{4}{r} = \frac{7}{5r}$   $(r \neq 0)$

**SOLUTION**
$$5r\left(2 - \frac{4}{r}\right) = 5r\left(\frac{7}{5r}\right)$$

$$5r \cdot 2 - 5r \cdot \frac{4}{r} = 7$$

$$10r - 20 = 7$$

$$10r = 27$$

$$r = \frac{27}{10}$$

$$r = 2.7$$

*Check:* If $r = 2.7$, $2 - \frac{4}{r}$ | If $r = 2.7$, $\frac{7}{5r}$

$$= 2 - \frac{4}{\frac{27}{10}} \qquad\qquad = \frac{7}{5\left(\frac{27}{10}\right)}$$

$$= \frac{54}{27} - \frac{40}{27} \qquad\qquad = \frac{7}{\frac{27}{2}}$$

$$= \frac{14}{27} \qquad\qquad = \frac{14}{27}$$

The root is 2.7, or the solution set is $\{2.7\}$.

**EXAMPLE 3**
$$\frac{7}{t} = \frac{5}{t} + \frac{3}{t-5}$$

**SOLUTION**
$$t(t-5) \cdot \frac{7}{t} = t(t-5)\left(\frac{5}{t} + \frac{3}{t-5}\right)$$

[Note that $t(t-5)$ is a good choice of replacement for $z$ in the **Equation Principle for Multiplication**

We must keep in mind that $t \neq 0$ and $t - 5 \neq 0$ or $t \neq 5$. Why?

$$(t-5) \cdot 7 = (t-5) \cdot 5 + t \cdot 3$$
$$7t - 35 = 5t - 25 + 3t$$
$$7t - 35 = 8t - 25$$
$$-35 + 25 = 8t - 7t$$
$$-10 = t$$

The root of the last equation is $-10$.

*Check:* If $t = -10$, $\frac{7}{t}$ | If $t = -10$, $\frac{5}{t} + \frac{3}{t-5}$

$$= \frac{7}{-10} \qquad\qquad = \frac{5}{-10} + \frac{3}{-10-5}$$

$$= -\frac{7}{10} \qquad\qquad = \frac{5}{-10} + \frac{3}{-15}$$

$$= \frac{-5}{10} + \frac{-1}{5}$$

$$= \frac{-5}{10} + -\frac{2}{10}$$

$$= \frac{-7}{10}$$

Hence, the solution set of $\frac{7}{t} = \frac{5}{t} + \frac{3}{t-5}$ ($t \neq 0$, $t \neq 5$) is $\{-10\}$

Solve 43 to 68 using principles with which you are familiar.

**43.** $6c - 3c = 9$

**44.** $5t - 7t = -12$

**45.** $x - 2x = -\frac{1}{2}$

**46.** $\frac{1}{3}r + \frac{1}{2}r = 5$

**47.** $1.7d - .3d = -\frac{1}{2}$

**48.** $4s - \frac{1}{2}s = 2s + 3$

**49.** $3 + 4z = z - 4$

**50.** $\frac{1}{4}m - \frac{3}{4}m + \frac{1}{2} = 2m - \frac{5}{4}$

**51.** $3x - 2 + x = \dfrac{1}{2}x - 4x$

**52.** $3.6b - 1.7b = 2b - .5$

**53.** $\dfrac{1}{2} - z = 2z + \dfrac{3}{4}$

**54.** $8a - .73 = .36 - 7a$

**55.** $-19 = \dfrac{3}{2}x - 13$

**56.** $.07r - 1.3 = 4.7$

**57.** $\dfrac{x}{-5} + 7 = -11$

**58.** $\dfrac{-3}{y} - 1.7 = 7.6$

**59.** $\dfrac{4}{3}x - 7 = 6 - \dfrac{7}{3}x$

**60.** $\dfrac{6}{7 - x} = -4$

**61.** $7x + 13 = 13x - 16$

**62.** $7 - 12x = 7x + 17$

**63.** $\dfrac{7}{t} - 6 = \dfrac{-9}{t}$

**64.** $-5 + \dfrac{4}{y} = \dfrac{7}{y} - 6$

**65.** $3(x + 4) = -7$

**66.** $\dfrac{7}{3}(7 - y) = -21$

**67.** $\dfrac{y - 6}{y} = -3$

**68.** $7 = \dfrac{3 + s}{s}$

Determine the roots of the following equations. Check.

**69.** $\dfrac{y}{y - 6} = \dfrac{7}{3}$

**70.** $\dfrac{6 - x}{7} = 4x$

**71.** $\dfrac{x + 13}{-5} = -7x$

**72.** $-\dfrac{4}{3}x + 5 = \dfrac{7}{9}x + 7$

**73.** $7 = -\dfrac{x + 3}{x}$

**74.** $3(5 + v) = 4v + 7$

**75.** $-7s + \dfrac{4}{9} = \dfrac{7s - 11}{3}$

**76.** $\dfrac{3}{7}w - \dfrac{7}{6} = \dfrac{8}{9} + 3w$

**77.** $-\dfrac{7}{8} + 2r = \dfrac{5(6 + 7r)}{2}$

**78.** $-\dfrac{7}{9}s = \dfrac{3}{5} + 2s$

**79.** $-5 = \dfrac{-7}{x + 9}$

**80.** $\dfrac{5}{3}x + 13 - \dfrac{7}{3}x = 15$

**81.** Review the proof, given on page 162, that every real number has exactly one opposite (additive inverse). In a similar way, prove that every real number except zero has exactly one reciprocal (multiplicative inverse).

## 5 · Equations Involving Absolute Value

From your study of the absolute value, you will recall that the equation

$$| a | = 3$$

has two roots, $-3$ and $3$, because $|-3| = 3$ and $|3| = 3$. Thus, the equation $|a| = 3$ is equivalent to

$$a = 3 \text{ or } a = -3. \text{ (see pp. 55-56)}$$

This observation will help us in solving more complicated equations than the one above. Consider, for example, the following equation:

$$|2m + 7| = 5$$

According to what we observed above, and the meaning of absolute value, this equation is equivalent to the following sentence:

$$2m + 7 = 5 \text{ or } 2m + 7 = -5$$

Let us solve these equations:

$$(1) \quad 2m + 7 = 5$$
$$2m = -2 \quad \text{[Why?]}$$
$$m = -1 \quad \text{[Why?]}$$

$$(2) \quad 2m + 7 = -5$$
$$2m = -12 \quad \text{[Why?]}$$
$$m = -6 \quad \text{[Why?]}$$

We must check to see whether $-1$ and $-6$ are the roots of the equation $|2m + 7| = 5$:

(1)  If $m = -1$, $|2m + 7| =$     (2)  If $m = -6$, $|2m + 7| =$
$$|2 \cdot (-1) + 7| = \qquad\qquad |2 \cdot (-6) + 7| =$$
$$|-2 + 7| = \qquad\qquad\quad |-12 + 7| =$$
$$|5| = 5 \qquad\qquad\qquad\quad |-5| = 5$$

Thus, the solution set of the equation $|2m + 7| = 5$ is $\{-1, -6\}$. As you see, it is a set consisting of two elements.

## EXERCISES

Solve each of the following equations and check:

**1.**  $|n| = 10$

**2.**  $|3d| = 12$

**3.**  $\left|\dfrac{1}{2}x\right| = .7$

**4.**  $|5 + y| = 3$

5. $| 2b - 1 | = 9$

6. $| a + 2 | = 1$

7. $\left| 3n - \dfrac{1}{2} \right| = \dfrac{3}{4}$

8. $\left| \dfrac{1}{3}z + 6 \right| = 15$

9. $\left| \dfrac{1}{2}t + \dfrac{3}{4}t - \dfrac{1}{2} \right| = \dfrac{2}{3}$

10. $| 3p - 5 | = 4$

11. $| 2r | = |-3|$

12. $| 2b + 5 | = 0$

13. $| s + 1 | = \dfrac{1}{2}$

14. $\left| \dfrac{3}{5}r \right| = 7$

15. $| 7x - 3 | = 22$

16. $\left| \dfrac{6x + 1}{5} \right| = 11$

17. $\left| 4 + \dfrac{5}{x} \right| = 3$

18. $14 = | 4 - z |$

19. $\left| \dfrac{4 - x}{x} \right| = 3$

20. $\left| \dfrac{6 - y}{-5} \right| = 7$

21. $\left| \dfrac{7}{9} + x \right| = \dfrac{3}{7}$

22. $4 = \left| \dfrac{3}{5}t \right|$

23. $2 = \left| \dfrac{3y - 1}{y} \right|$

24. $\left| \dfrac{2 - v}{3} \right| = 2$

25. $\left| \dfrac{7x - 13}{-3} \right| = 4$

26. $| w + w | = \dfrac{1}{2}$

## 6 · Writing Equivalent Expressions

You have already had some experience in writing an expression equivalent to a given expression. For example, $3x - 5x + 1.5 + 4x$ and $2x + 1.5$ are two equivalent expressions, because upon replacing $x$ throughout by the name of any one number, each expression will name the same number. Let us replace $x$ by, say, $-5$ in each expression.

$$
\begin{aligned}
&3x - 5x + 1.5 + 4x \\
&= 3 \cdot (-5) - 5 \cdot (-5) + 1.5 + 4 \cdot (-5) \\
&= -15 + 25 + 1.5 - 20 \\
&= 10 + 1.5 - 20 \\
&= 11.5 - 20 \\
&= -8.5
\end{aligned}
$$

Thus, the value of $3x - 5x + 1.5 + 4x$, when $x$ is replaced by $-5$, is $-8.5$.

Similarly,

$$2x + 1.5$$
$$= 2 \cdot (-5) + 1.5$$
$$= -10 + 1.5$$
$$= -8.5.$$

Thus, $-5$ for $x$ in $2x + 1.5$ also yields $-8.5$.

Try some other replacements for $x$ in each of the two expressions. You no doubt observe that, for many purposes, the second expression above is "simpler" than the first expression.

In solving equations, it is frequently convenient to write, in place of expressions containing parentheses, equivalent expressions which do not contain parentheses. Let us consider, for example, $2(x + 3)$. An expression which is equivalent to this, and which does not contain parentheses, is $2x + 6$. $2x + 6$ is obtained from $2(x + 3)$ by applying the Distributive Principle.

Let us make some replacements for $x$ to see that each expression yields the same number.

1 for $x$:

$$2(x + 3) \qquad\qquad 2x + 6$$
$$2(1 + 3) \qquad\qquad 2 \cdot 1 + 6$$
$$= 2 \cdot 4 \qquad\qquad = 2 + 6$$
$$= 8 \qquad\qquad = 8$$

$-7$ for $x$:

$$2(x + 3) \qquad\qquad 2x + 6$$
$$2(-7 + 3) \qquad\qquad 2 \cdot (-7) + 6$$
$$= 2 \cdot (-4) \qquad\qquad = -14 + 6$$
$$= -8 \qquad\qquad = -8$$

$-\dfrac{4}{7}$ for $x$:

$$2(x + 3) \qquad\qquad 2x + 6$$
$$2\left(-\frac{4}{7} + 3\right) \qquad\qquad 2 \cdot \left(-\frac{4}{7}\right) + 6$$
$$= 2\left(-\frac{4}{7} + \frac{21}{7}\right) \qquad\qquad = -\frac{8}{7} + 6$$
$$= 2 \cdot \frac{17}{7} \qquad\qquad = -\frac{8}{7} + \frac{42}{7}$$
$$= \frac{34}{7} \qquad\qquad = \frac{34}{7}$$

$$0 \text{ for } x: \quad 2(x + 3) \qquad\qquad 2x + 6$$
$$2(0 + 3) \qquad\qquad 2 \cdot 0 + 6$$
$$= 2 \cdot 3 \qquad\qquad = 0 + 6$$
$$= 6 \qquad\qquad = 6$$

**EXAMPLE 1**   Write an expression equivalent to $-3(y + 7)$

**SOLUTION**
$$-3(y + 7)$$
$$= -3y + (-3) \cdot 7$$
$$= -3y - 3 \cdot 7$$
$$= -3y - 21$$

Thus $-3(y + 7)$ and $-3y - 21$ are equivalent expressions. One contains parentheses, the other does not.

Replace the variable in each expression by $1$, $-7$, $-\dfrac{4}{7}$,

and 0 to see whether both expressions will yield the same number for the same replacement of $y$.

**EXAMPLE 2**   $4(a - b)$

**SOLUTION**
$$4[a + (-b)]$$
$$4a + 4 \cdot (-b)$$
$$4a + (-4b)$$
$$4a - 4b$$

Thus $4(a - b)$ and $4a - 4b$ are equivalent expressions.

Let us make a few replacements for the variables $a$ and $b$.

$$1 \text{ for } a, -3 \text{ for } b: \quad 4(a - b) \qquad\qquad 4a - 4b$$
$$4[1 - (-3)] \qquad\qquad 4 \cdot 1 - 4 \cdot (-3)$$
$$= 4 \cdot 4 = 16 \qquad\qquad = 4 - (-12) = 16$$

$$-\frac{1}{3} \text{ for } a, \frac{2}{5} \text{ for } b: \quad 4(a - b) \qquad\qquad 4a - 4b$$

$$4\left(-\frac{1}{3} - \frac{2}{5}\right) \qquad\qquad 4 \cdot \left(-\frac{1}{3}\right) - 4 \cdot \frac{2}{5}$$

$$= 4\left(-\frac{5}{15} - \frac{6}{15}\right) \qquad\qquad = -\frac{4}{3} - \frac{8}{5}$$

$$= 4 \cdot \left(-\frac{11}{15}\right) \qquad\qquad = -\frac{20}{15} - \frac{24}{15}$$

EXAMPLE 3     $-2(m - n - 5)$
SOLUTION
$$= -2[m + (-n) + (-5)]$$
$$= -2m + (-2) \cdot (-n) + (-2) \cdot (-5)$$
$$= -2m + 2n + 10$$

Thus $-2(m - n - 5)$ and $-2m + 2n + 10$ are equivalent expressions.

Let us make some replacements for variables; 3 for $m$, $-4$ for $n$:

$$-2(m - n - 5) \qquad\qquad -2m + 2n + 10$$
$$-2[3 - (-4) - 5] \qquad\qquad -2 \cdot 3 + 2 \cdot (-4) + 10$$
$$= -2(7 - 5) \qquad\qquad = -6 + (-8) + 10$$
$$= -2 \cdot 2 = -4 \qquad\qquad = -14 + 10 = -4$$

$-5$ for $m$, $-\dfrac{2}{3}$ for $n$:

$$-2(m - n - 5) \qquad\qquad\qquad -2m + 2n + 10$$
$$-2\left[-5 - \left(-\frac{2}{3}\right) - 5\right] \qquad -2 \cdot (-5) + 2 \cdot \left(-\frac{2}{3}\right) + 10$$
$$= -2\left[-\frac{15}{3} - \left(-\frac{2}{3}\right) - \frac{15}{3}\right] \qquad = 10 + \left(-\frac{4}{3}\right) + 10$$
$$= -2\left(-\frac{13}{3} - \frac{15}{3}\right) \qquad\qquad = \frac{30}{3} + \left(-\frac{4}{3}\right) + \frac{30}{3}$$
$$= -2 \cdot \left(-\frac{28}{3}\right) = \frac{56}{3} \qquad\qquad = \frac{56}{3}$$

EXAMPLE 4     $(5c - 3d) \cdot \left(-\dfrac{1}{2}\right)$

SOLUTION     $[5c + (-3d)] \cdot \left(-\dfrac{1}{2}\right)$

$$= -\frac{1}{2} \cdot [5c + (-3d)]$$

$$= -\frac{1}{2} \cdot 5c + \left(-\frac{1}{2}\right) \cdot (-3d)$$

$$= -\frac{5}{2}c + \frac{3}{2}d$$

Thus $(5c - 3d) \cdot \left(-\dfrac{1}{2}\right)$ and $-\dfrac{5}{2}c + \dfrac{3}{2}d$ are equivalent expressions.

## EXERCISES

For each expression below, write an expression which is equivalent to it and which does not contain parentheses:

**1.** $3(m + 2)$

**2.** $-1(2x + 5)$

**•3.** $-\dfrac{3}{4}(6 + 3d)$

**4.** $(x + y) \cdot (-5)$

**5.** $12(a - 4)$

**6.** $-3(b - 7)$

**7.** $9(M - N)$

**•8.** $-\dfrac{2}{5}(3k - 5s)$

**•9.** $(1.5u - 3.7) \cdot 5$

**10.** $4(a + b - c)$

**11.** $-3(s - t + 11)$

**12.** $(-2x - 3y - 4z) \cdot (-2)$

**13.** $(u + v + w) \cdot a$

**•14.** $-b \cdot (2a + 3c - 4d)$

**•15.** $-\dfrac{3}{4}k \cdot (-m - p - r)$

**•16.** $\dfrac{7}{8}\left(16x + \dfrac{8}{7}y\right)$

**17.** $\left(-\dfrac{3}{4}\right) \cdot (r - 2s + 3t)$

**•18.** $(-3) \cdot \left(\dfrac{x - y}{2}\right)$

**19.** $6 \cdot \left(\dfrac{x}{y} + 13\right)$

**20.** $(3.5 + v) \cdot (-6)$

**21.** $(-3) \cdot (w + 3t)$

**22.** $\left(\dfrac{1}{4}\right) \cdot \left(\dfrac{2}{3}y - \dfrac{3}{4}x\right)$

**23.** $(.07 - 1.3r) \cdot (- .2)$

**24.** $4 \cdot \left(\dfrac{3x - y}{x}\right)$

**25.** $-5 \cdot (x - 2y + 3z)$

**26.** $(w + 7v - 9t) \cdot (-3)$

**27.** $\left(\dfrac{3}{4}\right) \cdot \left(\dfrac{1}{2x + y}\right)$

**28.** $\left(\dfrac{3}{7x - 3y}\right) \cdot \left(-\dfrac{5}{6}\right)$

**29.** $\left(\dfrac{3}{4}\right) \cdot \left(3x - \dfrac{4}{5}y - 6z\right)$

**30.** $\left(\dfrac{2x - 3y}{5}\right) \cdot \left(-\dfrac{7}{3}\right)$

**31.** $\left(\dfrac{3}{5}\right) \cdot \left(\dfrac{4}{x + 2y}\right)$

**32.** $\left(-\dfrac{7}{8}\right) \cdot (13 - x)$

**33.** $\left(7 - \dfrac{x}{3}\right) \cdot \left(-\dfrac{1}{7}\right)$

**34.** $\left(-\dfrac{4}{9}\right)(3x - 2w)$

**35.** $(-7) \cdot (3x - 4y - 7z)$

**36.** $(4w - 7r + 6t) \cdot \left(-\dfrac{3}{7}\right)$

## 7 · Monomials and Polynomials

Algebraic expressions are commonly classified according to the number of terms they contain.

Each of the following is a monomial:

$$5$$
$$3x$$
$$-\frac{1}{2}y$$
$$.7ab$$
$$3xyz$$
$$-1.6amxr$$

Look up the meaning of the prefix "mono" in your dictionary.

Each of the following is a binomial:

$$a + x$$
$$-ay + bx$$
$$3 + acxy$$
$$-\frac{1}{2}ab + \left(-\frac{1}{3}xyz\right)$$
$$.6 + 3x$$
$$4xmu - 2ya$$

Look up the meaning of the prefix "bi" in your dictionary.

Each of the following is a trinomial:

$$2 + x + y$$
$$3x - 2y + 7xyz$$
$$-\frac{1}{2}a + .7b + (-3abc)$$
$$\frac{1}{5} - 4m + \frac{ab}{c}$$
$$\frac{x}{y} + \frac{y}{z} + \frac{z}{w}$$
$$-anr + 2bc - 1.7an$$

Look up the meaning of the prefix "tri" in your dictionary.

Expressions consisting of one term, two terms, three terms, and more than three terms are called *polynomials*. Look up the meaning of the prefix "poly" in your dictionary.

You have already learned how to find expressions equivalent to a given expression by the use of basic principles. You found, for example, that the Distributive Principle is extremely useful in finding equivalent expressions.

To find an expression equivalent to a given expression, you perform some operations. Each operation must be justified by basic principles. Study the examples below and verify whether the principle stated in each case is the correct one.

**EXAMPLE 1**   Multiplication of two monomials.

$$(3a) \cdot (-2c) = 3[a \cdot (-2)]c \quad \text{[Associative Principle of Multiplication]}$$

$$= 3[-2 \cdot a]c \quad \text{[Commutative Principle of Multiplication]}$$

$$= [3 \cdot (-2)]ac \quad \text{[Associative Principle of Multiplication]}$$

$$= -6ac \quad [3 \cdot (-2) = -6]$$

Thus, $(3a) \cdot (-2c) = -6ac$

**EXAMPLE 2**   $(-\frac{1}{2}xy) \cdot (-18ab) = -\frac{1}{2}x(-18yab)$   [Associative and Commutative Principles of Multiplication]

$$= -\frac{1}{2}(-18xyab) \quad \text{[Associative and Commutative Principles of Multiplication]}$$

$$= 9xyab$$

Thus, $(-\frac{1}{2}xy) \cdot (-18ab) = 9xyab$

**EXAMPLE 3**   Multiplication of a binomial and a monomial.

$$4m[-2x + (-3y)]$$
$$= 4m \cdot (-2x) + 4m \cdot (-3y) \quad \text{[Distributive Principle]}$$

$$= [4 \cdot (-2)]mx + [4 \cdot (-3)]my \quad \text{[Commutative and Associative Principles of Multiplication]}$$

$$= -8mx + (-12)my \quad [4 \cdot (-2) = -8; \\ 4 \cdot (-3) = -12]$$

$$= -8mx + [-(12my)] \quad [\forall_{a,b}, (-a)b = \\ -(ab)]$$

$$= -8mx - 12my \quad \text{[Principle of Subtraction]}$$

**EXAMPLE 4**    $[4am + (-xy)](-2ay)$

$= (-2ay)[4am + (-xy)]$                    [Commutative Principle of Multiplication]

$= (-2ay) \cdot 4am + (-2ay) \cdot (-xy)$    [Distributive Principle]

$= -2 \cdot 4aaym + (-2ay) \cdot (-1xy)$    [Commutative and Associative Principles of Multiplication, and Principle of $-1$ (Multiplication)]

$= -8aaym + 2axyy$    [$-2 \cdot 4 = -8$; $-2 \cdot (-1) = 2$; and Commutative and Associative Principles of Multiplication]

Thus, $[4am + (-xy)](-2ay) = -8aaym + 2axyy$

**EXAMPLE 5**    Multiplication of two binomials.

$(a + b)(x + y) = (a + b)x + (a + b)y$

[Distributive Principle]

$= ax + bx + ay + by$

[Distributive Principle]

Thus, $(a + b)(x + y) = ax + bx + ay + by$

**EXAMPLE 6**    $[2m + (-n)][-3c + (-5)]$

$= [2m + (-n)](-3c) + [2m + (-n)](-5)$

[Distributive Principle]

$= -3c[2m + (-n)] + (-5)[2m + (-n)]$

[Commutative Principle of Multiplication]

$= -3c \cdot 2m + (-3c) \cdot (-n)$
$\qquad + (-5) \cdot 2m + (-5) \cdot (-n)$

[Distributive Principle]

$= -3 \cdot 2cm + (-3) \cdot (-1cn)$
$\qquad + (-5) \cdot 2m + (-5) \cdot (-1n)$

[Why?]

$= -6cm + 3cn - 10m + 5n$    [Why?]

Thus, $[2m + (-n)][-3c + (-5)]$
$= -6cm + 3cn - 10m + 5n$

There are certain binomials which recur quite frequently in algebra. It is to your advantage to be thoroughly familiar with the results of multiplying these binomials. The first of these is the result of multiplying a binomial by itself.

**EXAMPLE 7**
$$(x + y)(x + y) = (x + y)x + (x + y)y$$
$$= xx + yx + xy + yy$$
$$= x^2 + xy + xy + y^2$$
$$= x^2 + 2xy + y^2$$

Thus, $\forall_{xy}$, $(x + y)(x + y) = x^2 + 2xy + y^2$.
($x^2$ means $xx$ and is read "$x$ squared.")

Another important result is that of multiplying a sum of two terms by their difference.

**EXAMPLE 8**
$$(x + y)(x - y) = (x + y)x - (x + y)y$$
$$= xx + yx - xy - yy$$
$$= x^2 + xy - xy - y^2$$
$$= x^2 - y^2$$

Thus, $\forall_{xy}$, $(x + y)(x - y) = x^2 - y^2$

# EXERCISES

1. Classify each of the following as a monomial, binomial, or trinomial:

   **a.** $2x + 3y$      **g.** $-3$
   **b.** $m + p + s$      **h.** $5u - 7v$
   **c.** $-2s + 3t - 4xy$      **i.** $25dx$
   **d.** $3x$      **j.** $-xy + \dfrac{xz}{t}$
   **e.** $-2xyz$      **k.** $4abc$
   **f.** $105a + 2b - c$      **l.** $u + m$

2. Multiply and simplify as far as possible:

   **a.** $3x \cdot 4y$      **f.** $(\frac{1}{2}r + \frac{1}{3}s)(-6)$
   **b.** $4(m + n)$      **g.** $13(.3t - .4u)$
   **c.** $-3(x + y)$      **h.** $15[-5d + (-7f)]$
   **d.** $(2a + 5)(5)$      **i.** $100(-2r + s)$
   **e.** $(3c + 4d)(-8)$      **j.** $(a + b)(x + t)$

k.  $(2f - g)(f + 2g)$
l.  $(m + s)(m - s)$
m.  $(3a + 4b)(3a - 4b)$
n.  $(2c + d)(2c + d)$
o.  $(q + u)(3u - q)$
p.  $5(x + z)(x + z)$
q.  $13(5m + 3)(3n - 7)$
r.  $\frac{1}{3}(6n + 15)(6n - 15)$

s.  $(m + n)(m + n)(m + n)$
t.  $(a + b + c)(a + b + c)$
u.  $(x + y + z + w)(x + y + z + w)$
v.  $[(x + y) - z][(x + y) + z]$
w.  $(x - w + v)(x + w - v)$
x.  $(3r + 4s)(7r + 5s)$
y.  $(3y + 4x)(7x + 13y)$
z.  $(11r + 6s)(7r - 5s)$

## 8 · More Equations

Frequently, in solving equations, you first find expressions which are simpler looking and which are equivalent to the expressions involved in the equations. For example, in solving the equation $4m - 1.5m = 2m + 5$, you would proceed as follows:

$$4m - 1.5m = 2m + 5$$
$$2.5m = 2m + 5$$
$$2.5m - 2m = 2m + 5 - 2m$$
$$.5m = 5$$
$$m = 10$$

*Check:* If $m = 10$,
$$4m - 1.5m$$
$$= 4 \times 10 - 1.5 \times 10$$
$$= 40 - 15$$
$$= 25$$

If $m = 10$,
$$2m + 5$$
$$= 2 \times 10 + 5$$
$$= 20 + 5$$
$$= 25$$

The solution set is $\{10\}$. This is sometimes written as $\{m \mid 4m - 1.5m = 2m + 5\} = \{10\}$
and is read "the set of all real numbers $m$ such that $4m - 1.5m = 2m + 5$ is the set consisting of the number 10."

Now let us solve other equations.

**EXAMPLE 1**

**SOLUTION**

$$-\tfrac{1}{2}(3t - 5) = 4t - 3(t + \tfrac{1}{4})$$
$$-\tfrac{3}{2}t + \tfrac{5}{2} = 4t - 3t - \tfrac{3}{4}$$
$$-\tfrac{3}{2}t + \tfrac{5}{2} = t - \tfrac{3}{4}$$
$$-\tfrac{3}{2}t + \tfrac{5}{2} - t = t - \tfrac{3}{4} - t$$
$$-\tfrac{5}{2}t + \tfrac{5}{2} = -\tfrac{3}{4}$$
$$-\tfrac{5}{2}t + \tfrac{5}{2} - \tfrac{5}{2} = -\tfrac{3}{4} - \tfrac{5}{2}$$
$$-\tfrac{5}{2}t = -\tfrac{13}{4}$$
$$(-\tfrac{2}{5})(-\tfrac{5}{2}t) = (-\tfrac{2}{5})(-\tfrac{13}{4})$$
$$t = \tfrac{26}{20}$$
$$t = \tfrac{13}{10}, \text{ or } t = 1.3.$$

*Check:*

If $t = 1.3$, $-\frac{1}{2}(3t - 5)$   If $t = 1.3$, $4t - 3(t + \frac{1}{4})$

$= -\frac{1}{2}(3 \cdot 1.3 - 5)$         $= 4 \cdot 1.3 - 3(1.3 + \frac{1}{4})$

$= -\frac{1}{2}(3.9 - 5)$            $= 5.2 - 3 \cdot 1.55$

$= -\frac{1}{2} \cdot (-1.1)$           $= 5.2 - 4.65$

$= .55$                   $= .55$

The solution set is $\{1.3\}$.

As before, this can be stated:

$$\{t \mid \tfrac{1}{2}(3t - 5) = 4t - 3(t + \tfrac{1}{4})\} = \{1.3\}$$

**EXAMPLE 2** Consider the equation:

$$5(y + \tfrac{2}{5}) - 3y = -5 - (-2y - 7)$$

**SOLUTION** Simplifying, we get

$$5y + 2 - 3y = -5 + 2y + 7$$
$$2y + 2 = 2y + 2$$
$$2 = 2$$

$2 = 2$ is a true statement no matter what replacement is made for $y$. Hence the equation $5(y + \frac{2}{5}) - 3y = -5 - (-2y - 7)$ has as its roots *all* real numbers. Its solution set is the set of all real numbers. This can be written as

$$\{y \mid 5(y + \tfrac{2}{5}) - 3y = -5 - (-2y - 7)\}$$
$$= \text{the set of all real numbers.}$$

This set is equivalent to the set $\{y \mid 2 = 2\}$, meaning the set of all $y$ for which $2 = 2$. The last sentence is true no matter what replacement is made for $y$.

**EXAMPLE 3** Consider one more equation:
$$5(x - 2) + 2(x + 6) = 3x + 6 + 4(x + 1)$$

**SOLUTION** Simplifying,
$$5x - 10 + 2x + 12 = 3x + 6 + 4x + 4$$
$$7x + 2 = 7x + 10$$
$$2 = 10$$

There is no replacement for $x$ such that $2 = 10$, hence we say that the equation

$$5(x - 2) + 2(x + 6) = 3x + 6 + 4(x + 1)$$

has no roots, or that its solution set is the *empty set.* [We are essentially thinking of a set of values of $x$ such that $5(x - 2) + 2(x + 6) = 3x + 6 + 4(x + 1)$ is true.] This is frequently written in the following manner:

$$\{x \mid 5(x - 2) + 2(x + 6) = 3x + 6 + 4(x + 1)\} = \phi$$

and is read "the set of all $x$ (assumed to be real numbers) such that $5(x - 2) + 2(x + 6)$ equals $3x + 6 + 4(x + 1)$ is the empty set." This can also be written, as has been shown,

$$\{x \mid 2 = 10\} = \phi$$

## EXERCISES

Determine the elements of the following sets if the universal set is the set of real numbers:

**1.** $\{m \mid 5(m + 2) = 10\}$

**2.** $\{x \mid 3(x - 6) = 5\}$

**3.** $\{t \mid -2(2t - 3) = 7\}$

**4.** $\{y \mid -6(7y + 5) = 17\}$

**5.** $\{a \mid 3(2a + 5) - 7(a - 6) = 4a - 6\}$

**6.** $\{r \mid -1 + 3r = 3(r - 1)\}$

**7.** $\left\{y \mid \dfrac{y - 7}{6} = 2y + 1\right\}$

**8.** $\{x \mid 3x + 2 + x = -(x + 2) + 3\}$

**9.** $\left\{v \mid 4(3v + 2) = 5\left(v + \dfrac{8}{5}\right) + 7v\right\}$

**10.** $\{x \mid 3(x - 5) = 3(4 - x)\}$

**11.** $\left\{v \mid \dfrac{1}{v} + \dfrac{3}{v - 1} = \dfrac{7}{v}\right\}$

**12.** $\{x \mid 7 + 6x + 5 = -3(2 - 2x) + 18\}$

**13.** $\left\{y \mid \dfrac{1}{4}y + 13 = -(y + 3)\right\}$

**14.** $\left\{x \mid \dfrac{x + 3}{2} = 7\right\}$

**15.** $\{v \mid 5(3 - 2v) = 4(2 - v) - 6v\}$

**16.** $\{x \mid 3(x - 3) = 4(3 - x)\}$

17. $\left\{ y \left| \dfrac{\frac{2}{5}y}{\frac{1}{3}} = \dfrac{7}{8} \right. \right\}$

18. $\left\{ r \left| \dfrac{3}{r-3} + \dfrac{5}{r} = \dfrac{1}{r} \right. \right\}$

19. $\{ x \mid 3x - 7 = -(7 - 3x) \}$

20. $\left\{ t \left| \dfrac{t + 0.6}{4} = 2(t + .3) \right. \right\}$

21. $\left\{ x \left| \dfrac{4x + 7}{3} = \dfrac{4}{3}x + 7 \right. \right\}$

22. $\{ y \mid y - 1 = -y - (y + 1) + 2y \}$

23. $\left\{ v \left| \dfrac{v - 3}{v} = \dfrac{1}{4} \right. \right\}$

24. $\left\{ x \left| \dfrac{4(x - 1)}{2} = 2x - 3 \right. \right\}$

25. $\left\{ s \left| \dfrac{4}{3}(s - 3) = s + 2 - \left( 6 - \dfrac{s}{3} \right) \right. \right\}$

26. $\left\{ x \left| \dfrac{4}{x} + \dfrac{3}{x} + \dfrac{7}{8} = \dfrac{6}{x} \right. \right\}$

27. $\left\{ t \left| 4t = \dfrac{1}{3}t - 7 \right. \right\}$

28. $\left\{ y \left| \dfrac{7}{y + 2} = \dfrac{11}{y} \right. \right\}$

29. $\left\{ v \left| \dfrac{3}{2 - v} = \dfrac{3}{v - 2} \right. \right\}$

30. $\left\{ s \left| \dfrac{3}{4 - s} = \dfrac{1}{2s - 5} \right. \right\}$

31. $\left\{ r \left| \dfrac{5}{r - 3} = \dfrac{9}{3r - 1} \right. \right\}$

32. $\left\{ c \left| \dfrac{1}{3}(c + 5) - 5\left( 3c - \dfrac{1}{3} \right) = -2(c + 6) - \dfrac{1}{2}(2c + 7) \right. \right\}$

33. $\left\{ s \left| -4s + 3(2s - 5) = 3(s - 6) + \dfrac{1}{2}(4 - 2s) \right. \right\}$

34. $\{ n \mid (n - 5) \times 3 + (3n - 7) \times 4 = 4n \}$

35. $\{ z \mid 17(z + 7) = 15(z + 7) \}$

36. $\{ d \mid 5(2d - 6) = 5(6 - 2d) \}$

37. $\{ u \mid 6 \cdot |u + 5| = 6 \}$

**38.** $\left\{w \,\middle|\, \dfrac{1}{2} \cdot |4w - 1| = 13\right\}$

**39.** $\{f \,|\, 1.5(12 - f) = 3(1.6 + f)\}$

**40.** $\left\{x \,\middle|\, \dfrac{1}{2}(3x - 5) = -\dfrac{1}{2}(3x - 5)\right\}$

**41.** $\{x \,|\, 2 \cdot |3 - x| = 2\}$

**42.** $\left\{r \,\middle|\, 5 - 6r = \dfrac{3(7 + 13r)}{-4}\right\}$

**43.** $\left\{x \,\middle|\, \dfrac{7}{x} - \dfrac{3}{x} - \dfrac{5}{x} = \dfrac{1}{2}\right\}$

**44.** $\left\{x \,\middle|\, \dfrac{1 - 3x}{-7x} = \dfrac{1}{5}\right\}$

**45.** $\left\{y \,\middle|\, y + 3 = \dfrac{3y + 14}{-11}\right\}$

**46.** $\left\{x \,\middle|\, \left(\dfrac{x - 19}{7}\right) \cdot \left(-\dfrac{3}{8}\right) = 5x - 7\right\}$

**47.** $\left\{y \,\middle|\, 7 + \dfrac{4}{y} = \dfrac{1}{y} - \dfrac{3}{y}\right\}$

**48.** $\{r \,|\, |7r - 3| = 17\}$

**49.** $\{x \,|\, |x| - 7(x + 3) - 4(3 - x) = -15\}$

**50.** $\left\{t \,\middle|\, \left(\dfrac{11 - t}{2}\right) \cdot \left(-\dfrac{5}{8}\right) = \dfrac{3t + 4}{7}\right\}$

**51.** $\{s \,|\, (s - 7) \cdot 3 + 5(6 - s) = 8 \cdot (s + 9)\}$

**52.** $\{x \,|\, 8 \cdot (4x - 7) = (6 + 7x) \cdot (-4)\}$

**53.** $\{y \,|\, 6y + 9 = y\}$

**54.** $\left\{s \,\middle|\, \dfrac{4}{s} - 3 = \dfrac{5}{s} - 7\right\}$

**55.** $\left\{t \,\middle|\, \dfrac{4}{6t} + \dfrac{1}{4t} = \dfrac{1}{t} - 3\right\}$

**56.** $\{u \,|\, |u| = -2\}$

**57.** $\left\{x \,\middle|\, \dfrac{x - 3}{7} = 3x + 4\right\}$

**58.** $\{r \,|\, .3r + 1.5 = 1.5r + .5\}$

**59.** $\left\{x \,\middle|\, \dfrac{5}{3}(x - 3) - 6x = 13\right\}$

**60.** $\left\{x \,\middle|\, \dfrac{2x + 11}{4} - 5x = \dfrac{3x - 7}{5}\right\}$

**61.** $\left\{x \left| \dfrac{x-4}{5} = 3(x-5) \right.\right\}$

**62.** $\left\{x \left| -5 \cdot (x+11) = 3x - \dfrac{4}{3} - 7x \right.\right\}$

**63.** $\left\{r \left| \dfrac{3r-1.8}{-7} = 7r + 9 \right.\right\}$

**64.** $\left\{t \left| \left(\dfrac{5t-7}{11}\right) \cdot \left(-\dfrac{7}{3}\right) = 4t + 2 \right.\right\}$

**65.** $\left\{x \left| \dfrac{4x-7}{x+3} = -\dfrac{7}{9} \right.\right\}$

**66.** $\left\{x \left| \dfrac{7}{2x+4} = \dfrac{-5}{x-3} \right.\right\}$

## 9 · Using Equations to Solve Problems

Equations are a useful, and frequently an indispensable, tool in solving various kinds of problems. Consider, for example, the following puzzle-type problem:

> I thought of a number, multiplied it by 2, added 5 to the product, and obtained 3 as a result. What is the number I thought of?

Since we don't know what this number is, we shall use a letter, say $x$, in place of a name of this number. Now we shall write expressions corresponding to the things said about this number in the problem:

$$\text{multiplied the number by 2:} \qquad x \cdot 2 \text{ or } 2x$$
$$\text{added 5 to the product:} \qquad 2x + 5$$
$$\text{the result is 3:} \qquad 2x + 5 = 3$$

Now we have the equation:

$$2x + 5 = 3$$

Solving this equation, we find that the root is $-1$. Thus, I thought of the number $-1$.

Let us check:

$$\text{multiply the number by 2:} \qquad -1 \times 2 = -2$$
$$\text{add 5 to the product:} \qquad -2 + 5 = 3$$

The result is 3, and therefore $-1$ *is* the correct answer to the problem; or, $\{x \,|\, 2x + 5 = 3\} = \{-1\}$.

# EXERCISES

Choose a letter in place of a name of a number and write an expression for each of the following:

**EXAMPLE 1**   A number increased by 3, divided by one-half of the number

**SOLUTION**   Let $n$ stand in place of a name of the number. Then the number increased by 3 is $n + 3$; one-half the number is $\frac{1}{2}n$; and the expression is

$$\frac{n + 3}{\frac{1}{2}n}$$

**EXAMPLE 2**   The sum of two numbers multiplied by their difference

**SOLUTION**   Let $x$ and $y$ stand in place of names of the two numbers. The expression is:

$$(x + y)(x - y)$$

1. The sum of a number and twice the number.
2. One-third of a number.
3. The opposite of a number.
4. The absolute value of a number.
5. The sum of absolute values of two numbers.
6. The absolute value of the sum of two numbers.
7. A number squared.
8. A number cubed.
9. A number to the 7th power.
10. The sum of a number squared and another number squared.
11. The product of three numbers; the second number is one more than the first, and the third number is one more than the second.
12. A number subtracted from one-half of the number.
13. The sum of two numbers divided by their difference.
14. The sum of the product and quotient of two numbers.
15. The sum of three numbers multiplied by the product of the three numbers.
16. The sum of $x - 2$ and $3x + 7$.
17. Five more than six times a number.
18. Three less than the square of a number.

**19.** The number by which $4s + 3$ exceeds $-2s + 1$.

**20.** .30 less than $6r$.

**21.** A number added to the square of one-half the number.

**22.** Three less than three-fourths of a number

**23.** The quotient of seven less than a number divided by that number.

**24.** An even integer.

**25.** An odd integer.

Write an algebraic expression for each of the following:

**EXAMPLE 1** If $a$ is the number of minutes in one hour, what is the number of minutes in 5 hours?

**SOLUTION** $5a$

**EXAMPLE 2** If $x$ is the number of length units in one side of a square, what is the number of square units in the area of the square?

**SOLUTION** $x^2$

**26.** If $n$ is the number of feet in a mile, what is the number of feet in 3 miles? $\frac{1}{2}$ mile? 1.6 miles? $p$ miles?

**27.** If $c$ is the number of noops in a yap, what is the number of noops in 5 yaps? $\frac{4}{7}$ yaps? 7.8 yaps? $d$ yaps?

**28.** If $m$ is the number of ounces in a pound, what is the number of ounces in 2 pounds? $\frac{3}{4}$ pounds? 1.8 pounds? $y$ pounds?

**29.** If $a$ is the number of length units in the width of a rectangle, and $b$ the number of the same length units in the length of the rectangle, what is the number of square units in the area of the rectangle?

**30.** If $r$ is the number of length units in the radius of a circle, what is the number of these length units in the circumference of the circle? The number of square units in the area of the circle? The number of length units in the diameter of the circle?

Solve each of the following problems:

**1.** A number is multiplied by 3; $3\frac{1}{2}$ is added to the product, yielding 2. What is the number?

**2.** If 2 is added to a number and the sum is multiplied by 3, the result is zero. What is the number?

**3.** If $\frac{1}{2}$ is subtracted from a number, and the difference is multiplied by 4, the result is 5. What is the number?

**4.** The sum of two numbers is added to their difference. The result is 6. What is one of the numbers? What can you tell about the other number?

**5.** Add 5 to a number, divide the sum by the difference of 5 from the number. The result is 2. What is the number?

**6.** Subtract a number from 1, divide the difference by this number subtracted from 3. The result is 0. What is the number?

**7.** In each problem, do the required computations:

**EXAMPLE**   The formula for the volume of a rectangular solid is
$V = lwh$

Compute the volume when the length is 12 in., the width is 9 in., and the height is 3 in.

**SOLUTION**    $V = 12 \cdot 9 \cdot 3$ cu. in.
$= 324$ cu. in.

The volume is 324 cu. in.

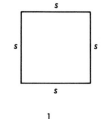

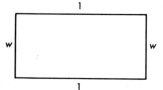

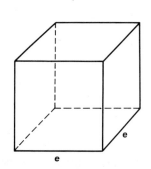

**a.** The formula for the perimeter of a square is, $p = 4s$.
Compute the perimeter when $s = 7$ in.

**b.** Using the formula in Exercise **a**, compute the length of the side of the square when $p = 37$ in.

**c.** The formula for the perimeter of a rectangle is, $p = 2l + 2w$.
Compute the perimeter when $l = 2$ ft., $w = 13$ in.

**d.** Using the formula in Exercise **c**, compute the length of the rectangle if the perimeter is 100 in. and the width is 15 in.

**e.** The formula for the volume of a cube is, $V = e^3$. Compute the volume of the cube if $e = 7$ in.

**f.** Using the formula in Exercise **e**, compute the length of one edge if $V = 1000$ cu. in.

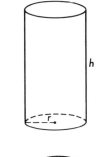

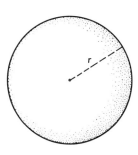

**g.** The formula for the volume of a right circular cylinder is $V = \pi r^2 h$.
Compute the volume when $r = 3.5$ in., $h = 17$ in. (use $\pi = 3.1$)

**h.** Using the formula in Exercise **g**, compute the height when $V = 255$ cu. in., $r = 2$ in.

**i.** The formula for the volume of a sphere is, $V = \frac{4}{3}\pi r^3$. Compute the volume when $r = 5$ in.

**j.** Using the formula in Exercise **i,** compute the length of a radius of a sphere if $V = 1200$ cu. in.

**k.** The formula for the area of a sphere is, $A = 4\pi r^2$. Compute the area when $r = 1.5$ ft.

## 10 · Making Problems to Fit Equations

In the previous section you learned to make equations which fit given problems. You solved the equations in order to find the answers to the problems. It should be interesting to start out with an equation and make up a story which will fit the given equation. It should be possible to make up several different stories which fit one equation. This equation may be viewed as a generalization, and the stories which fit this equation may be viewed as specific instances of that generalization. Answers to the specific instances may be found by solving the equation.

**EXAMPLE**      Let us make up stories which fit the equation:

$$2x + 3 = 11$$

**SOLUTIONS**     Here are some stories:

1. I thought of a number, multiplied it by 2, and added 3 to the product. The result is 11. What is the number? Do you see that the root of the equation $2x + 3 = 11$ is the answer to this problem?

2. Mary has 11¢. She buys two apples at a certain price and has 3¢ left. What is the cost of one apple?

Do you think the equation $2x + 3 = 11$ fits this situation? How is $x$ used in this situation?

3. If the area in square feet of a certain rectangle is doubled, and 3 square feet added, an area of 11 square feet is obtained. What is the area of the rectangle? Does the equation $2x + 3 = 11$ fit this situation? What is the meaning of $x$ in this case?

4. Johnny lives a certain number of miles from school. If this number is doubled and 3 miles added, then the distance of 11 miles is obtained. How many miles from school does Johnny live?

It is possible to make up a story for a given equation such that, after solving the equation, you will discover that the answer is not realistic; that is, the answer does not make sense.

**EXAMPLE**     $3y + 6 = 3$

**SOLUTION**     Suppose you made up the following story:
If I multiply the number of years in Susie's age by 3 and add 6 to the product, I obtain 3.

Now let us solve the equation:

$$3y + 6 = 3$$
$$3y = -3$$
$$y = -1$$

Thus, the root of the equation is $-1$. Therefore, Susie is $-1$ years old. This answer is not realistic in terms of the story. The number $-1$ is not in the replacement set of the variable. When we speak of the age of a person, the replacement set of the variable is the set of positive numbers.

## EXERCISES

For each equation below, make up three stories which fit the equation. After you have made up each story, solve the equation. If the root to the equation is not realistic in terms of any of the stories, tell why it is not.

1. $4m + 1 = 9$

2. $\dfrac{5t - 3}{3} = 9$

3. $2 - \dfrac{1}{2}y = 0$

4. $4x + 1 = 2x + 11$

5. $\dfrac{1}{3}s + \dfrac{1}{3} = 0$

## 11 · More Practice in Using Equations to Solve Problems

You have seen that in order to solve a problem by using an equation you need to write an equation that fits the problem, find the root of the equation, then convince yourself that the root of the equation "works" in the problem.

It is very important that you first read the problem thoughtfully until you fully understand it. Then you should write the conditions of the problem in the form of mathematical sentences.

Below are several examples of problems and their solutions. You should always attempt to develop your own ways of solving problems. There are often many different ways of solving the same problem. Use your ingenuity and be clever about it!

**PROBLEM**

Alice has a bank which contains $2.65 in dimes and nickels. If Alice has eleven more nickels than dimes, how many of each type of coin does she have?

**SUGGESTED SOLUTION**

Since there are only two kinds of coins, we know that the product of .05 (value of a nickel) and the number of nickels, added to the product of .10 (value of a dime) and the number of dimes will yield 2.65 ($2.65 in the bank).

We don't actually know how many dimes or nickels she has, but we do know that there are more nickels than dimes.

If we let $x$ stand for the number of dimes, then $x + 11$ would stand for the number of nickels. (Why?) Then the following equation fits the story of the problem.

$$.05(x + 11) + .10x = 2.65$$

Solving the equation,

$$100[.05(x + 11) + .10x] = 100 \times 2.65$$

(Do you see why it is good to use 100 here as a multiplier?)

$$5(x + 11) + 10x = 265$$
$$5x + 55 + 10x = 265$$
$$15x = 210$$
$$x = 14$$

Thus, there are 14 dimes; and 14 nickels + 11 nickels = 25 nickels.

Checking,

Dimes   $14 \times .10 = 1.40$   or   $1.40
Nickels  $25 \times .05 = 1.25$   or   $1.25 giving the total
of $2.65.

Use another method to solve this problem.

**PROBLEM**

A family vacation budget allowed three times as much for food as for camping expenses and four times as much for travel as for camping expenses. If the total allowed for food, camping expenses, and travel was $168, how much was allotted to travel?

**SUGGESTED SOLUTION**

We note the relationship between food and camping expenses. And also between camping expenses and travel.

If we let $x$ stand for the number of dollars spent on food, then $\frac{1}{3}x$ would stand for the number of dollars spent for camping expenses. It would then follow that $\frac{4}{3}x$ would stand for the number of dollars allowed for travel. The sum of $x$, $\frac{1}{3}x$, and $\frac{4}{3}x$ should be 168.

Another approach would be to let $y$ stand for the number of dollars spent for camping; then $3y$ would stand for food expense and $4y$ would stand for the travel expense in dollars.

Thus, our equation is

$$y + 3y + 4y = 168$$
$$8y = 168$$
$$y = 21$$

The camping expense was $21. The travel expense allotment was $4 \times 21 = 84$, or $84. The food allotment was $3 \times 21 = 63$, or $63.

Checking,

|         |       |
|---------|-------|
| food    | $63   |
| camping | $21   |
| travel  | $84   |
| total   | $168  |

Solve the problem using the first suggested approach.

**PROBLEM**   Joe is now fifteen years younger than Jane. In six years Jane will be twice as old as Joe will be then. What are their ages now?

**SUGGESTED SOLUTION**   We know that the difference in their ages is fifteen years.

If we let $x$ stand for Jane's present age in years, then we can express Joe's age in terms of $x$. It is $x - 15$. We may represent Jane's age six years from now by $x + 6$, and Joe's age six years from now by $(x - 15) + 6$, or $x - 9$. Are these expressions, $x + 6$ and $x - 9$ equivalent? Rereading the problem reveals that Jane's age six years from now is twice as great as Joe's age. That is, Joe's age must be doubled (multiplied by 2) to make it equal to Jane's age. Thus, we have

$$2(x - 9) = x + 6$$

Simplifying,

$$2(x - 9) = x + 6$$
$$2x - 18 = x + 6$$
$$x = 24$$

Thus, Jane is 24 years old, and Joe is $24 - 15 = 9$ years old.

Checking,                          Ages six years from now
    Jane 24 years                    Jane 30
    Joe   9                         Joe   15

Difference 15 years

Hence, Jane will be twice as old as Joe at that time.

**PROBLEM**   The sum of two numbers is 97. One number is 19 greater than the other number. What are the two numbers?

**SUGGESTED SOLUTION**   One number is 19 greater than the other. If we let $y$ stand for the smaller number, the larger number may be represented by $y + 19$.

Our equation is

$$y + (y + 19) = 97$$

Solving,

$$2y + 19 = 97$$
$$2y = 78$$
$$y = 39$$

Thus, the smaller number is 39 and the larger of the two is $39 + 19 = 58$.

Checking,

smaller number 39

larger number  58

———

sum      97

The difference is $58 - 39 = 19$.

Use a different method to solve this problem.

**PROBLEM**

215 tickets were sold for a church supper. Adult tickets were $.75 each and children's tickets were $.35 each. The sale of both kinds of tickets amounted to $135.25. How many adult tickets were sold?

**SUGGESTED SOLUTION**

The product of .75 and the number of adults, added to the product of .35 and the number of children will yield 135.25. (We are dropping the dollar signs temporarily to simplify the problem.) If we sold 100 adult tickets, we would have $215 - 100 = 115$ children. If we had 150 adults, we would have $215 - 150 = 65$ children. Thus, if we let $r$ stand for the number of adult tickets, then $215 - r$ will stand for the number of children's tickets.

Thus, our equation is

$$.75r + .35(215 - r) = 135.25$$

Solving,

$$100[.75r + .35(215 - r)] = 100 \times 135.25$$
$$75r + 35(215 - r) = 13{,}525$$
$$75r + 7{,}525 - 35r = 13{,}525$$
$$40r + 7{,}525 = 13{,}525$$
$$40r = 6{,}000$$
$$r = 150$$

Thus, 150 adult tickets and 215 − 150 = 65 children's tickets were sold.

Checking,

$$150 \times .75 = 112.50 \quad \text{or} \quad \$112.50$$
$$65 \times .35 = \phantom{1}22.75 \quad \text{or} \quad \$\phantom{1}22.75$$
$$\text{Total} \quad \$135.25$$

Use a different approach in solving this problem.

**PROBLEM**

Jim and Joe ride their motorbikes in opposite directions from Joe's house on the highway, starting at the same time. We find them 19 miles apart 15 minutes later. The average speed of Joe's bike is 8 miles per hour less than the average speed of Jim's bike. Can we determine the average speed of Joe's bike?

**SUGGESTED SOLUTION**

We know that if one travels at an average speed of 15 miles per hour for two hours he has covered a distance of 30 miles; or if one covered a distance of 40 miles in a time of 2 hours, his average speed would be 20 miles per hour. You are probably familiar with the formula

$$d = rt$$

where $d$ is distance, $r$ is speed (or rate), and $t$ is time.

We know the two bikes end up 19 miles apart after 15 minutes. We observe that both bikes have been traveling for the same period of time, but they have covered different distances because of traveling at unequal rates. However, the sum of their distances will be equal to the distance they are apart. If we let $z$ stand for the speed of Jim's bike in m.p.h., then we may represent the speed of Joe's bike in m.p.h. by $z - 8$.

To find the distance traveled by Joe, we find the product of Joe's speed $(z - 8)$ m.p.h., and the number of hours he traveled, $\frac{15}{60}$ or $\frac{1}{4}$ hour. Thus, $\frac{1}{4}(z - 8)$ represents the miles traveled by Joe.

Similarly, we determine that $\frac{1}{4}z$ represents the distance traveled by Jim in the same length of time.

We may now write the following equation:

$\frac{1}{4}(z - 8) + \frac{1}{4}z = 19$

Solving,

$$4[\tfrac{1}{4}(z - 8) + \tfrac{1}{4}z] = 4 \times 19$$
$$(z - 8) + z = 76$$
$$2z - 8 = 76$$
$$2z = 84$$
$$z = 42$$

Thus, Jim's average speed was 42 m.p.h., and Joe's average speed was $42 - 8 = 34$ m.p.h.

Checking,                             Distance

$$\text{Joe} \ (\tfrac{1}{4} \text{ hr.}) \times (34 \text{ m.p.h.}) = \tfrac{34}{4} \text{ miles}$$
$$\text{Jim} \ (\tfrac{1}{4} \text{ hr.}) \times (42 \text{ m.p.h.}) = \tfrac{42}{4} \text{ miles}$$
$$\text{Total} \quad \tfrac{34}{4} + \tfrac{42}{4} = \tfrac{76}{4} = 19 \text{ miles}$$

Can you obtain the same answer, using a different approach?

**PROBLEM**

A seed dealer mixed grass seed selling at $1.20 a pound with clover seed selling at $1.60 a pound. If he wanted a mixture of 90 lbs. to sell at $1.24 a pound, how many pounds of each did he use in the mixture?

**SUGGESTED SOLUTION**

We know that the cost of the mixture is obtained by multiplying the cost per pound ($1.24) by the number of pounds (90 lbs.). The cost of this mixture is $111.60.

We don't know how many pounds of the grass seed or clover we have, but we know their total weight is 90 pounds. Thus, if we let $x$ stand for the lbs. of grass used, then $90 - x$ is the lbs. of clover used. $1.20x$ is the cost of grass in dollars, $1.60(90 - x)$ is the cost of clover in dollars. Thus, our equation is

$$1.20x + 1.60(90 - x) = 111.60$$

Solving,

$$100[1.20x + 1.60(90 - x)] = 100 \times 111.60$$
$$120x + 160(90 - x) = 11{,}160$$
$$120x + 14{,}400 - 160x = 11{,}160$$
$$-40x = -3{,}240$$
$$x = 81$$

Thus, we used 81 lbs. of grass seed and $90 - 81 = 9$ lbs. of clover seed.

Checking,                                 Cost

grass 81 lbs. at $1.20 per pound     $ 97.20
clover 9 lbs. at $1.60 per pound     $ 14.40

                                         $111.60 total cost

**PROBLEM**

How long is a rectangular plot if its length is 10 ft. longer than its width, and its perimeter is 52 ft.?

**SUGGESTED SOLUTION**

Let $m$ be the number of feet in the width of the rectangle. Then the number of feet in the length is $m + 10$.

Let us draw a picture to help us analyze and solve the problem:

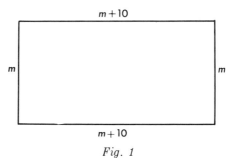

*Fig. 1*

The number of feet in the perimeter is:

$m + (m + 10) + m + (m + 10)$, or
$4m + 20$.

We are ready now to write an equation which fits the problem.

$4m + 20 = 52$

Solving the equation,

$$4m + 20 = 52$$
$$4m = 32$$
$$m = 8$$

Thus, the rectangle is 8 feet wide and 18 feet long.

Checking,

The length is 10 ft. longer than the width, because $18 - 8 = 10$.

The perimeter is
$8 + 18 + 8 + 18 = 52$

★ **PROBLEM**     A 20% antifreeze solution contains one volume of pure antifreeze in every five volumes of solution (or one volume of pure antifreeze to every 4 volumes of water— it would contain 80% water). Suppose we had 10 quarts of such a solution. How much pure antifreeze does it contain? How much water should be added to yield a solution containing 15% antifreeze?

**SUGGESTED SOLUTION**     Since 20% of the solution is pure antifreeze, it contains .20 × 10 = 2 quarts of pure antifreeze.

If we added two quarts of water, our total volume of solution would be twelve quarts. The amount of pure antifreeze remains the same; therefore, the mixture is $\frac{2}{10+2} = \frac{1}{6}$ antifreeze, or it would contain $16\frac{2}{3}\%$ antifreeze.

If we added six quarts of water, our total volume is sixteen quarts. Again, the amount of pure antifreeze is the same both before and after diluting with water. We have $\frac{2}{10+6} = \frac{1}{8}$, or 12.5% antifreeze solution.

If we add ten quarts of water, the resulting mixture would be 10% antifreeze. In all cases, the amount of pure antifreeze is the same before and after diluting with water.

Can we reverse the question? How much water need be added to 10 quarts of the 20% solution to produce a $16\frac{2}{3}\%$ solution?

We see that the original solution contains two quarts of pure antifreeze. $16\frac{2}{3}\%$ or $\frac{2}{3}$ of the sum of the original volume and the amount of water added should be equal to two. Do you see why?

What amount of water should be added to our original 10 qts. of 20% solution to produce a 15% solution? 15% or $\frac{15}{100}$ of the sum of the original volume (10 qts.) and the amount of water added should be equal to 2.

If we let $x$ stand for the number of quarts of water added, we formulate the following equation:

$$2 = \tfrac{15}{100}(10 + x)$$

Solving,

$$200 = 15(10 + x)$$
$$200 = 150 + 15x$$
$$50 = 15x$$
$$x = 3\tfrac{1}{3}$$

Thus, if $3\tfrac{1}{3}$ quarts of water are added to our original 10 quarts of 20% antifreeze, a 15% solution is produced.

Checking,

We are starting with 10 quarts of 20% antifreeze solution. Therefore, there are .20 × 10 or 2 quarts of antifreeze in the solution. By adding $3\tfrac{1}{3}$ quarts of water, we obtain $13\tfrac{1}{3}$ quarts of weaker solution. The solution still contains 2 quarts of antifreeze.

$13\tfrac{1}{3}$ quarts of solution

2 quarts of antifreeze in it

What per cent of the total solution is antifreeze? It is

$$\frac{2}{13\tfrac{1}{3}} \times 100 = \frac{2}{\dfrac{40}{3}} \times 100 = \frac{6 \times 100}{40} = \frac{600}{40} = 15$$

Thus the new solution *is* 15% solution.

## EXERCISES

Solve each problem and check:

1. The sum of the perimeters of two squares is 100 in. If the perimeter of one square is three times the perimeter of the other, find the length of the side of each square.

2. The measure of the length of a rectangle is 4 times the measure of the width. The perimeter is 300 inches. Determine the length of each side of the rectangle.

3. The sum of the perimeters of two equilateral triangles is 30 inches. Determine the length of the sides of each triangle if a side of the larger triangle is 9 times as long as a side of the smaller triangle.

4. The perimeter of an isosceles triangle is 29 inches. If one leg is 4 inches longer than the base, determine the length of each side of the triangle. [An isosceles triangle has two sides of the same length. Each of these sides is called a leg. The third side is called the base.]

5. In a $\triangle ABC$, the measure of $\angle A$ is twice the measure of $\angle B$ and three times that of $\angle C$. Determine the measure of each angle in $\triangle ABC$. (The sum of the measures of three angles in a triangle is 180°.)

6. A square and a rectangle have the same perimeter. The rectangle's dimensions are: length 27 ft., width 12 ft. How long is a side of the square?

7. Supplementary angles are angles whose measures add to 180°. What are the measures of two supplementary angles if the measure of one is five times that of the other? If the measure of one is 37° more than that of the other?

8. Complementary angles are angles whose measures add to 90°. What are the measures of two complementary angles if the measure of one angle is five times that of the other angle? If one is 37° more than the other?

9. Complete the following table. The first line is completed for you.

| Measure of angle | Complement (1) | Supplement (2) | Difference (2) − (1) |
|---|---|---|---|
| 5° | 85° | 175° | 175 − 85 = 90 |
| 38° | | | |
| | 89° | | |
| | | 126° | |
| | 30°25′ | | |
| | | 179°59′ | |
| | | | |

Examine your answers in the column headed *Difference* above. What can you conclude on the basis of the answers in this column?

10. Miss Thrifty has $9.00 in nickels and dimes. She has twice as many dimes as she has nickels. How many coins of each kind does Miss Thrifty have?

11. Mr. Tight has a jar full of nickels. If he removes 50 nickels and replaces them with 70 dimes, he will have $1\frac{1}{2}$ times the original amount. How much money does Mr. Tight have in the jar?

12. A jar full of pennies and nickels contains 3 times as many nickels as pennies. The total amount of money in the jar is $5.60. How many coins of each kind are there in the jar?

13. There are 36 pupils in a mathematics class. The girls outnumber the boys 2 to 1. How many boys are there in the class?

**14.** Mr. Games has dice, marbles, and coins, 136 of these objects in all. If the number of marbles is twice the number of dice, and the number of coins is five times the number of dice, how many of each kind does he have?

**15.** Mrs. Homemaker buys three cans of different vegetables. Can $A$ weighs $2\frac{1}{2}$ ounces more than can $B$, and can $C$ weighs $10\frac{1}{3}$ ounces more than $B$. The total weight of the three cans is $48\frac{5}{6}$ ounces. How many ounces does can $A$ weigh?

**16.** Mr. Fleet can run 3 times as fast as Mr. Sluggish. They started from the same spot at the same time and ran in opposite directions. The distance between them after 5 minutes was $1\frac{1}{4}$ miles. What distance did Mr. Fleet run?

**17.** The sum of three consecutive integers is 45. What are the integers? [Example of consecutive integers: 7, 8, 9.]

**18.** The sum of four consecutive *even* integers is 276. What are the integers? [Example of four consecutive even integers: 4, 6, 8, 10.]

**19.** The sum of three consecutive *odd* integers is 273. What are the integers? [Example of three consecutive odd integers: 7, 9, 11.]

**20.** The sum of four consecutive odd integers is 104. What are the integers?

**21.** The average of three integers is 5. Can you find such integers? How many such sets of integers can you find?

**22.** Multiplying a number by 3 gives the same result as adding 4 to the number. What is the number?

**23.** Taking one-half of a number gives the same result as adding 5 to the number. What is the number?

**24.** Dividing a number by 5 gives the same result as adding 16 to the number. What is the number?

**25.** Multiplying a number by 3 and adding 5 to the product gives the same result as multiplying the number by $-2$. What is the number?

**26.** What two numbers have 59 as their sum and 11 as their difference?

**27.** A piggy bank contained 4 fewer dimes than quarters, 10 more nickels than dimes, 3 times as many half dollars as quarters. The total value of the coins was $11.30. How many dimes were there?

**28.** John is six years older than Jerry. In nine years Jerry will be $\frac{2}{3}$ as old as John. What is John's age now?

**29.** The number of women at a mixed gathering was 4 less than one-third of the entire group present. This number of women was also equal to one-fourth of the entire number of people present. How many women were present?

30. A candy store proprietor wishes to mix caramels selling at $.95 a pound with 32 lbs. of creams selling at $1.10 a pound. If he wishes to sell the resulting mixture for $1.00 a pound, how many pounds of caramels should he use in the mixture?

31. We have a two digit number. The sum of the tens digit and units digit is 11. If the tens digit is 3 greater than the units digit, what is the number?

32. A new car leaves Detroit traveling at an average speed of 45 m.p.h. One and one-half hours later another car leaves Detroit on the same route. If the second car catches up with the first car in $4\frac{1}{2}$ hours, find the speed of the second car.

33. Mr. Smith bought a new television set. He was allowed a discount of $25 more than one-fourth the price of the new set. He actually paid $155 in cash to make up the balance of the cost of the new set. What was the price of the television set?

34. On a trip to the city, Mr. G. traveled at an average speed of 45 m.p.h. His average speed on the return trip was 55 m.p.h. If the time of coming and returning over the same route amounted to 6 hours, how far was the city from Mr. G's house?

35. If three is added to the quotient of sixteen divided by a given number, the result is the reciprocal of the given number. Determine the given number.

36. The number of students in room A is $\frac{3}{4}$ of the number in room B. If room B has 8 more students than room A, determine the number of students in each room.

37. Mr. J. paid $2,678 for his new car, which included a 3% sales tax. What was the actual purchase price of the car, before tax?

38. A number is divided by a number 33 greater than itself. The quotient is added to one-third. The result is three-fourths. Determine the original numbers.

39. **a.** If it takes a woman nine days to clean house, by working at the same rate, how much of the job will she complete in six days? In three days? In one day? In $y$ days?

  **b.** If Mary completes one-third of a task in one day, how long would it take her to complete the whole task? Ann completes one-sixth of the same task in one day. Compare their rates of work. How long would it take Mary and Ann to complete the task working together? (We will assume their rate of work to continue at the same rate.)

**c.** If Jim completes one-fourth of a job in one day and Joe completes three-eighths of a job in one day, who is the faster worker? Compare their rates. How long would it take Jim to complete the job by himself? How long would it take Joe by himself? Working at the same rate, how long would it take them working together?

**d.** If two boys working together complete a job in 5 hours, what part of the job will they complete in one hour? If the combination of the boys requires $x$ hours to complete the task, what part of the task will they complete in one hour? What part of the job will each of them complete in $x$ hours? Each will complete a fraction of the job in $x$ hours. What will these two fractions total?

**e.** If it takes Ed 5 hours to complete a job, and Bob completes the same job in 3 hours, how much of the job would each boy complete in one hour? How long would it take both working together to complete the job?

**40.** Mr. J's property tax is \$339. This is a 13% increase over last year's tax. What was the tax last year?

**41.** College Y has 1431 students, and it has $3\frac{1}{2}$ times as many boys as girls. What is the enrollment of girls?

**42.** It would take Bill 4 hours to wash the windows by himself. Joe could complete the job in 6 hours. Working together at these same rates, how long will it take them to do the job?

**43.** Ann has \$4.75, made up of half dollars and quarters. If there is a total of thirteen coins, how many coins of each kind does she have?

**44.** Given the fraction $\frac{4}{11}$, what number may be added to the numerator and subtracted from the denominator to produce the fraction $\frac{7}{8}$?

**45.** It takes Roy one-half hour to cut the back lawn, while his brother, Bob, completes the task in 45 minutes. Working together at the same rates, how long will it take them to complete the job?

**★46.** John vacationed at a river resort featuring float trips. His motorboat ordinarily travels at an average speed of 12 m.p.h. He found that he could travel 18 miles upstream in the same time that he could travel 24 miles downstream. Compute the speed of the current.

**★47.** Three boys worked on a job. Harry received \$4 less than twice as much as John. George received \$7 more than Harry. How much did each receive if their total wages were \$199?

**★48.** Suppose your science teacher has 5 quarts of 25% sulphuric acid. He would like to obtain a sulphuric acid solution of 35% acid by adding a solution of 75% acid to his original solution. How much of the more concentrated acid must be added to achieve the desired concentration?

★ **49.** The difference between the squares of two consecutive odd numbers is 32. What are the numbers?

★ **50.** A chemist has 18 quarts of 90% solution of sulphuric acid. How much additional water must be used to have a 22% acid solution?

★ **51.** Jim agrees to help John paint his house. It would take Jim 44 hours to do it by himself, while John could do it alone in 40 hours. They want to complete the job in a two-day weekend. Working together at their usual rates, how many hours must they work to complete the job in the weekend?

★ **52.** An alloy of lead and tin weighs 78 pounds and contains 67% tin. How much lead must be melted in to make an alloy containing 60% lead?

★ **53.** John usually took 50 minutes to mow the front lawn. After mowing for five minutes, he persuaded Greg to bring over his power mower and help him. Together, they finished the task in 15 minutes. How long would it have taken Greg to do the mowing by himself?

★ **54.** A plane makes a trip of 900 miles. If the average speed had been increased by 75 m.p.h., the plane could have covered 1350 miles in the same time. Determine the average speed of the plane.

## 12 · Rectangles and Triangles

In studying the sizes of geometric figures, like rectangles, we are concerned with the number of length units in their sides and the number of square units in their areas. For the study of areas, the area of a square each of whose sides is one unit in length serves as our unit of area, or guide for comparison. The area of such a square is 1 square unit.

Since upper elementary school days, you have accepted the following principle:

The area of a rectangle is equal to the product of its length and width, or, written as a formula,

$$A = l \times w$$

The formula contains the variables $A$, $l$, and $w$. If $l$ and $w$ stand for the *measures* of the length and width of the rectangle, $l \times w$ stands for the *measure* of the area. In order to maintain a consistent unit of area, we require that the measures of both $l$ and $w$ be in terms of the same unit of length. Actually, a more precise expression of the above principle would be:

The number of square units in the measure of the area of a rectangle is equal to the product of the number of linear units in the measures of its length and width.

Suppose we were asked to determine the area of a rectangle whose length is 12 inches and whose width is 7 inches. If we replace $l$ by 12 and $w$ by 7, in the formula, we get

$$A = 12 \times 7$$

84 is the number which is the measure of the area. In this case, we would say that the area is 84 square inches.

**EXAMPLE 1**     Suppose we have a rectangle whose area is 78 square feet and whose length is 60 feet. Could we determine its width?

**SOLUTION**     In the formula, $A = lw$, if we replace $A$ by 78 and $l$ by 60, we obtain

$$78 = 60 \cdot w$$

Solving this equation,

$w = \frac{78}{60}$
or, $w = 1.3$

Thus, the width of this rectangle is 1.3 feet.

The formulas used in finding the areas of some of the other geometric figures are related to the formula for the area of the rectangle.

With a little experimenting, you will discover that cutting any rectangle into two parts by a diagonal divides the rectangle into two triangles which are exactly alike. Thus, the triangles $ADC$ and $ABC$ above have the same measure for their areas. Or, the area of each triangle is one-half the area of the rectangle.

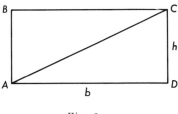

Fig. 2

Thus,

Area of $\triangle ADC = \frac{1}{2} bh$ and Area of $\triangle ABC = \frac{1}{2} bh$

Notice that each triangle is a right triangle.

In triangle $ABC$, *Figure 3*, page 206, we may form right triangles by constructing a perpendicular line from $C$ to $AB$, as in *Figure 4*.

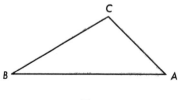

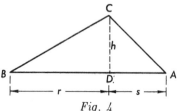

Fig. 3                                    Fig. 4

This perpendicular from one of the corners (called vertices) of the triangle to the opposite side of the triangle (or its extension) is called an altitude. We have two right triangles, $BCD$ and $CDA$. If we designate the measure of $CD$ as $h$, the measure of $BD$ as $r$, and the measure of $AD$ as $s$, the areas of the triangles are given by

$$A_{\triangle BCD} = \tfrac{1}{2} \cdot r \cdot h; \ A_{\triangle CDA} = \tfrac{1}{2} \cdot s \cdot h.$$

The total area of triangle $ABC$ is the sum of these areas

$$A_{\triangle ABC} = \tfrac{1}{2}rh + \tfrac{1}{2}sh.$$

Applying the distributive principle, and simplifying, we get

$$A_{\triangle ABC} = \tfrac{1}{2}h(r + s),$$

where $r + s$ merely stands for the measure of the side $AB$ to which the perpendicular (the altitude) was drawn from $C$. If we agree that the measure of $AB$ will be called the base and designated by $b$, we will have

$$A_{\triangle ABC} = \tfrac{1}{2} \cdot b \cdot h.$$

**EXAMPLE 2**   Suppose we are asked to determine the area of the following triangle:

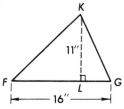

The measure of $KL$ (perpendicular to $FG$ from $K$) is 11 inches. The measure of $FG$ is 16 inches.

**SOLUTION**   Using the formula for area of a triangle, we have

$A = \tfrac{1}{2} \cdot b \cdot h$

$A = \tfrac{1}{2} \cdot 16 \cdot 11$

$A = 88$

The measure of the area is 88 square inches.

**EXAMPLE 3**　　Suppose the area given was 72 square inches, and the measure of the base 16 inches; could we determine the measure of the altitude $KL$?

**SOLUTION**　　Substituting in $A = \frac{1}{2} \cdot b \cdot h$, we get

$$72 = \frac{1}{2} \cdot 16 \cdot h$$

Solving this equation, we obtain $h = 9$. Thus, the measure of the altitude $KL$ would be 9 inches.

**EXAMPLE 4**　　If the altitude of a given triangle is tripled and the base is cut to $\frac{1}{4}$ of the original measure, how will the area of the new triangle compare with the original?

**SOLUTION**　　If we express the area of the original triangle as

$$A_1 = \frac{1}{2} \cdot b \cdot h, \text{ or } A_1 = \frac{b \cdot h}{2},$$

we may express the area of the new triangle as

$$A_2 = \frac{1}{2} \cdot (\tfrac{1}{4}b) \cdot (3h)$$

$$\text{or, } A_2 = \frac{3b \cdot h}{8}.$$

Thus, no matter what measure $b$ stands for in the original triangle, $\frac{1}{4}b$ will represent $\frac{1}{4}$ of this measure. In like manner, no matter what measure $h$ represents, $3h$ will always represent three times this measure.

Now,

$$\frac{A_1}{A_2} = \frac{\dfrac{bh}{2}}{\dfrac{3bh}{8}} = \frac{8bh}{6bh} = \frac{8}{6} = \frac{4}{3}$$

Thus, the area of the first triangle is $\frac{4}{3}$ the area of the second, or the area of the second triangle is $\frac{3}{4}$ the area of the first.

The perimeter of any polygon may be determined by adding the measures of the sides. Thus, the perimeter of a rectangle is given by the formula

$$P = l + w + l + w$$

or, $P = 2(l + w)$, where $l$ and $w$ stand for the measures of the length and width of the rectangle.

The perimeter of a square becomes $P = s + s + s + s,$

or, $P = 4s$, ($s$ represents the measure of one of the sides.)

The perimeter of any triangle $ABC$, whose sides are $a$, $b$, $c$ is

$$P = a + b + c$$

It is easy to see that the area of a square is found by using the formula for the area of a rectangle. For the square, the length and width are the same, thus

$$A_{\text{square}} = s^2$$

where $s$ stands for the measure of one of its sides.

## EXERCISES

1. Rectangle 1 has the width of 5″ and length of 7″. Rectangle 2 has the width of 5″ and length of 14″. Compare the areas of the two rectangles.

2. How does the area of a rectangle change if its length is doubled while the width is left the same? Its width is doubled while the length is left the same? Work out your answers using the general formula.

3. How does the area of a rectangle change if its length is tripled while the width is left the same? Its width is tripled while the length is left the same?

4. How does the area of a rectangle change if its length and the width are both doubled? Both tripled?

5. If the measure of one side of a rectangle is multiplied by $n$, what change takes place in the area?

6. If the measure of both the width and length of a rectangle is multiplied by $n$, what change takes place in the area of the rectangle?

7. How does the area of a square change if we double each of its sides? How does the area change, if we triple each of its sides?

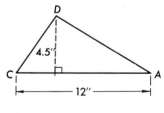

Ex. 8

8. Determine the area of triangle $ACD$.

9. *ABCD* and *FGHK* are rectangles. If the measure of *HG* is 4″ and the measure of *FG* is 7″, determine the area of the shaded region.

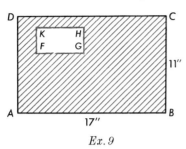

Ex. 9

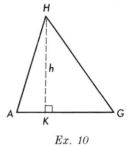

Ex. 10

10. If the area of triangle *AGH* is 72 sq. in. and the measure of *AG* is 12″, what is the measure of the altitude?

11. Determine the area of a square whose perimeter is 44″.

12. If the perimeter of triangle *GHK* is 144 in., find the measure of *HK*.

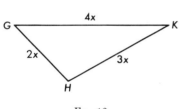

Ex. 12

Ex. 13

13. *ABGC* is a rectangle. If a triangular piece of the corner (*EGD*) is removed, what is the area of the remaining pentagon *ABDEC* if the measure of *DB* is 3″?

14. *ARST* is a rectangle. Determine the area of triangle *TSR*.

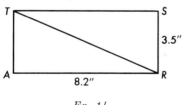

Ex. 14

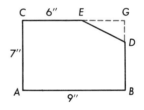

Ex. 15

15. If the area of the square *VTSR* is 84.6 sq. inches, determine the measure of *RS*.

16. The length of a rectangle is 3 times its width. If the measure of the perimeter of the rectangle is 114 in., determine the length and width.

**17.** If a rectangle is 13 inches long and 8 inches wide, what is the measure of the sides of a square of equal area.

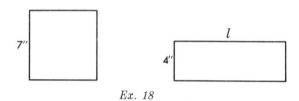

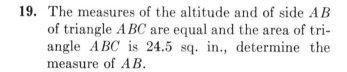

*Ex. 18*

**18.** If the areas of the square and the rectangle are equal, determine the measure of *l*.

**19.** The measures of the altitude and of side $AB$ of triangle $ABC$ are equal and the area of triangle $ABC$ is 24.5 sq. in., determine the measure of $AB$.

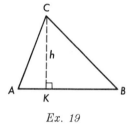

*Ex. 19*

## 13 · Formulas in Science

Mathematics has been instrumental in the development of our present age of science. We will concern ourselves in this section with some of the formulas which arise in various sciences. We will have neither space nor time to attempt explanation of all physical phenomena involved when using these formulas. Rather, we will be mainly concerned with the principles and manipulations which the scientist encounters when seeking answers to his problems.

We know water freezes at a temperature of 32° on the Fahrenheit scale, and it boils at 212° on the same scale. There is another important temperature scale in science called the Centigrade scale, on which the freezing point of water is 0° and the boiling point is 100°. It is necessary to be able to interchange temperature measurements from either of these scales to the other.

We let $F$ stand for the Fahrenheit reading and $C$ for the reading on the Centigrade scale. A formula which defines the relationship between these two scales is

$$F = 1.8C + 32$$

To verify this formula for the freezing point of water, we replace $C$ in the formula by 0.

$$F = 1.8 \times 0 + 32$$
$$F = 0 + 32$$
$$F = 32$$

Thus, the temperature of 0 degrees Centigrade is the same as 32 degrees Fahrenheit.

For the boiling point of water, we replace $C$ by 100.

$$F = 1.8 \times 100 + 32$$
$$F = 180 + 32$$
$$F = 212$$

Thus, the temperature of 100 degrees Centigrade is the same as 212 degrees Fahrenheit.

What Fahrenheit reading corresponds to the 25 degree Centigrade reading? To answer this, we replace $C$ by 25 in the formula.

$$F = 1.8(25) + 32$$
$$F = 45 + 32$$
$$F = 77; \text{ or } 25° \text{ } C \text{ corresponds to } 77° \text{ } F.$$

If we replace $F$ by 68, can we determine the value of $C$?

$$68 = 1.8 \text{ } C + 32$$
$$36 = 1.8 \text{ } C$$
$$C = \frac{36}{1.8}$$
$$C = 20; \text{ or } 68° \text{ } F \text{ is equivalent to } 20° \text{ } C.$$

Could we express $C$ in terms of $F$?

$$F = 1.8 \text{ } C + 32$$
$$F - 32 = 1.8 \text{ } C$$
$$\frac{F - 32}{1.8} = C$$
$$\text{or } C = \frac{F - 32}{1.8}$$

Justify each step on the basis of principles discussed earlier.

## EXERCISES

1. The formula for the specific heat of a substance is

$$S = \frac{H}{m(t_2 - t_1)}$$

   **a.** Given the following replacements:
   27 for $H$, 16 for $m$, 23 for $t_2$, and 19 for $t_1$; determine $S$.
   **b.** Determine the measure of $t_1$ for the following replacements:
   32 for $H$, 19 for $m$, .70 for $S$, 22 for $t_2$.
   **c.** Express $m$ in terms of the other variables.

2. The formula for distance traveled by a freely falling object is $d = \frac{1}{2} gt^2$

   Given the following replacements:
   32 for $g$, 6 for $t$, determine $d$.

3. The formula for electric current in a circuit of two cells connected in series is $I = \dfrac{2E}{R + 2r}$

   **a.** Given the following replacements:
   2.2 for $E$, 14 for $R$, and 7 for $r$; determine $I$.
   **b.** Determine $r$ for the following replacements:
   5 for $I$, 50 for $E$, and 2 for $R$.
   **c.** Express $R$ in terms of $I$, $E$, and $r$.
   **d.** Express $E$ in terms of $I$, $R$, and $r$.

4. The formula involving the effect of temperature and pressure on the volume of a confined gas is $\dfrac{P_1 V_1}{T_1} = \dfrac{P_2 V_2}{T_2}$

   **a.** If $P_1$ is replaced by 780, $T_1$ by 390, $P_2$ by 820, $V_2$ by 305, $T_2$ by 330, determine $V_1$.
   **b.** Solve for $T_1$ in terms of the other variables.
   **c.** Solve for $V_2$ in terms of the other variables.

5. The formula relating the density of an object to its weight and volume is $D = \dfrac{W}{V}$

   **a.** If $W$ is replaced by 13, $V$ by 6.5, determine $D$.
   **b.** If $D$ is replaced by 13.5, $W$ by 4.2, determine $V$.
   **c.** Express $V$ in terms of $D$ and $W$.

**6.** The formula for the resistance of two electrical conductors in parallel is

$$R = \frac{r_1 r_2}{r_1 + r_2}.$$

   **a.** If $r_1$ is replaced by 48, $r_2$ by 62, determine $R$.
   **b.** Express $r_1$ in terms of $r_2$ and $R$.

**7.** The formula relating the rate of flow of an electric current to the pressure and resistance is $I = \dfrac{E}{R}.$

   **a.** If $E$ is replaced by 110, $R$ by 20, determine $I$.
   **b.** If $R$ is replaced by 33, $I$ by 5, determine $E$.
   **c.** Express $R$ in terms of $I$ and $E$.

**8.** The formula for the energy of a moving object is $E = \dfrac{Wv^2}{2g}.$

   **a.** If $W$ is replaced by 11, $v$ by 52, $g$ by 32, determine $E$.
   **b.** Express $W$ in terms of the other variables.

**9.** The formula for greatest height attained by a body projected vertically upward is $h = \dfrac{v^2}{2g}.$

   **a.** If $v$ is replaced by 330, $g$ by 32, determine $h$.
   **b.** If $v$ is doubled, and $g$ remains the same, how will $h$ change?

**10.** The formula for the amount of heat developed from a current flowing through a wire is $H = \dfrac{Eit}{4.18}.$

   **a.** If $E$ is replaced by 210, $i$ by 15, $t$ by 25, determine $H$.
   **b.** Express $t$ in terms of $E$, $i$, and $H$.

**11.** The formula for the velocity of a liquid flowing through an opening is $v = \sqrt{2gh}.$
   If $g$ is replaced by 32, and $h$ by 2, determine $v$.

## 14 · Formulas in Business

Many problems encountered in business require an understanding of percentage. You recall that 2% is just another way of saying .02 or $\frac{2}{100}$ or $\frac{1}{50}$. Similarly, $\frac{6}{100}$ may be used interchangeably with 6%.

Suppose his employer deducts 6% of Mr. Jones's annual salary for a retirement fund. If the amount deducted is $348, can we determine Mr. Jones's annual salary?

We might reason that 6% of some number which is his salary is equal to 348. If we let $y$ stand for his salary, then

$$6\% \ y = 348$$
$$.06 \ y = 348$$
$$\tfrac{6}{100} \ y = 348$$
$$6 \ y = 34{,}800$$
$$y = 5800$$

Thus, we could conclude that Mr. Jones's annual salary is $5,800. If we replace $y$ with 5800 in $6\% \cdot y = 348$, a true statement is obtained:

$$6\% \cdot (5{,}800) = \tfrac{6}{100} \cdot (5800) = 348$$

Let us consider another business situation. Suppose the total cost of a lot and a new house is $16,000. If the cost of the lot is $3,200, what per cent of the total cost is the cost of the lot?

If we let $x$ be the per cent of total cost which was spent for the lot, we have

$$x \cdot 16000 = 3200$$
$$x = \tfrac{3200}{16000}$$
$$x = .20 = 20\%$$

Thus, the cost of the lot is 20% of the total cost.

When one borrows money from a bank, he pays a sum of money called interest for the privilege of using the bank's money. The amount paid for this privilege depends upon the amount borrowed, the length of time the money was needed, and the rate of interest. The amount borrowed is called the *principal*. The time is usually measured in years or fractions of a year. The rate of interest is expressed as a per cent. 6% annual interest would mean that one would pay $6 interest for using $100 of the bank's money for one year. The formula for this relationship is

$$i = p \, r \, t$$

where $i$ is interest, $p$ is principal, $r$ is the rate of interest, and $t$ is the time, in years.

When interest is determined on the basis of the original principal only, it is called simple interest.

**EXAMPLE**   Suppose Mr. Downs borrows $800. If the rate of interest is 5% and he repays the loan in 2 years, how much interest must he pay?

**SOLUTION**
$$i = p\,r\,t$$
$$i = (800) \times .05 \times 2$$
$$i = 80$$

Thus, Mr. Downs will pay $80 interest for using $800 for two years at 5% interest.

**EXAMPLE**
Mr. Jones borrowed $560 for 9 months. If the interest paid was $25.20, what was the rate of interest?

**SOLUTION**
$$i = p\,r\,t$$
If we solve for $r$ in terms of $i$, $p$, and $t$, we have

$$r = \frac{i}{p\,t}$$

Replacing the variables with their values gives us

$$r = \frac{25.20}{(560) \cdot \left(\frac{3}{4}\right)} = .06 \qquad \text{(9 months is } \tfrac{3}{4} \text{ of a year)}$$

Thus, the rate of interest paid was 6%.

## EXERCISES

Solve each problem:

1. A real estate salesman received a 5% commission for selling a house for $16,800. How much commission did he receive, and how much money did the house owner get?

2. An appliance salesman sells a record player for $145, making a profit of 15% on the sales price. How much did the record player cost the salesman originally?

3. If a house has an assessed valuation of $14,000 and the tax rate is $21 per $1000 of assessed valuation, how much tax will be paid on the property?

4. Mr. Smith invested money in two different businesses. One paid him 5% and the other paid him 7% on his investment. He invested $2,000 more in the business paying the higher rate than he did in the other business. If he received a total of $250 at the end of the year, how much did he have invested in each business?

5. The tax rate of a suburban area was 12 mills for every dollar assessed valuation. (A mill is $\frac{1}{10}$ of one cent). If Mr. J's assessed evaluation was $13,500, compute his tax.

6. A business man borrowed $1500, which he agreed to pay back with interest at $5\frac{1}{2}\%$. If we know that he paid $25 interest, determine how long he kept the money.

7. Mr. Enterprise borrowed $3300 for a period of 20 months at 5% interest. How much interest must he pay for the use of the money?

8. A rancher borrowed a sum of money for a period of 15 months. If he paid back $1800, which included the amount he borrowed in addition to his interest at 6%, how much money did he borrow?

9. A company developing a new shopping center borrowed $2,000,000 for a period of five years. If the interest paid was $550,000, determine the rate of interest.

10. How long will it take for a given amount of principal to double when invested at 4% simple interest?

## 15 · Equations in Two Variables

So far you have been studying equations with one variable. Now we shall consider equations with two variables. Let us take the following example:

$$x + 2y = 5$$

The variables in this equation are $x$ and $y$. In order to obtain meaningful sentences, we shall replace the variables $x$ and $y$ by numerals. We shall agree that the two variables may be replaced by names for the same number or for two different numbers.

We pick any number whatsoever for one variable, say $x$. Replacing $x$ by, say 1, we have

$$1 + 2y = 5$$

Solving for $y$,

$$1 + 2y = 5$$
$$2y = 4$$
$$y = 2$$

Thus 1 for $x$, 2 for $y$, gives us

$$1 + 2 \cdot 2 = 5$$

which is a true statement.

Now let us use $\frac{1}{2}$ for $x$.

$$\tfrac{1}{2} + 2y = 5$$
$$2y = 4\tfrac{1}{2}$$
$$y = 2\tfrac{1}{4}$$

$\frac{1}{2}$ for $x$ and $2\frac{1}{4}$ for $y$, gives us

$$\frac{1}{2} + 2 \cdot 2\frac{1}{4} = 5$$
$$\frac{1}{2} + 4\frac{1}{2} = 5$$

which also is a true statement.

Thus, the pairs

$$(1, 2); \text{ that is } 1 \text{ for } x, 2 \text{ for } y,$$
$$\text{and} \quad (\tfrac{1}{2}, 2\tfrac{1}{4}); \text{ that is } \tfrac{1}{2} \text{ for } x, 2\tfrac{1}{4} \text{ for } y$$

satisfy the equation $x + 2y = 5$.

There are many more number pairs which satisfy the equation above. Some of these are

$$(-1, 3); (4, \tfrac{1}{2}); (-2, 3\tfrac{1}{2}); (1.5, 1.75); (-4, 4\tfrac{1}{2})$$

Make appropriate replacements in the equation to see that each of these number pairs satisfies the equation. Keep in mind that the first number listed is for $x$, the second for $y$.

Find ten more number pairs which satisfy the equation. Given plenty of time, how many number pairs satisfying this equation would you be able to find?

## EXERCISES

Each equation below has two variables. For each equation, find five real number pairs each of which satisfies the equation.

1. $a + b = 7$
2. $3m - 4n = 2$
3. $\frac{1}{2}p + 3r = -4$
4. $1.7s - 3.6t = 1.5$
5. $3w = 2n + 4$
6. $3 - (2x + y) = 0$
7. $\dfrac{d - 2}{5} = \dfrac{u + 3}{4}$
8. $5(v + 6z) = \frac{1}{2}(3v + 9z)$
9. $|m + 2n| = 3$
10. $\frac{1}{2} \cdot |x + w| = \frac{1}{3} \cdot |x - w|$
11. $|x| - y = |x - y|$
12. $2a = 3 \cdot |b| - 1$

# VOCABULARY

altitude (206)
base (199)
binomial (176)
Equation Principle for Addition (EPA) (161)
Equation Principle for Multiplication (EPM) (164)
equivalent expressions (171)
false sentence (154)
if and only if (160)
interest (214)
isosceles triangle (199)
leg (199)
monomial (176)
open sentence (154)

ordered pair (219)
perimeter (207)
polynomial (176)
principal (214)
rate (214)
root (157)
satisfy an equation (157)
solution set (157)
solving an equation (157)
trinomial (176)
true sentence (154)
value of an expression (171)
vertices (206)

∙∙∙∙∙∙∙∙∙∙∙∙∙∙∙∙∙∙∙∙∙∙∙∙∙∙∙∙∙∙∙∙∙∙∙∙∙∙∙∙∙∙∙∙∙∙∙∙∙∙∙∙∙∙∙∙∙∙∙∙∙∙∙∙∙∙∙∙∙∙∙∙∙∙∙∙∙∙∙∙∙∙∙∙∙∙∙∙∙∙∙∙∙∙∙∙∙

# REVIEW EXERCISES

Classify each of the following sentences below into one of the following categories:

(1) True sentence
(2) False sentence
(3) Sentence which is neither true nor false but in which at least one replacement for the variable or variables, but not all, will result in a true sentence. Find at least one such replacement.
(4) Sentence which is neither true nor false and which has no replacement for the variable or variables which will result in a true sentence.
(5) Sentence which is neither true nor false and in which all replacements of the variables result in true sentences.

1. $16\% = \dfrac{4}{25}$

2. $|-4| = -4$

3. $x + 3 = -1$

4. $a^4 = 0$

5. $y(y + 1) = 0$

6. $x^3 - 1 = 0$

7. $2m - m = 5$

8. $|u| = u$

9. $\dfrac{4}{x} = 0$

10. $y + 1 = y + 2$

**11.** $\dfrac{u+3}{u} = 1$

**12.** $\dfrac{c}{c} = 1; \; (c \neq 0)$

**13.** $m + n = 3$

**14.** $2t + s = s$

**15.** $\dfrac{z+y}{z+y} = 2$

**16.** $3x - 2x = x$

**17.** $-2(m + t) + 2m + 2t = 0$

**18.** $\left|\dfrac{n}{n}\right| = 1; \; (n \neq 0)$

Solve each of the following equations:

**19.** $2x = 4$

**20.** $3y = 17$

**21.** $15z = 8$

**22.** $-4a = 9$

**23.** $-\dfrac{2}{3}c = -\dfrac{4}{5}$

**24.** $-1.6d = 7.8$

**25.** $3u + 5 = 1$

**26.** $x - 6 = 7$

**27.** $2w + 3 = 5$

**28.** $7 - 5m = .5$

**29.** $\dfrac{1}{2} + \dfrac{1}{3}v = 1$

**30.** $6 + 3h = -2$

**31.** $3n + 47 = -13$

**32.** $\dfrac{p+1}{2} = 2$

**33.** $2(x + 1) = 1$

**34.** $3y + 2(y + 2) = 4$

**35.** $7(z + 1) - 2(2z - 3) = 0$

**36.** $3(2t - 1) - 10(t + 13) = 12$

**37.** $-4(s - 5) + 2(3s + 6) = 10$

For each equation, give five pairs $(x, y)$ which satisfy it:

**38.** $x + y = 2$

**39.** $1 - y = 2x$

**40.** $\dfrac{x + 2y}{x} = 1$

**41.** $3(2x - y) = 2(x + y)$

**42.** $\dfrac{1}{2}(3x + 5y) = \dfrac{1}{3}(2x - 7y)$

**43.** $.3(6x - y) = .1(2x - 11y)$

The *ordered pairs* $(1, 2)$ and $(-1, -1)$ satisfy the equation $3x - 2y = -1$. Replace each of the variables below to obtain number pairs which also satisfy this equation:

**44.** $(2, y)$

**45.** $(x, -3)$

**46.** $(-4, y)$

**47.** $(x, 5)$

For each mathematical sentence, make up a story which fits it:

**EXAMPLE**     $(2t + 5) + t = 200$

**SOLUTION**     Mr. Jones and his son, Bob, weigh a total of 200 lbs. Mr. Jones weighs 5 lbs. more than twice Bob's weight.

**48.** $(5r - 6) - 2r = 30$

**49.** $(6y - 5) - y = 140$

**50.** $3x + (5x + 3) = 128$

**51.** $r + 5 > 12$

**52.** $2y - 3 < 14$

**53.** $3(x - 6) \leq 32$

Solve each problem:

1. A number added to three times that number is 8. What is the number?

2. The average of three consecutive odd numbers is 17. What are the three numbers? Do you see a quick way of telling the numbers? Can the average of three consecutive odd numbers be an even number? Why?

3. The average of three consecutive even numbers is 12. What are the three numbers? If the average is 102, what are the three numbers? Do you see a quick way of telling the numbers? Can the average of three consecutive even numbers be an odd number?

4. An article usually selling at $1.75 is put on sale at the reduction of 15% of the regular price. What is the reduced cost of the article?

5. An article sells at a certain price. After the reduction of 25% of the selling price, the article sold for $1.65. What was its original selling price?

6. The perimeter of a square is the same as the length of a rectangle. The width of the rectangle is one-fourth of the length of the side of the square. If the width of the rectangle is 2″, what is the area of the square? Of the rectangle?

## CHAPTER TEST

In Exercises 1–10 choose the correct answer:

1. Which of the following pairs of equations is a pair of equivalent equations?

   (a) $\dfrac{x + 3}{x + 2} = 5; 4x + 10 = 3$

   (b) $5 - x = 7; 2(x - 8) + 3(7 - x) = 7$

   (c) $-3 = \dfrac{-5}{x - 5}; x - 5 = \dfrac{5}{3}$

   (d) All of the above

   (e) None of the above

**2.** An equation whose solution set is $\left\{-\dfrac{8}{7}\right\}$ is

(a) $\dfrac{7}{8}y + 4 = 5$

(c) $-\dfrac{7}{8}y + 4 = -5$

(b) $\dfrac{8}{7}y + 5 = 4$

(d) $-\dfrac{7}{8}y - 4 = 5$

(e) None of the above

**3.** Which of the following sets is equivalent to $\left\{x\,\Big|\,\dfrac{4}{3}x + \dfrac{5}{6}x = 2\right\}$

(a) $\{x\,|\,4x + 5x = 36\}$

(c) $\{x\,|\,4x + 5x = 18\}$

(b) $\{x\,|\,x = 4\}$

(d) $\{x\,|\,8x + 5x = 6\}$

(e) None of the above

**4.** The solution set of the equation $|\,3r + 5\,| = 8$ is

(a) $\left\{\dfrac{13}{3},\,1\right\}$

(c) $\left\{1,\,-\dfrac{13}{3}\right\}$

(b) $\left\{\dfrac{3}{13},\,-1\right\}$

(d) $\phi$

(e) None of the above

**5.** The cost in dollars of 111 tickets, if $n$ of them are 75¢ tickets and the remainder are 90¢ tickets is

(a) $.90n + .75(n - 111)$

(c) $.90(111 - n) + .75n$

(b) $.75n + .90(n - 111)$

(d) $.75(111 - n) + .90n$

(e) None of the above

**6.** The age of a boy now, if 7 years ago he was two-thirds as old as his mother and his mother is now $t$ years of age, is given by the expression

(a) $\dfrac{2}{3}(t + 7) + 7$

(c) $\dfrac{3}{2}(7 + t) + 7$

(b) $\dfrac{3}{2}(t - 7) + 7$

(d) $\dfrac{2}{3}(t - 7) + 7$

(e) None of the above

**7.** The selling price of a house which sells at a profit of 16% of its cost $c$ is given by the expression

(a) $c + 16c$

(c) $c - .16c$

(b) $.16c + c$

(d) $.16(c + .16)$

(e) None of the above

8. If Jerry were three years younger, he would be two-thirds as old as Jim. Jim is 12 years older than Jerry. If we let $x$ stand for Jerry's age, which of the following open sentences would lead to a correct solution of the problem?

(a) $\frac{2}{3}(x - 3) = x + 9$

(c) $x - 3 = \frac{2}{3}(x + 12)$

(b) $\frac{2}{3}(x + 3) = x + 9$

(d) $x + 3 = \frac{2}{3}(x - 12)$

(e) None of the above

9. Which of the following sentences are true statements for every replacement of the variable?

(a) $(3r + 7) + (-9s) = (7 - 9s) + 3r$

(b) $\frac{4}{3}(r + 6) - 9t = \frac{4}{3}r + 8 - 12t$

(c) $x\left(y + \frac{2}{3}\right) = y\left(x + \frac{2}{3}\right)$

(d) $1.3x + .8 + 4.2y = 2(2.1y + .4 + 1.3x)$

(e) None of the above

10. If $2n$ and $2n + 2$ represent two consecutive even integers, their product is represented by

(a) $4n + 4$

(c) $4n^2 + 4n$

(b) $4n + 2$

(d) $2n + 4n^2$

(e) None of the above

11. Determine the solution set of the following equations, using the set of integers as the replacement set of the variable.

a. $4(3t - 5) - 3(2t + 1) = 2t + 1$

b. $\dfrac{5(x - 2)}{x} = 7$

c. $\dfrac{2(3 - r)}{r + 4} = -4$

12. Choose a letter in place of numeral and write an expression for each of the following:

a. Eleven less than one third of a number.

b. Seven more than the square of a number.

c. Difference of two numbers multiplied by their sum.

13. Mary has a total of eighty 4¢-stamps and 6¢-stamps, the total value of which is $4.04. How many stamps of each type does she have?

14. Two small planes leave cities 970 miles apart and travel toward each other. One plane's average speed is 40 miles per hour greater than that of the other plane. If they meet in two and one-half hours, determine the speed of each plane.

15. How much pure weed killer should be added to seven gallons of a 12% solution to produce an 18% solution?

16. If $x$ represents the tens digit and $y$ the units digit of a two-digit numeral, the value of every two-digit numeral can be represented as (choose the correct answer)

    (a) $y + x$                      (c) $yx$

    (b) $xy$                        (d) $10x + y$

                    (e) None of these

17. If $x = y$, then $rx = ry$ is always true only if (choose the correct answer)

    (a) $x$ and $y$ are integers.

    (b) $r \neq 0$.

    (c) $x \neq 0$ and $y \neq 0$.

    (d) $x$ and $y$ are rational numbers.

    (e) None of these.

18. For each of the following expressions, write an expression which is equivalent to it and which does not contain parentheses:

    a. $-3\left(x - \dfrac{4}{3}\right)$

    b. $(r - 2t + 5) \cdot (-4)$

19. For each step, state the principle which justifies it:

    a. $[r6 \cdot (-7)]t \overset{(1)}{=} [6r \cdot (-7)] \cdot t$

                  $\overset{(2)}{=} [6(-7) \cdot r] \cdot t$

                  $\overset{(3)}{=} (-42 \cdot r) \cdot t$

                  $\overset{(4)}{=} -42(rt)$

    b. $(r + t)(x + y) \overset{(1)}{=} (r + t) \cdot x + (r + t)y$

                    $\overset{(2)}{=} x \cdot (r + t) + y \cdot (r + t)$

                    $\overset{(3)}{=} xr + xt + yr + yt$

## CUMULATIVE REVIEW

Determine the elements of the following sets if the universal set is the set of real numbers:

1. $\left\{ t \mid 6 - \dfrac{3}{t} = \dfrac{5}{3t} \right\}$

2. $\left\{ x \mid \dfrac{7}{x} = \dfrac{2}{x-4} \right\}$

3. $\left\{ t \mid 6 = \dfrac{5+t}{-2t} \right\}$

4. $\left\{ x \mid -3 = \dfrac{-5}{x-5} \right\}$

5. $\{ x \mid \ |2x - 4| = 11 \}$

6. $\{ r \mid -7.6r + (-2.2) = 2.6 \}$

7. $\left\{ x \mid \dfrac{-3+x}{-2x} = 4 \right\}$

8. $\{ x \mid 5(x+3) - 4 = 16 \}$

9. $\{ x \mid 5(2x - 3) + 6 = 4(3 - x) \}$

10. $\{ x \mid 5x + (2 - 3x) = -19 \}$

11. $\{ x \mid x - (5 - x) + 7 = -11 \}$

12. $\{ t \mid 6t - 3(t - 4) - 6(7 - 5t) = 13 \}$

13. $\{ z \mid 7z - [11z + (-5)] = -14 \}$

14. $\left\{ y \mid \dfrac{5y}{3} - \dfrac{6+y}{4} = 11 \right\}$

15. $\{ y \mid 7(y - 2) + 3(y + 7) - 3(3 - y) = 0 \}$

16. $\{ y \mid -11 + 5(y - 5) = -19 \}$

17. $\left\{ x \mid \dfrac{7}{8}(x - 3) + \dfrac{5}{9}(4 - x) = -3 \right\}$

18. $\left\{ x \mid \dfrac{17x}{5} + \dfrac{3+x}{-5} = -2 \right\}$

19. $\left\{ x \mid \dfrac{5}{x+3} + \dfrac{-7}{3+x} = 11 \right\}$

20. $\left\{ x \mid \dfrac{x-6}{7-x} = -3 \right\}$

21. $\left\{ x \mid \dfrac{6}{3-x} = \dfrac{-7}{x-5} \right\}$

22. $\left\{ x \mid \dfrac{-6}{x-2} = \dfrac{1}{2-x} \right\}$

**23.** $\left\{ x \left| \dfrac{x}{3} - \dfrac{2x}{4} = \dfrac{5(x+3)}{6} \right. \right\}$

**24.** $\left\{ y \left| \dfrac{2y+3}{5} = \dfrac{7y-6}{-9} \right. \right\}$

**25.** $\left\{ r \left| \dfrac{r+(-7)}{-6} = \dfrac{-5+r}{2} \right. \right\}$

**26.** $\left\{ w \left| w - \dfrac{3}{4} = -\dfrac{5}{9} \right. \right\}$

**27.** $\left\{ x \left| \dfrac{7}{6} - 2x = -\dfrac{3}{5} \right. \right\}$

**28.** $\left\{ t \left| \dfrac{-9.4}{t} = -4.7 \right. \right\}$

**29.** $\left\{ r \left| \dfrac{3}{11}r = \dfrac{5}{7} \right. \right\}$

**30.** $\left\{ t \left| -\dfrac{8}{13} = \dfrac{7}{t} \right. \right\}$

**31.** $\left\{ x \left| -9.3 = \dfrac{x}{3.1} \right. \right\}$

True or false?

**32.** $-11 \not< 1$

**33.** $|-6| > 2$

**34.** $7 \neq -6$

**35.** $6 \leq 6$

**36.** $4 \leq |-5|$

**37.** $-6 \not> -5$

Replace the frames with natural number names to obtain true statements:

**38.** $\dfrac{4[(7+\triangle)+18]}{6} > 9$

**39.** $\dfrac{5(\square+6)}{3} \neq 6\square$

**40.** $11 \leq \dfrac{2}{3}(9+\bigcirc)$

**41.** Does every point on the number line have a rational number as its coordinate?

**42.** Is the set of negative numbers closed under addition and under multiplication?

**43.** If $B = \{0, 1, 2\}$ and $C = \{0, 1\}$, are these sets closed under the operations of addition and multiplication?

**44.** Explain what it means to have a one-to-one correspondence between two sets.

**45.** Let $U = \{a, b, c, d, f, g\}$; $A = \{a, b, d\}$;
$B = \{c, f, g\}$; $D = \{a, b, f, d, g\}$

Determine

    **a.** $A \cap B$

    **b.** $A \cup B$

★ **c.** $\overline{A}$

★ **d.** $A \cap \overline{B}$

    **e.** $B \cup D$

★ **f.** $\overline{A} \cup D$

    **g.** $B \subset D$ (True or false?)

    **h.** $A \subset D$ (True or false?)

Give the simplest numeral for the following:

**46.** $(-\frac{1}{3}) \cdot \{[(3)(-9) - 5(-3) + 1 \cdot 7] \div 2\}$

**47.** $7 + \{[(3) \cdot (-7) + (-4)] + [(-6) \cdot (-2) + 7]\}$

**48.** Is addition distributive with respect to multiplication? Explain.

**49.** For each step, state the principle justifying it:

**a.** $(-5) \cdot (1 - 6) + 5 \cdot (-6) \overset{(1)}{=} (-5) \cdot [1 + (-6)] + 5 \cdot (-6)$

$\overset{(2)}{=} (-5) \cdot 1 + (-5) \cdot (-6) + 5 \cdot (-6)$

$\overset{(3)}{=} (-5) + (-5) \cdot (-6) + 5 \cdot (-6)$

$\overset{(4)}{=} (-5) + (-6) \cdot (-5) + (-6) \cdot 5$

$\overset{(5)}{=} -5 + (-6)[(-5) + 5]$

$\overset{(6)}{=} -5 + (-6)[5 + (-5)]$

$\overset{(7)}{=} -5 + (-6) \cdot 0$

$\overset{(8)}{=} -5 + 0$

$\overset{(9)}{=} -5$

**b.** $\dfrac{r}{t} + \dfrac{x}{v} \overset{(1)}{=} \dfrac{rv}{tv} + \dfrac{xt}{vt}$

$\overset{(2)}{=} \dfrac{rv}{tv} + \dfrac{xt}{tv}$

$\overset{(3)}{=} rv \cdot \left(\dfrac{1}{tv}\right) + xt \cdot \left(\dfrac{1}{tv}\right)$

$\overset{(4)}{=} (rv + xt)\left(\dfrac{1}{tv}\right)$

$\overset{(5)}{=} \dfrac{rv + xt}{tv}$

**c.** $(y - x) + (x - y) \overset{(1)}{=} [y + (-x)] + [x + (-y)]$

$\overset{(2)}{=} [x + (-y)] + [y + (-x)]$

$\overset{(3)}{=} x + [(-y) + y] + (-x)$

$\overset{(4)}{=} x + [y + (-y)] + (-x)$

$\overset{(5)}{=} x + 0 + (-x)$

$\overset{(6)}{=} x + (-x)$

$\overset{(7)}{=} 0$

**50.** Describe the difference between rational and irrational numbers.

**51.** Compute the following to three decimal places.

    **a.** $\sqrt{7.78}$                          **b.** $\sqrt{79.66}$

**52.** Replace the frames with real number symbols to obtain true sentences:

    **a.** $\square + (-7) \leq -6$          **l.** $\square \div (-6) = 43$

    **b.** $\triangle - 7 > 11$             **m.** $(-9) \times (-6) = \triangle$

    **c.** $\dfrac{8}{\triangle - 11} \not> -6$         **n.** $\bigcirc \times (-5) = -13$

    **d.** $(-6)(5 + \triangle) \neq -2$      **o.** $\square - (-6) = -11$

    **e.** $5\bigcirc + 7 = -9$           **p.** $-7 \div \triangle = 38$

    **f.** $\dfrac{6[(-5) + \triangle]}{5} = -7$     **q.** $-14 \times 4 = \square$

    **g.** $3\triangle + (-9) = 13$        **r.** $7 \div \square = 0$

    **h.** $5 \cdot (-6) = 7 - 6\triangle$     **s.** $[6 + \square] + 13 = 13 + [\square + 6]$

    **i.** $\dfrac{-6}{7 + \triangle} = -5$        **t.** $6(\triangle + 3) = 6 \cdot (-4) + 6 \cdot (3)$

    **j.** $(-7) \times \square = 6$          **u.** $\dfrac{0}{9} = \triangle$

    **k.** $-7 - \triangle = 16$

**53.** Label each of the following as true or false:

    **a.** $-\left(-\dfrac{1}{3}\right)$ is the opposite of $-\left(\dfrac{1}{3}\right)$.

    **b.** $-\dfrac{2}{7}$ is the reciprocal of $\dfrac{7}{2}$.

    **c.** For every $x$ and $y$, $\dfrac{x}{y} \geq 0$ $(y \neq 0)$.

    **d.** For every $x$ and $y$, $xy \leq |x| \cdot |y|$.

    **e.** If $x < 0$ and $y < 0$, then $xy = -|x| \cdot |y|$.

    **f.** For every $x$ and $y$, $|x + y| \geq |x| - |y|$.

    **g.** If $x < 0$, then $|-x| = -x$.

    **h.** For every $x$ and $y$, $-y - x = -x - y$.

    **i.** If $y < 0$ and $x < 0$, then $\dfrac{x}{y} = \dfrac{|x|}{|y|}$.

    **j.** For every $x$ and $y$, $x + y = -[(-x) + y]$.

**54.** Is the set $\{\cdots, -6, -3, 0, 3, 6, 9, 12, \cdots\}$ closed under the operations of addition and multiplication?

**55.** For each of the following, derive an expression which is equivalent to it and which is in a simpler form.

    **a.** $d - 13d + 5c + (-7d) + (-5c)$

    **b.** $-11(y - 3z) + 5[z + (-5)] - 6$

    **c.** $-15 + 3(x - 5) + 15(2 - x) - 7[x + (-3)]$

    **d.** $(-z)(-3y)(5y)$

    **e.** $(-5x)(-2y)(-7)$

**56.** For each expression, write a single fractional expression equivalent to it:

    **a.** $\dfrac{\dfrac{x}{y} + 7}{\dfrac{7}{x}}$
                             **d.** $\dfrac{5}{z} \cdot \left(\dfrac{-2}{y}\right)$

    **b.** $\dfrac{s}{3} - \dfrac{t}{5}$
                                **e.** $\dfrac{x + r}{t} - \dfrac{y + r}{5}$

    **c.** $(16x + 3y) \div \dfrac{2}{y}$
                        **f.** $\dfrac{x - y}{3} + \dfrac{2x + y}{-3}$

**57.** There are 49 marbles in a box. If the number of red marbles is twice the number of white marbles, and the number of green marbles is twice the number of red marbles, how many marbles of each color are there in the box?

**58.** One-half of a number plus one-fourth of the number is 9. What is the number?

**59.** How many miles will Johnny travel on his bicycle in 4 hours and 10 minutes if his average speed is 10 mph?

**60.** The selling price of an article is $1.54. This price includes 10% markup computed on the basis of the cost. What is the cost of the article?

**61.** Joe is at present twice as old as his sister. In eight years he will be $1\frac{1}{2}$ times as old as she will be. Determine their present ages.

**62.** The sum of one-fifth of a number and two-thirds of the number is 36. What is the number?

    Give the simplest mathematical expression for each of the following statements:

**EXAMPLE**        What is the sum of any number $r$, and 7?

**SOLUTION**       $r + 7$

**63.** What is the product of any number $t$, and 11?

**64.** What is the quotient of any number $r$, and 6?

**65.** What is the difference between any number $x$, and 7?

**66.** What is the sum of any number $r$, and the number seven greater than $r$?

**67.** What is the sum of any number $t$, and twice $t$?

**68.** What is the difference of any number $s$ subtracted from a number 3 times $s$?

**69.** If $\triangle$ is any number, what is $\frac{1}{3}$ of that number?

**70.** If $r$ is any number, what is six more than twice this number?

**71.** If $t$ is any number, what is its reciprocal?

**72.** If $\triangle$ is any number, what is its opposite?

**73.** If $u$ is any number, what is the number which is 13 less than twice $u$?

**74.** If $r$ is any number, what is the difference between 4 times this number and this number increased by 6?.

**75.** If $t$ is any number, what is the product of five more than this number and sixteen?

## BIBLIOGRAPHY

Bakst, A., *Mathematics, Its Magic and Mastery*, Van Nostrand, Toronto, 1952, pages 186–208, "The Grammar of Algebra," pages 209–223, "Algebra, the Boss of Arithmetic."

Bakst, A., *Mathematical Puzzles and Pastimes*, Van Nostrand, Toronto, 1954, pages 56–69, "Mathematical Hands Across the Sea."

School Mathematics Study Group, *Mathematics for High School: First Course in Algebra (Revised Edition)*, SMSG, New Haven, Connecticut, 1960, pages 74–94.

School Mathematics Study Group, *Mathematics for Junior High School: Supplementary Units*, SMSG, New Haven, Connecticut, 1959, pages 89–112.

University of Illinois Committee on School Mathematics, *Unit 3*, "*Equations and Inequations*," UICSM, Urbana, Illinois, 1960.

# Systems of Equations and Inequalities

### 1 · More About Equations With Two Variables

At the end of the last unit, you learned that an equation of the form $Ax + By = C$ has many number pairs which satisfy it.

The equation $3x + 2y = 7$ is of such form. This equation is obtained from $Ax + By = C$ by replacing $A$ by 3, $B$ by 2, and $C$ by 7. Upon replacement of $A$, $B$, and $C$ by various numerals, we obtain many different equations.

If either $A$ or $B$ is replaced by 0, an equation is obtained which has one variable in it. For example,

$$0 \text{ for } A, \ -5 \text{ for } B, \text{ and } 6 \text{ for } C \text{ yields}$$
$$-5y = 6$$
$$1 \text{ for } A, \ 0 \text{ for } B, \text{ and } 0 \text{ for } C \text{ yields}$$
$$x = 0$$

The set of replacements which does not result in an equation with at least one variable is

$$0 \text{ for } A \text{ and } 0 \text{ for } B.$$

What is the result of such replacement? What can you tell about the resulting equation?

An equation with two variables is not always in the form $Ax + By = C$. For example, the equation $2y = 3(x - 5) + 12 - 5y$ is *not* in this form. We can find, however, an equation which is equivalent to the above and which is of the form $Ax + By = C$. Study the way it is done below and state the principle involved at each step.

230

**EXAMPLE**

$$2y = 3x - 15 + 12 + [-(5y)]$$
$$2y + 5y = 3x - 3 + [-(5y)] + 5y$$
$$7y = 3x - 3$$
$$7y + [-(3x)] = 3x - 3 + [-(3x)]$$
$$7y + [-(3x)] = 3x + [-(3x)] - 3$$
$$-3x + 7y = -3$$
$$(-1)(-3x + 7y) = (-1)(-3)$$
$$3x - 7y = 3$$

In the development above, we have written each step in great detail. With some practice, you will be able to "skip" some steps. You should not be too hasty in skipping steps, however, especially when you are not sure of yourself.

The last equation, $3x + (-7)y = 3$, is of the form

$$Ax + By = C$$

where $A$ is replaced by 3, $B$ by $-7$, and $C$ by 3. We shall call this form *the standard form of a linear equation in two variables.*

The equation $3x - 7y = 3$ is, of course, equivalent to $3x + (-7y) = 3$.

## EXERCISES

For each equation below, find an equivalent equation in standard form. At each point, you should be prepared to justify what you do by the appropriate basic principle.

In the sample, not every step is shown. If you are unsure of any of the steps, fill in the intermediate steps.

**EXAMPLE**        $$3 - 7y + 3x = 6(x - y) + 3y$$

**SOLUTION**

$$3 - 7y + 3x = 6(x - y) + 3y$$
$$3 - 7y + 3x = 6x - 6y + 3y$$
$$3 - 7y + 3x = 6x - 3y$$
$$3 - 7y + 3x - 6x = 6x - 3y - 6x$$
$$3 - 7y - 3x = -3y$$
$$3 - 7y - 3x + 3y = -3y + 3y$$
$$3 - 4y - 3x = 0$$
$$3 - 4y - 3x - 3 = 0 - 3$$
$$-4y - 3x = -3$$
$$-3x + (-4)y = -3$$

1. $x = y + 7$
2. $2x = -3 - 8y$
3. $-5(x + y) = 17$
4. $3x = 2(y + 6)$
5. $-5(2x + y) = -3(x - 2)$
6. $-10(x - 3y) = 2y - 3x + 6$
7. $6(y - 6x) + 17 = 13 - 4(x + 10y)$
8. $\dfrac{y - x}{y + x} = 3$
9. $\dfrac{2x - 3}{3y + 7} = -9$
10. $\dfrac{3}{5} = \dfrac{6x - y + 15}{3x + 7y - 1}$

## 2 · Inequalities

You will recall from Chapter 4 that an open sentence like $x > 5$ is called an inequality. It is read "$x$ is greater than 5." The sentence "$5 < x$" means the same as the previous sentence. It is read "5 is less than $x$."

The sentence "$x \not< 5$" is read "$x$ is not less than 5," which, of course, means that $x$ is either 5 or greater than 5. What is the meaning of $x \not> 5$?

Inequalities, like equations, have *solution sets*. Solution sets of inequalities are sets of those numbers which satisfy the inequalities. For example, in the system of real numbers, the solution set of the inequality $x > 5$ is the set of all numbers greater than 5. If we call this set $A$, we will write

$$A = \{x \mid x > 5\}$$

which is read "$A$ is the set of all $x$ such that $x$ is greater than 5."

At the beginning of this course, you learned to establish a one-to-one correspondence between numbers and points on a number line. Using the number line, we can locate points which correspond to the numbers which make up the solution set $A = \{x \mid x > 5\}$. On the graph below, this set is pictured by the part of the number line marked with a heavy line.

$$A = \{x \mid x > 5\}$$

You should notice, however, how we have shown that the point corresponding to the number 5 does not belong to the set. How would you write an inequality to include the point with the coordinate 5 in its solution set? Here is another inequality and its graph:

$$-5 \leq m < 3$$

It is read "$m$ is less than three *and* greater than or equal to negative five."

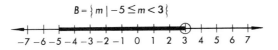

$$B = \{m \,|\, -5 \leq m < 3\}$$

The set $B$ is a set of numbers satisfying the inequality $-5 \leq m < 3$. The sentence "$-5 \leq m < 3$" means the same as "$m \geq -5$ *and* $m < 3$." The graph of this set is a set of points making up a line segment with one end point missing. Notice that one end point belongs to the line segment (which?) and the other does not (which?). Explain why one point is a part of the graph of the solution set and the other is not.

# EXERCISES

1. Write out in words the description of each set listed below. Graph the solution set and describe the graph in words. Assume in each case that the numbers are chosen from the set of real numbers.

**EXAMPLE** $A = \{n \,|\, 0 \leq n \leq 1\}$

**SOLUTION** (1) $A$ is a set of numbers $n$, where $n$ is less than or equal to one and is greater than or equal to zero.

(2)

$$A = \{n \,|\, 0 \leq n \leq 1\}$$

(3) The graph is a line segment.

**a.** $B = \{p \,|\, p > -3\}$

**b.** $R = \{a \,|\, a < 0\}$

**c.** $M = \{s \,|\, s \geq 3\}$

**d.** $X = \{b \,|\, b \leq -1\}$

**e.** $Y = \{t \,|\, -2 < t < 3\}$

**f.** $C = \{r \,|\, -\frac{1}{2} \leq r < \frac{1}{2}\}$

**g.** $T = \{u \,|\, 1 \leq u \leq 2.3\}$

**h.** $V = \{w \,|\, w \neq 0\}$

**i.** $G = \{c \,|\, c \neq -2 \text{ and } c \leq \frac{4}{5}\}$

**j.** $W = \{m \,|\, m < 5 \text{ or } m > 7\}$

**k.** $J = \{x \,|\, -1 \leq x \leq 1 \text{ and } x \leq \frac{1}{2}\}$

**l.** $S = \{d \,|\, -1 \leq d \leq 1 \text{ or } d \leq \frac{1}{2}\}$

2. Graph the following sentences and tell which ones have the null set as their solution set. (Assume that the replacement set is the set of real numbers.)

**EXAMPLE 1**    $B = \{a \,|\, a < -1 \text{ and } a > \frac{1}{2}\}$

**SOLUTION**    Graphing,

We observe that the graphs of $\{a \,|\, a < -1\}$ and $\{a \,|\, a > \frac{1}{2}\}$ have no points in common; therefore the solution set is the null set. Thus,

$B = \{a \,|\, a < -1 \text{ and } a > \frac{1}{2}\} = \phi$

This can also be written as

$B = \{a \,|\, a < -1\} \cap \{a \,|\, a > \frac{1}{2}\} = \phi$

**EXAMPLE 2**    $R = \{s \,|\, s \geq 3 \text{ and } s < 4\frac{1}{2}\}$

**SOLUTION**    Graphing,

We see that there are points common to both parts of the graph. Therefore the solution set is not the null set. Thus,

$R = \{s \,|\, s \geq 3 \text{ and } s < 4\frac{1}{2}\} \neq \phi$

This can also be written as

$R = \{s \,|\, s \geq 3\} \cap \{s \,|\, s < 4\frac{1}{2}\} \neq \phi$

a. $A = \{x \,|\, x > 5 \text{ and } x < -1\}$
b. $M = \{a \,|\, a \leq -1\} \cap \{a \,|\, a \geq -1\}$
c. $P = \{n \,|\, n > -5 \text{ or } n < -5\}$
d. $E = \{c \,|\, c \leq 6 \text{ or } c \geq 6\}$
e. $X = \{s \,|\, \frac{1}{2} < s < 0\}$
f. $C = \{g \,|\, -1 < g < -2\}$
g. $D = \{r \,|\, r < 2 \text{ or } r < -3\}$

3. Frequently we do not choose the solution sets from the real numbers. The members of the solution sets may belong to the set of natural numbers, the set of integers, or to the set of rational numbers.

**EXAMPLE 1**

$T = \{x \mid x \; \epsilon \; \text{Integers}, \; -2 < x < 3\}$
is read
"the set of elements $x$ such that $x$ is an element of the set of integers *and* $x$ is less than 3 and greater than $-2$."

**SOLUTION**

If we graph on the "number line" the points which we associate with these numbers, we have

(Note that for integers, the "number line" consists of points which are not connected.)

**EXAMPLE 2**

However, if the set $R = \{w \mid w \; \epsilon \; \text{Real numbers and} \; -2 < x < 3\}$ is graphed on the number line, we have

Write out in words the description of each set listed below. Graph the solution set and describe the graph in words.

   **a.** $T = \{s \mid s \; \epsilon \; \text{Integers}, \; s > 9 \text{ or } s < 13\}$
   **b.** $G = \{x \mid x \; \epsilon \; \text{Naturals}, \; 6 < x < 9\}$
   **c.** $H = \{r \mid r \; \epsilon \; \text{Reals}, \; r < 3.5 \text{ and } r > 2.5\}$
   **d.** $J = \{t \mid t \; \epsilon \; \text{Integers}, \; -3 \le t \le 5\}$
   **e.** $C = \{y \mid y \; \epsilon \; \text{Reals}, \; -2.5 < y < 1 \text{ or } y > 5\}$
   **f.** $K = \{z \mid z \; \epsilon \; \text{Naturals}, \; z \not> 8\}$
   **g.** $L = \{x \mid x \; \epsilon \; \text{Reals}, \; x > 2\frac{1}{2} \text{ and } x \ne 4\}$
   **h.** $M = \{p \mid p \; \epsilon \; \text{Integers}, \; -7 < p < -5\}$

## 3 · The Coordinate Plane and Ordered Number Pairs

You have already seen that an equation of the form $Ax + By = C$ has many number pairs which satisfy it. For example, in the system of real numbers, each of the number pairs $(1, 1)$, $(7, 5)$, $(-\frac{1}{2}, 0)$, $(-6, -\frac{11}{3})$, $(0, \frac{1}{3})$ satisfies the equation

$$2x - 3y = -1.$$

You will recall that, at the beginning of this course, we examined a one-to-one correspondence between numbers and points on the number-line. Now we shall examine a one-to-one correspondence between real *number pairs* and the *points in the plane*.

To do this, we take two number lines—it is customary to take one horizontal and one vertical line—that cross each other at their zero points. The point where the lines meet is called the *origin*. The surface on which the points are located is called a *plane*.

Now we can assign to each point a number pair and to each number pair we can assign a point. It is the usual practice to assign number pairs as in the diagram. The first number in the number pair is sometimes called the "first component," and the second number, the "second component"; together they are known as "coordinates." We are now ready to make an agreement by which a one-to-one correspondence between number pairs and points will be established.

Consider the number pair (4, 2). To find the point corresponding to this pair, we shall agree that the first number tells us the number of units we are to move from the origin to the right or to the left—positive number, to the right; negative number, to the left. The second number, then, tells us how many units to move up or down—positive number, up; negative number, down.

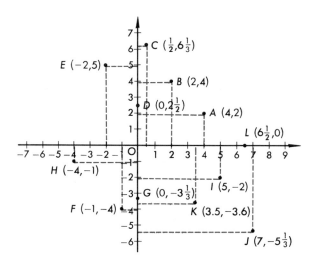

Thus, (4, 2) means move 4 units to the right, 2 units up. The point thus obtained is the point $A$ in the diagram. Do you see that there is only *one* point corresponding to the number pair (4, 2)?

Examine the figure to see how the points corresponding to the following number pairs were located:

$(2, 4)$; $(\frac{1}{2}, 6\frac{1}{3})$; $(0, 2\frac{1}{2})$; $(-2, 5)$;
$(-1, -4)$; $(0, -3\frac{1}{3})$; $(-4, -1)$; $(5, -2)$; $(7, -5\frac{1}{3})$;
$(3.5, -3.6)$; $(6\frac{1}{2}, 0)$.

What are the coordinates of the origin?

If we should agree that the form of the number pair names is $(x, y)$, then we could refer to the horizontal line by the name "$x$-axis," and to the vertical line by the name "$y$-axis."

Each real number pair has exactly one point corresponding to it. The numbers in the pair are the **coordinates** of that point. The first number is called the **first coordinate** or **abscissa** and the second number is called the **second coordinate** or **ordinate.**

For example, in the number pair $(4, 2)$, 4 is the abscissa of the point corresponding to $(4, 2)$ and 2 is the ordinate of that point. Abscissa is sometimes called $x$-coordinate, and ordinate, $y$-coordinate.

It is important to note that the numbers in a number pair cannot be interchanged. For example, do you see that $(4, 2)$ and $(2, 4)$ are two different number pairs, and that there are two different points corresponding to them? We call such number pairs **ordered number pairs.** Thus in $(4, 2)$, 4 is the first number, and 2 is the second number. In $(2, 4)$, 2 is the first number, and 4 is the second number, and, $(4, 2) \neq (2, 4)$.

The plane in which we locate points corresponding to given ordered number pairs is called "the coordinate plane" or "the Cartesian plane," after the name of the French mathematician Descartes who first introduced the idea. The two axes superimposed upon the plane are referred to as the rectangular coordinate system.

How would you convince someone that there is exactly *one* point corresponding to a given ordered number pair, and that there is exactly *one* ordered pair corresponding to a given point in a coordinate plane?

## EXERCISES

1. Make a coordinate system on a sheet of paper and locate points corresponding to the following ordered number pairs. Label points as in the diagram above.

   **a.** $(4, 1)$  
   **b.** $(1, 4)$  
   **c.** $(3\frac{1}{2}, 3\frac{1}{2})$  
   **d.** $(0, 7)$  
   **e.** $(-1, 2)$  
   **f.** $(0, 0)$  

   **g.** $(-3\frac{1}{2}, -4)$  
   **h.** $(0, -1\frac{1}{2})$  
   **i.** $(2.2, -4.5)$  
   **j.** $(6, 0)$  
   **k.** $(-7\frac{1}{2}, 0)$  
   **l.** $(0, -3.1)$

2. In the coordinate system below, the points are named by capital letters of our alphabet. List each letter on your paper, and next to it write the name of the number pair corresponding to the point. (The exercise is done for point *A*.)

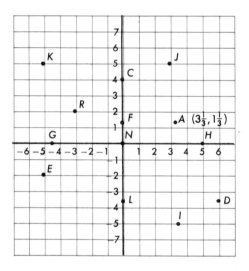

3. You have probably observed that the two axes of the rectangular coordinate system divide the plane into four parts. It is customary to name these parts as below:

|                    |                   |
|--------------------|-------------------|
| Second Quadrant    | First Quadrant    |
| Third Quadrant     | Fourth Quadrant   |

Thus, we can say that the point corresponding to the ordered number pair (1, 175), for example, belongs to the first quadrant. The points *on* the *x*-axis, or *on* the *y*-axis do *not* belong to any quadrant.

Tell to which quadrant each of the points corresponding to the ordered number pairs below belongs:

**a.** $(-16, -137)$  
**b.** $(1007, -2)$  
**c.** $(10, 1000)$  
**d.** $(-.007, 137.99)$  
**e.** $(\frac{13}{29}, -.003)$  
**f.** $(-111, -3)$  
**g.** $(-37, -678)$  
**h.** $(-\frac{1}{3}, 99)$  
**i.** $(127, 12)$  

**j.** $(-13, 13)$  
**k.** $(13, -13)$  
**l.** $(-128, 378)$  
**m.** $(-998, 998)$  
**n.** $(1027, -368)$  
**o.** $(11, -11)$  
**p.** $(2006, 2006)$  
**q.** $(|-17|, |-1389|)$  
**r.** $(|\frac{1}{2}|, |-\frac{1}{2}|)$  

**4.** Examine your answers in Exercise 3. What can you tell about the coordinates of points in the first quadrant? In the second quadrant? In the third quadrant? In the fourth quadrant?

**5.** What can you tell about the coordinates of the points on the $x$-axis? On the $y$-axis?

**6.** Describe each of the resulting sets: (Use diagram at the right.)

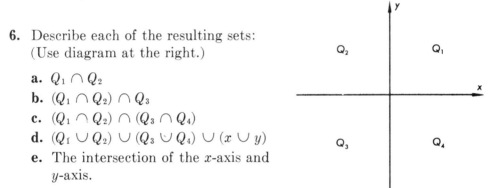

**a.** $Q_1 \cap Q_2$  
**b.** $(Q_1 \cap Q_2) \cap Q_3$  
**c.** $(Q_1 \cap Q_2) \cap (Q_3 \cap Q_4)$  
**d.** $(Q_1 \cup Q_2) \cup (Q_3 \cup Q_4) \cup (x \cup y)$  
**e.** The intersection of the $x$-axis and $y$-axis.

## 4 · Graphs of Linear Equations in Two Variables

You have seen that an equation of the form

$$Ax + By = C$$

where $A$, $B$, and $C$ may have as replacements the real number names ($A$ and $B$ are not both 0) has many number pairs which satisfy it. Now you also know that to each ordered number pair there corresponds exactly one point in a coordinate plane. The points are *graphs* of the ordered number pairs.

Let us consider the following equation:

$$2x + 5y = -3$$

Its solution set can be described as $\{(x, y) \mid 2x + 5y = -3\}$. This is read "the set of all ordered number pairs $x$ and $y$ for which $2x + 5y = 3$." Here are some ordered number pairs $(x, y)$ which satisfy this equation:

$$(1, -1); (-4, 1); (0, -\tfrac{3}{5}); (11, -5); (3.5, -2); (6, -3).$$

Let us locate the graphs of these number pairs on the coordinate system below:

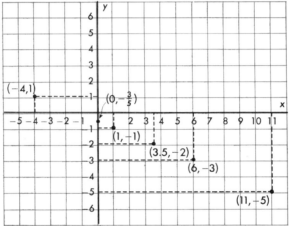

If you try to fit an edge of a ruler to these points, you will notice that they line up pretty well along the edge. As a matter of fact, later in your study of mathematics you will be able to prove that the graph of the equation $2x + 5y = -3$ is a straight line. Moreover, you will be able to prove that the graph of any equation of the form $Ax + By = C$, where the replacement set of $A$, $B$, and $C$ is the set of real numbers ($A$ and $B$ not both 0) is a straight line. For now, we will *assume* that it is so. In fact, let us agree to accept the following pair of principles concerning straight lines:

**Line Principle 1.** In the system of real numbers the graph of every equation of the form $Ax + By = C$ is a straight line.

**Line Principle 2.** There is only one straight line which passes through two given points.

According to Line Principle 1, the graph of the equation $2x + 5y = -3$ is a straight line.

According to Line Principle 2, we need to locate only two points whose coordinates satisfy the equation $2x + 5y = -3$ in order to locate the graph of this equation.

## EXERCISES

Graph the following sets. Use the set of real numbers as the replacement set for both $x$ and $y$.

**1.** $\{(x, y) \mid x + y = 6\}$

**2.** $\{(x, y) \mid 2x + 3y = -2\}$

**3.** $\{(x, y) \mid 4x - 5y = 10\}$

**4.** $\{(x, y) \mid x = y + 1\}$

**5.** $\{(x, y) \mid 3x = 4 - 7y\}$

**6.** $\{(x, y) \mid 5(x + 3) = 2(y - 1)\}$

**7.** $\{(x, y) \mid -2(3 - 2x) = 3(1 + 3y)\}$

**8.** $\{(x, y) \mid -6x + 4 = -11y\}$

**9.** $\left\{(x, y) \mid \dfrac{x}{3} + y = -5\right\}$

**10.** $\left\{(x, y) \mid 5 + \dfrac{4}{3}x = -7y\right\}$

**11.** $\{(x, y) \mid -4y + 3x = 7\}$

**12.** $\{(x, y) \mid 2x - 5 = -13y\}$

## 5 · Solving Systems of Equations by Graphing

In the previous section you learned to graph a linear equation in two variables. Since the graph of such an equation is a straight line and since two points determine a line, you needed to determine only two number pairs which satisfy the equation. The two points corresponding to these number pairs determine the line.

Let us consider the equation:

$$3x - 4y = 12$$

In order to find real number pairs satisfying the equation, let us first replace $x$ by 0.

$$3 \cdot 0 - 4y = 12$$
$$-4y = 12$$
$$y = -3$$

Thus, $(0, -3)$ should be one pair which satisfies the equation. To check,

$$3 \cdot 0 - 4(-3) = 0 - (-12)$$
$$- 12$$

so we know that $(0, -3)$ does, in fact, satisfy the equation.

Now let us replace $y$ by 0.

$$3x - 4 \cdot 0 = 12$$
$$3x = 12$$
$$x = 4$$

Thus, (4, 0) should be another pair which satisfies the equation. To check,

$$3 \cdot 4 - 4 \cdot 0 = 12 - 0$$
$$= 12$$

Let us locate points corresponding to the ordered number pairs $(0, -3)$ and (4, 0) and draw a picture of the line through them. This line is the graph of the equation $3x - 4y = 12$.

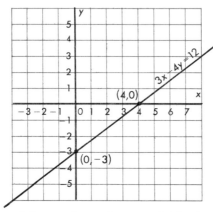

The distance from the origin to the point at which the line cuts an axis is called an *intercept*. Thus the distance from the origin to (4, 0) on the graph of $3x - 4y = 12$ is the *x-intercept* and the distance from the origin to $(0, -3)$ is the *y-intercept*.

It is sometimes convenient to locate the intercepts than to find any other two points. The two intercepts, of course, determine a line except under one special set of conditions. (What are these conditions?)

We can follow this procedure because every number pair that satisfies the equation names a point on its graph *and* every point on the graph has coordinates that satisfy the equation.

Now we are ready to consider two linear equations in two variables, taken together. Each of these equations has a straight line for its graph. Thus, the graph of the two equations consists of two straight lines; and two straight lines in the same plane either intersect in one point or do not intersect at all, or else the lines are not distinct. In the last case we have two equivalent equations; that is, two equations for the same line. What do we call two lines which do not intersect?

Consider the following system of two linear equations in two variables:

$$-x + 2y = 5$$
$$3x - 2y = -13$$

Below are graphs of these two equations. Examine the graphs to see how they were obtained.

From the graph we find that the coordinates of the point in which the two lines intersect are $(-4, \frac{1}{2})$. Since this point is on both lines, its coordinates must satisfy both equations; that is, since this number pair is a member of each set of number pairs specified by the equations, it is an element of their intersection—and we know the lines can intersect in no more than one point.

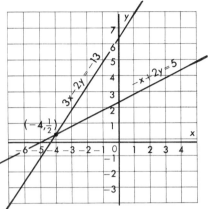

Let us check.

In the first equation:

$$-4 \text{ for } x; \tfrac{1}{2} \text{ for } y$$
$$-(-4) + 2 \cdot \tfrac{1}{2} = 4 + 1$$
$$= 5$$

Therefore $(-4, \frac{1}{2})$ checks the first equation.

In the second equation:

$$-4 \text{ for } x; \tfrac{1}{2} \text{ for } y$$
$$3(-4) - 2 \cdot \tfrac{1}{2} = -12 - 1$$
$$= -13$$

Therefore $(-4, \frac{1}{2})$ checks the second equation.

Thus we have a way of finding the number pair which satisfies two equations in two variables. The set $\{(-4, \frac{1}{2})\}$ is the solution set of the system.

## EXERCISES

For each pair of equations below, do the following:

(1) Graph the solution set of each equation.

(2) List the coordinates of the point of intersection of the two graphs as an ordered pair of real numbers.

(3) Check to see whether the coordinates of the point of intersection satisfy both equations in the pair.

**EXAMPLE**

$$2x + y = -4$$
$$3y = 5x - 1$$

**SOLUTION** (1) Two ordered pairs satisfying the first equation:
$(0, -4)$; $(-5, 6)$
Two ordered pairs satisfying the second equation:
$(2, 3)$; $(-4, -7)$

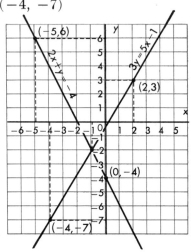

(2) $(-1, -2)$

(3) Check:

$$-1 \text{ for } x; \; -2 \text{ for } y$$

$$
\begin{array}{ll}
2(-1) + (-2) = -2 + (-2) & \qquad 3y \;\big|\; 5x - 1 \\
\qquad\qquad\quad = -4 & = 3(-2) \;\big|= 5(-1) - 1 \\
& = -6 \;\big|= -5 - 1 = -6
\end{array}
$$

**1.** $x + y = 4$
$2x - y = 2$

**2.** $3x + 2y = 10$
$-x + 6y = 0$

**3.** $3x - y = -1$
$x - 2y = 8$

**4.** $2x = 2y + 1$
$x + 2y = 8$

**5.** $7y = x - 4$
$x = y - 10$

**6.** $-2 - 3x = 4y$
$y = -x$

**7.** $y = x - 1$
$2y = 2x + 2$

**8.** $6x = 2y - 7$
$2y = 13x$

**9.** $x = y$
$y = -x$

**10.** $x = 0$
$x = y$

**11.** $y = 0$
$x = -y$

**12.** $-x = -y$
$x = -2$

**13.** $x = 4$
$y = -2$

## 6 · More About Graphing Equations

In the previous section, you learned to find the coordinates of a point common to two straight lines. The two lines were graphs of two linear equations each in two variables. You found that the coordinates of the common point satisfied both equations. The ordered number pair corresponding to the common point was the solution set of the given system of equations. In each case, the equations that you were asked to graph were selected so that their graphs had a common point.

Consider now the following system of two equations in two variables:

$$2x + y = -1$$
$$2y = -2 - 4x$$

Let us find two ordered number pairs which satisfy the first equation and two pairs which satisfy the second equation.

First equation:  $(-1, 1)$; $(4, -9)$
Second equation:  $(1, -3)$; $(-3, 5)$

Examine the following graph:

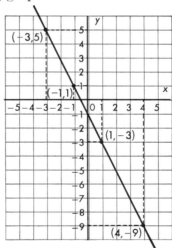

From the graph, you observe that each of the pairs of points determines the same line. That is, both equations are equations for the same line. Let us examine more closely the two equations:

$$2x + y = -1$$
$$2y = -2 - 4x$$

We shall use equation principles to attempt to get the second equation from the first. In doing this, we shall not fill in all of the steps. If you are not certain about any of the steps, you should fill in the details for yourself.

$$2x + y = -1$$
$$2x + y - 2x = -1 - 2x$$
$$y = -1 - 2x$$
$$2y = 2(-1 - 2x)$$
$$2y = -2 - 4x$$

Thus we see that the two original equations are equivalent and their graphs are the same line. Check a few ordered pairs to convince yourself that every pair of numbers which satisfies the first equation also satisfies the second equation. Such a pair of equations is frequently called *a dependent system of two linear equations in two variables.*

Now consider the following pair of equations:

$$x + 2y = 3$$
$$2x + 4y = -2$$

The first equation is satisfied, say, by

$$(-1, 2) \text{ and } (5, -1)$$

The second equation is satisfied, say, by

$$(1, -1) \text{ and } (-1, 0)$$

Study the graph below.

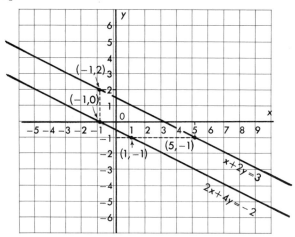

From the graph it appears that the two lines will not meet. They are therefore parallel lines. Parallel lines are lines in the same plane which do not meet no matter how far extended. In that case there would be no intersection point. If it is true that the two lines have no common point, then it should be true that there is no number pair which satisfies both equations.

It can be easily seen that the equation

$$x + 2y = -1$$

is equivalent to the equation $2x + 4y = -2$, which is our second equation. Therefore, we can use the pair of equations

$$x + 2y = 3$$
$$x + 2y = -1$$

in place of the original pair. But we see that in this pair of equations we want $x + 2y$ to yield 3 and $-1$ for the same replacements of $x$ and $y$. This is not possible.

We can conclude, then, that the equations

$$x + 2y = 3$$
$$2x + 4y = -2$$

have no common solutions. Such a pair of equations is frequently called *an inconsistent system of two linear equations in two variables.*

A pair of linear equations in two variables having exactly one number pair satisfying both equations is frequently called *an independent, or a simultaneous system of two linear equations in two variables.*

## EXERCISES

**1.** For each pair of equations below, do the following:

(1) Graph the solution set of each equation.

(2) Tell whether the system is independent, dependent, or inconsistent.

(3) Determine the solution set, and check, if the system is a simultaneous system; or use equation principles to convince yourself that the system is a dependent or inconsistent system.

**EXAMPLE 1**     $x + 2y = -1$
$2x + 4y = 4$

**SOLUTION**     (1)    $x + 2y = -1$          $(1, -1); (-3, 1)$
$2x + 4y = 4$          $(2, 0); (-4, 3)$

(2)   The lines as graphed on page 248 appear parallel.

In that case, the two equations will be inconsistent.

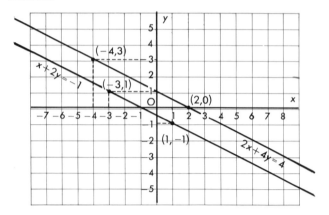

(3)   Let us take the second equation and obtain an equation equivalent to it.

$$2x + 4y = 4$$
$$\tfrac{1}{2}(2x + 4y) = \tfrac{1}{2} \times 4$$
$$x + 2y = 2$$

Thus, we now have the pair of equations

$$x + 2y = -1$$
$$x + 2y = 2$$

There are no ordered pairs of numbers which will satisfy both of these equations, since they lead to the conclusion that $-1 = 2$. Therefore, this system of equations is an inconsistent system.

Since the equation $x + 2y = 2$ is equivalent to the equation $2x + 4y = 4$ we can conclude that the original system

$$x + 2y = -1$$
$$2x + 4y = 4$$

is an inconsistent system.

**EXAMPLE 2**    $-m + 3n = 7$
$2m + 4n = 16$

**SOLUTION**    (1)    $-m + 3n = 7$        $(5, 4); (-1, 2)$
$2m + 4n = 16$        $(8, 0); (-3, 5\tfrac{1}{2})$

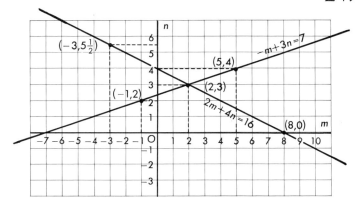

(2)   The system is simultaneous.

(3)   (2, 3)

Check: 2 for $m$; 3 for $n$

$$-m + 3n = -2 + 3 \cdot 3 \qquad 2m + 4n = 2 \cdot 2 + 4 \cdot 3$$
$$= -2 + 9 \qquad\qquad\qquad = 4 + 12$$
$$= 7 \qquad\qquad\qquad\qquad = 16$$

**EXAMPLE 3**   $z = 4 - w$
$2w + 2z = 8$

**SOLUTION**   (1)   $z = 4 - w$ $\qquad\qquad$ $(5, -1); (1, 3)$
$\qquad\qquad$ $2w + 2z = 8$ $\qquad\quad$ $(2, 2); (-1, 5)$

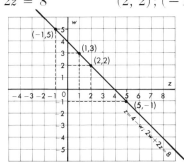

(2)   The system is a dependent system.

(3)   Finding equivalent equations to $z = 4 - w$ gives us

$$w + z = 4$$
$$2(w + z) = 2 \cdot 4$$
$$2w + 2z = 8$$

Thus, the first equation is equivalent to the second, and the system is dependent.

Reread the instructions on page 247.

1.  $u + v = 2$
    $2u + 5v = 7$

2.  $2x = 3 - 5y$
    $10y = 6 - 4x$

3.  $-s = 2t - 4$
    $4t + 2s = 1$

4.  $\frac{1}{2}k + \frac{1}{3}m = -6$
    $k + m = -15$

5.  $2n + 5 = r$
    $-3r = -15 - 6n$

6.  $7 - 3p = 4t$
    $2t + 1.5p = 17$

7.  $x = -y$
    $x = y$

8.  $2t - 3u = 1$
    $3t - 2u = 1$

9.  $2(a - 2b) = 3$
    $2b - a = 1$

10. $5w - 4v = 6$
    $3 + 2v = 2.5w$

## ★7 · Graphing Equations and Inequalities

The idea of a one-to-one correspondence between ordered pairs of real numbers and points in the coordinate plane is very important in the study of equations and inequalities. Equations and inequalities are open sentences in which the number replacements which make these sentences true are referred to as *solution sets*. The sets from which we may choose replacements for the variables are called *universal sets*. The open sentences serve as the *selectors* of the number pairs for the solution set. The universal set may be the set of real numbers, integers, or any set we choose.

From the correspondence between number pairs and points in the coordinate plane we view the open sentence

$$x + y = 4$$

as the selector of a set of points corresponding to the solution set. We indicate this set as

$$\{(x, y) \mid x + y = 4\}$$

We read this as

"the set of ordered real number pairs $(x, y)$ for which $x + y = 4$."
We say that the graph of $\{(x, y) \mid x + y = 4\}$ is the graph of $x + y = 4$.

Usually, we will choose the first members and the second members of the ordered pairs from the universe of real numbers, but we may restrict our choice to any set desired.

It is clear that

$$A = \{(x, y) \mid x, y \in \text{Real numbers}, x + y = 4\} \text{ and}$$
$$B = \{(x, y) \mid x, y \in \text{Integers}, x + y = 4\}$$

are different sets. We agree, as before, to associate the first components with the points on the horizontal axis, and the second components with the points on the vertical axis. The graph of set $A$ is given below.

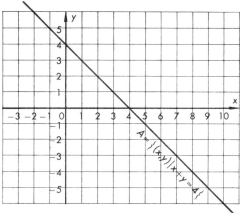

Consider another set:

$$C = \{(s, t) \,|\, s, t \,\epsilon \text{ Real numbers}, s \geq t\}$$

A graph of this set is

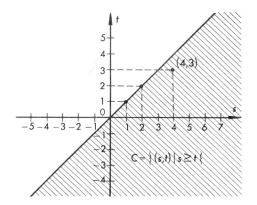

Note that the graph of the set of points which belong to $C$ extends indefinitely. Do you see that every point in the shaded area belongs to the set $C$? For example, $(4, 3) \,\epsilon\, C$, because $4 \geq 3$. Check a few more points in the shaded area to see whether they belong to $C$.

Do the points which make up the straight line, the boundary of the set, belong to the set? Why?

Let us now graph the set $R = \{(u, v) \,|\, |u| > -v\}$ if the replacement set for $u$ and $v$ is the set of real numbers.

First, let us name a few number pairs which belong to this set. Remember that for each pair in the set, the absolute value of the first member in the set must be greater than the opposite of the second member.

$(5, 1) \epsilon R$ because $|5| > -1$

$(3, 17) \epsilon R$ because $|3| > -17$

$(5, -4) \epsilon R$ because $|5| > -(-4)$ or $5 > 4$

but $(5, -6) \not\epsilon R$. Why?

$(0, 255) \epsilon R$ because $|0| > -255$

but $(0, -1) \not\epsilon R$. Why?

From these examples, it is becoming clear that, if the second member of the pair is any positive number, then the first member may be any non-negative number.

Observe that

$(4, -3) \epsilon R$, because $|4| > -(-3)$

but $(4, -5) \not\epsilon R$, because $|4| \not> -(-5)$

Now we can begin to make the graph. It is good practice first to identify the graph of

$$\{(u, v)\mid |u| = -v\}$$

Here are a few pairs which belong to this set. (See graph below.)

$$(3, -3), (2, -2), (-2, -2), (-1, -1), (0, 0)$$

Do you see that every pair belonging to $\{(u, v)\mid |u| = -v\}$ has for its second member a non-positive number? Explain why this is so.

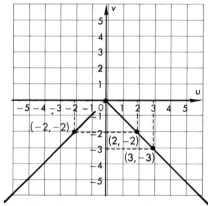

Above is the graph of $\{(u, v)\mid |u| = -v\}$

Now we are in a position to graph the set

$$R = \{(u, v)\mid |u| > -v\}$$

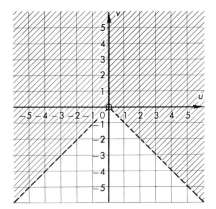

Do you see that only the points in the shaded regions belong to the set? Does (0, 0) belong to $R$? Do the boundaries (dashed lines) belong to $R$? Does (1, −2) belong to $R$?

**EXAMPLE**

Graph the set $T = \{(m, n) \mid m + n < 1\}$ if the replacement set for $m$ and $n$ is the set of integers.

**SOLUTION**

Here are a few pairs which belong to $T$.

$(-7, 7)$, because $-7 + 7 < 1$

$(-2, 1)$, because $-2 + 1 < 1$

$(-2, 2)$, because $-2 + 2 < 1$

    but  $(-2, 3) \notin T$, because $-2 + 3 \not< 1$

$(0, -5)$, because $0 + (-5) < 1$

$(8, -8)$, because $8 + (-8) < 1$

Are you beginning to see the relationship between the first number and the second in each pair which makes a pair belong to $T$?

Let us first graph the set, $\{(m, n) \mid m + n = 1\}$.

Here are some pairs that belong to this set.

$(-2, 3), (5, -4), (0, 1), (1, 0), (-4, 5), (-3, 4)$

No doubt you notice that the points belonging to the graph of $\{(m, n)\,|\,m + n = 1\}$ make up a "line." It is not the ordinary line you are used to when the replacement set is the set of real numbers. Since we we have only integers, we have a "dot line". How far does this "line" extend?

Now here is the graph of $T = \{(m, n)\,|\,m + n < 1\}$.

In the graph above, the points of the boundary are circled. Do they belong to $T$, Why? Do all the points marked ⊡ belong to $T$? How far does the graph extend?

## EXERCISES

1. Graph each of the following sets. The replacement set of the variable in each case is the set of real numbers.

   a. $X = \{(a, b)\,|\,a + 2b = 3\}$

   b. $Y = \{(c, d)\,|\,c = 5d - 4\}$

   c. $A = \left\{(m, n)\,\Big|\,\dfrac{m}{n} = 1\right\}$

   d. $B = \{(x, y)\,|\,2x < y\}$

   e. $C = \{(p, q)\,|\,2q + 3 < 2p\}$

   f. $D = \{(r, t)\,|\,|r| < t\}$

   g. $E = \{(s, r)\,|\,|s| > |r|\}$

   h. $M = \{(g, h)\,|\,g + h \neq 4\}$

   i. $P = \{(u, v)\,|\,u \geq v - 1\}$

2. Graph each of the following sets:

   a. $G = \{(x, y)\,|\,x, y \in \text{Integers}, x + 3 > y\}$

   b. $H = \{(r, s)\,|\,r, s \in \text{Natural numbers}, 2x + 3 = y\}$

   c. $K = \{(w, v)\,|\,w, v \in \text{Real numbers}, w < v + 3\}$

   d. $T = \{(m, p)\,|\,m, p \in \text{Integers}, m + p \geq -4\}$

**3.** Graph the sets in Exercise 1, using the set of integers as the universal set for the first and second components of the ordered pairs. Compare the graphs with those of Exercise 1, when the universal set was the set of real numbers.

**4.** If the universal set from which we choose the first and second components of the ordered pairs is the set $\{1, 2, 3, 4, 5\}$, graph the following sets:

**a.** $G = \{(x, y) \,|\, x + y < 4\}$      **c.** $L = \{(x, y) \,|\, y + 2 \geq x\}$

**b.** $K = \{(x, y) \,|\, y > x + 2\}$      **d.** $T = \{(x, y) \,|\, y \geq x\}$

## ★ 8 · Graphing More Complicated Sentences

When you solved systems of two equations with two variables by means of graphs, you looked for the *intersection* of the two sets. If the intersection was the null set, you knew that the two equations had no common solution.

Let us now consider sentences which involve equations and inequalities.

**EXAMPLE 1**     Let us graph the set:

$$A = \{(m, n) \,|\, m = n \text{ or } -1 < m < 3\}$$

The replacement set of $m$ and $n$ is the set of real numbers.

**SOLUTION**     To obtain the graph, we will consider the two sets separately.

(1)   $B = \{(m, n) \,|\, m = n\}$

(2)   $C = \{(m, n) \,|\, -1 < m < 3\}$

Graphs of each of the sets are below.

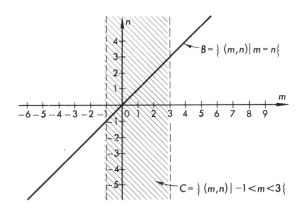

Do the vertical lines which make up the boundaries of the set $C$ belong to $C$? Why? How is this fact indicated in the graph? Now the set

$$A = \{(m, n) \mid m = n \ or \ -1 < m < 3\}$$

is the *union* of the sets $B$ and $C$. Why? Use the graph above to describe the graph of the union of $B$ and $C$.

**EXAMPLE 2**

Let us consider another example,

$$X = \{(p, q) \mid p \leq 2 \ and \ 2 \leq |q| < 5\},$$

where the replacement set of $p$ and $q$ is the set of real numbers.

**SOLUTION**

The two sets involved here are

(1)   $Y = \{(p, q) \mid p \leq 2\}$
(2)   $Z = \{(p, q) \mid 2 \leq |q| < 5\}$

Let us graph both sets on the same coordinate system.

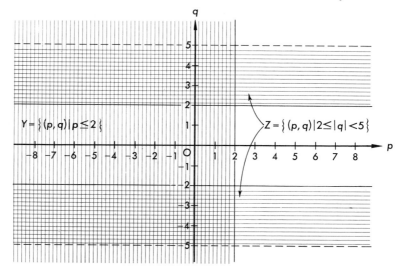

Does the boundary of the graph of the set $Y$ belong to the graph? How is this fact indicated in the graph?

Do the boundaries of the graph of $Z$ belong to the set? Why? How is this fact indicated in the graph?

Now we need to identify the graph of

$$X = \{(p, q) \mid p \leq 2 \ and \ 2 \leq |q| < 5\}$$

To do this, we find the points which belong to *both*

sets $Y$ and $Z$; that is, we find the *intersection* of the sets $Y$ and $Z$. The picture of the set $X$ is that part of the above graph which is shaded with both kinds of shadings. Describe in detail the boundaries of the graph of $X$.

Of what geometric figure does the graph of $X$ remind you?

**EXAMPLE 3**    Now let us graph the set

$$M = \{(s, t) \mid |s| \leq 2 \text{ and } |t| \geq 3\}$$

where the replacement set of $s$ and $t$ is the set of real numbers.

**SOLUTION**    Again we have two sets to graph:

$$A = \{(s, t) \mid |s| \leq 2\}$$

In the set $A$ only the first coordinate $s$ has a restriction on it ($|s| \leq 2$). Since nothing is said about $t$, $t$ can assume all values in the specified replacement set.

$$B = \{(s, t) \mid |t| \geq 3\}$$

Here there is a restriction on $t$, but no restrictions on $s$. Therefore, $s$ can assume all values in the replacement set. Here is the graph of both sets on one coordinate system.

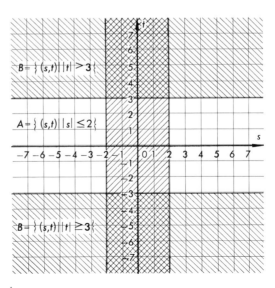

Note that the graph of $A$ consists of one part. The graph of $B$ has two separate parts.

Now $M = A \cap B$   (Why?)

Thus, the graph of $M$ is the set of points common to the graphs of $A$ and $B$. (Explain.)

Identify the parts of the graph which consist of points common to $A$ and $B$. This is the graph of $M$.

**EXAMPLE 4**    Now, let us graph $M$ when the replacement set of $s$ and $t$ is the set of integers.

**SOLUTION**

Each point which belongs to $A = \{(s, t)\mid |s| \leq 2\}$ is marked like this $\odot$. Points which belong to $B = \{(s, t)\mid |t| \geq 3\}$ are marked like this $\boxdot$. Points which are marked like this $\boxdot$ belong to *both* $A$ and $B$; that is, to the intersection of $A$ and $B$. And $A \cap B = M = \{(s, t)\mid |s| \leq 2$ and $|t| \geq 3\}$.

How far does the graph of $M$ extend? What would be the graph of $M$ if the replacement set of $s$ and $t$ were the set of natural numbers? To what quadrant would this graph be confined?

# EXERCISES

1. Graph each of the following sets using the set of real numbers as the universal set for first and second components:

   **a.** $A = \{(x, y)\mid x + y = 7$ or $x < 3\}$
   **b.** $B = \{(m, n)\mid m < 2$ or $n < 2\}$

**c.** $C = \{(r, t) \mid |r| > 4 \text{ or } r + t < 2\}$

**d.** $D = \{(s, w) \mid -3 \le s \le 2 \text{ or } 1 < w < 5\}$

**e.** $E = \{(z, u) \mid z + u < 2 \text{ or } z - u > 5\}$

**f.** $F = \{(a, b) \mid 0 < |a + b| < 1 \text{ or } |a| < 3\}$

**g.** $G = \{(c, d) \mid |c| > |d| \text{ or } c = d\}$

**h.** $H = \{(p, r) \mid 2p + r < 1 \text{ or } p > 0\}$

**i.** $K = \{(u, t) \mid 0 \le |u| \le 1 \text{ or } 0 \le |t| \le 1\}$

**j.** $L = \{(k, m) \mid 0 \le |k + m| \le 1 \text{ or } |k| = |m|\}$

**2.** In each problem in Exercise 1, replace the word *or* by *and* and identify the graph of each sentence thus obtained.

**3.** Graph the sets in Exercise 1, using the set of integers as the universal set from which to choose the first and second components of the ordered pairs.

··················································································

# VOCABULARY

| | |
|---|---|
| abscissa (237) | plane (236) |
| Cartesian plane (237) | quadrant (238) |
| coordinate (236) | rectangular coordinate system (237) |
| coordinate plane (237) | second component (236) |
| dependent system (246) | selector (250) |
| first component (236) | simultaneous system (247) |
| graph (239) | standard form (231) |
| inconsistent system (247) | system of equations (242) |
| independent system (247) | union (256) |
| inequality (232) | x-axis (237) |
| intercepts (242) | x-coordinate (237) |
| intersection (255) | x-intercept (242) |
| Line Principles (240) | y-axis (237) |
| ordinate (237) | y-coordinate (237) |
| origin (236) | y-intercept (242) |
| parallel lines (246) | |

# REVIEW EXERCISES

1. In each of the following, there is given a series of equivalent equations. State the principles involved in going from one step to another:

a.

$$5y + 3 = -6x$$
$$5y + 3 + 6x \overset{(1)}{=} -6x + 6x$$
$$5y + (3 + 6x) \overset{(2)}{=} (-6 + 6) \cdot x$$
$$5y + (6x + 3) \overset{(3)}{=} [6 + (-6)] \cdot x$$
$$5y + 6x + 3 \overset{(4)}{=} 0 \cdot x$$
$$5y + 6x + 3 \overset{(5)}{=} 0$$
$$5y + 6x + 3 + (-3) \overset{(6)}{=} 0 + (-3)$$
$$5y + 6x + [3 + (-3)] \overset{(7)}{=} -3$$
$$5y + 6x + 0 \overset{(8)}{=} -3$$
$$5y + 6x \overset{(9)}{=} -3$$
$$6x + 5y \overset{(10)}{=} -3$$

b.

$$2(y + 7) = 5(x - 3)$$
$$2y + 14 \overset{(1)}{=} 5x - 15$$
$$2y + 14 \overset{(2)}{=} 5x + (-15)$$
$$2y + 14 \overset{(3)}{=} (-15) + 5x$$
$$2y + 14 + (-5x) \overset{(4)}{=} (-15) + 5x + (-5x)$$
$$2y + 14 + (-5x) \overset{(5)}{=} (-15) + 0$$
$$2y + [14 + (-5x)] \overset{(6)}{=} -15$$
$$2y + [(-5x) + 14] \overset{(7)}{=} -15$$
$$[2y + (-5x)] + 14 \overset{(8)}{=} -15$$
$$2y + (-5x) + 14 + (-14) \overset{(9)}{=} -15 + (-14)$$
$$[2y + (-5x)] + 0 \overset{(10)}{=} -15 + (-14)$$
$$2y + [-5x + 0] \overset{(11)}{=} -15 + (-14)$$
$$2y + (-5x) \overset{(12)}{=} -15 + (-14)$$
$$-5x + 2y \overset{(13)}{=} -15 + (-14)$$
$$-5x + 2y \overset{(14)}{=} -29$$

**c.**

$$3x = -5 - 9y$$
$$\overset{(1)}{3x} = -5 + (-9y)$$
$$\overset{(2)}{3x + 9y} = -5 + (-9y) + 9y$$
$$\overset{(3)}{3x + 9y} = -5 + 0$$
$$\overset{(4)}{3x + 9y} = -5$$

**d.**

$$3(x - y) - 3 = -7$$
$$\overset{(1)}{3x - 3y - 3} = -7$$
$$\overset{(2)}{3x + (-3y) + (-3)} = -7$$
$$\overset{(3)}{3x + (-3y) + (-3) + 3} = -7 + 3$$
$$\overset{(4)}{3x + (-3y) + 0} = -7 + 3$$
$$\overset{(5)}{3x + (-3y)} = -7 + 3$$
$$\overset{(6)}{3x + (-3y)} = -4$$

**2.** For each equation, find an equivalent equation in the standard form. Then solve for $x$.

**EXAMPLE**      $5y + 2x + 3 = 6x + 3y - 8$

**SOLUTION**

$$5y + 2x + 3 + (-3) = 6x + 3y + (-8) + (-3)$$
$$2x + 5y = 6x + 3y + (-11)$$
$$2x + 5y + (-3y) = 6x + 3y + (-11) + (-3y)$$
$$2x + 2y = 6x + (-11)$$
$$2x + 2y + (-6x) = 6x + (-11) + (-6x)$$
$$-4x + 2y = -11$$

This equation is in the standard form of a linear equation in two variables.
Now, to solve for $x$:

$$-4x + 2y = -11$$
$$-\tfrac{1}{4}(-4x + 2y) = -\tfrac{1}{4} \cdot (-11)$$
$$x - \tfrac{1}{2}y = \tfrac{11}{4}$$
$$x + (-\tfrac{1}{2}y) + \tfrac{1}{2}y = \tfrac{11}{4} + \tfrac{1}{2}y$$
$$x = \tfrac{1}{2}y + \tfrac{11}{4}$$

The last sentence has $x$ expressed in terms of remaining terms.

**a.** $4x + 3y = 19$

**b.** $7y - 13 = 5x - 3y$

**c.** $17 + 14y = 6x - 11 - 5y$

**d.** $3(x - y) + 17 = 7 + 2x$

**e.** $8(x + y) - 5y = 6x + 8$

**f.** $14 - 6(2x + 3) = 7x - 3(y + 1)$

**g.** $17x - 6y + 4 - 3y + 4x = 21 + 5(x - y) - 6x$

**h.** $13(x - 3y) + 5(2y - x) + 4 = 7(7 + y) - 3x$

**i.** $5(y + 2x) - 3x + 14 = 5(x - 3y) + 17$

**j.** $\dfrac{3(x + 4)}{y - 5} = 5$

**k.** $\dfrac{2y + x}{x - y} = -3$

3. Graph the following:

   **a.** $B = \{(x, y) \mid x, y \in \text{Real numbers}, x \geq 0 \text{ and } y \geq 0\}$

   **b.** $C = \{(x, y) \mid x, y \in \text{Real numbers}, x \leq 0 \text{ and } y \leq 0\}$

   **c.** $D = \{(x, y) \mid x, y \in \text{Real numbers}, x \leq 2 \text{ and } y \leq 2\}$

   **d.** $E = \{(x, y) \mid x, y \in \text{Real numbers}, x + y = 5 \text{ and } y \geq 2\}$

   **e.** $F = \{(x, y) \mid x, y \in \text{Real numbers}, x > y\}$

   **f.** Graph the sets in **a** through **e** choosing $x$ and $y$ from the universe of integers.

   **g.** Graph the sets **a** through **e** letting $U = \{-1, 0, 1, 2, 3, 4, 5\}$.

4. Graph the solution set of the following:

   **a.** $-2x + y = -6$    **b.** $x - 3 = -5y$
       $x - 3y = 4$             $5y - 2y = 4$

   **c.** In what quadrant does the intersection lie in **a**? in **b**?

5. For each pair of equations below, do the following:

   (1) Graph the solution set for each equation.

   (2) Tell whether the system is independent, dependent, or inconsistent.

   **a.** $x + 3y = 7$      **b.** $5x + 9 = -3y$
       $3x + 4 = -9y$          $5y + 4 = -2x$

   **c.** $5x + 3 = -2y$
       $4y + 6 = -10x$

6. Graph each of the following:

   **a.** $B = \{(x, y)\,|\,x, y \,\epsilon$ Real numbers, $x + y \geq 5$ or $x > 2\}$

   **b.** $G = \{(r, s)\,|\,r, s \,\epsilon$ Integers, $r \geq s$ and $r + s = 7\}$

   **c.** $K = \{(w, v)\,|\,w, v \,\epsilon$ Real numbers, $|w| + 2 = v\}$

# CHAPTER TEST

1. For each of the following equations, find an equivalent equation in standard form:

   **a.** $-3y + \dfrac{5}{2} = -4x$         **b.** $\dfrac{-2x + 3}{5y + 7} = -2$

2. Graph the following sets on the number line:

   **a.** $G = \{w\,|\,w \,\epsilon$ Integers, $-4 \leq w < 5\}$

   **b.** $H = \{r\,|\,r \,\epsilon$ Real numbers, $r > 2$ and $r \leq 5\}$

   **c.** $K = \{x\,|\,x \,\epsilon\, U, 4 < x < 7\}, U = \{1, 2, 3, 4, 5, 6, 7\}$

   **d.** $T = \{y\,|\,y \,\epsilon$ Real numbers, $y < -5$ or $y > 3\}$

   **e.** $V = \{x\,|\,x \,\epsilon$ Real numbers, $x > -4$ and $x < -4\}$

3. Locate the points in the coordinate plane corresponding to the following number pairs:

   **a.** $(-3, -7)$                **d.** $(4, -9)$

   **b.** $(9, 5)$                   **e.** $(0, -3)$

   **c.** $(-11, 3)$               **f.** $(6, 0)$

4. If $B = \{(x, y)\,|\,x, y \,\epsilon$ Real numbers, $x + y \geq 5\}$, classify each of the following as true or false:

   **a.** $(1, 4) \,\epsilon\, B$         **b.** $(2, -3) \,\epsilon\, B$         **c.** $(4, 2) \,\epsilon\, B$

5. $G = \{(x, y)\,|\,x, y \,\epsilon$ Real numbers, $x \geq 0$ and $y \leq 0\}$:

   **a.** Describe in words the graph of $G$.

   True or false?

   **b.** $(5, -2) \,\epsilon\, G$

   **c.** $(0, 0) \,\epsilon\, G$

   **d.** $(175, 6) \,\epsilon\, G$

   **e.** $(-1106, 299) \,\epsilon\, G$

   **f.** $(-12, -3709) \,\epsilon\, G$

6. For each pair of equations, (1) graph the solution set, and (2) tell whether the system of equations is simultaneous, dependent, or inconsistent:

    **a.** $-3y + 5 = -7x$  
        $2x + 5 = -3y$

    **b.** $-6x + 2 = +4y$  
        $-2y = 2(3 + 1.5x)$

    **c.** $\dfrac{x + 2y}{3} = 2x + 1$  
        $2y = 5x + 3$

7. Graph the following ($U = \{-3, -2, -1, 0, 1\}$):

    **a.** $\{(x, y) \mid x, y \in U, x > -2 \text{ and } y < -1\}$  
    **b.** $\{(x, y) \mid x, y \in U, x \geq y\}$

# CUMULATIVE REVIEW

1. Using the word descriptions of the following sets, rewrite them using shorthand set notation:

**EXAMPLE**    $S$ is a set of real numbers $x$, such that $x$ is greater than $-3$ and less than 4.

**SOLUTION**    $S = \{x \mid x \in \text{Reals}, -3 < x < 4\}$

    **a.** $R$ is a set of integers $t$, such that $t$ is greater than or equal to $-2$ *and* less than or equal to 4.

    **b.** $P$ is a set of natural numbers $r$, such that $r$ is greater than four and less than seven.

    **c.** $T$ is the set of real numbers $y$, such that $y$ is greater than $-6$.

    **d.** $V$ is the set of integers $r$, such that $r$ is greater than or equal to 2 *and* less than or equal to 3.

    **e.** $G$ is the set of real numbers $s$, less than 5 or greater than 6.

    **f.** $D$ is the set of natural numbers $n$, such that $n$ is greater than seven *and* less than nine.

    **g.** $Q$ is the set of integers $t$ such that $t$ is less than $-4$ and greater than $-7$.

2. Names of rational numbers can be considered to be of the form $\dfrac{p}{q}$, in which $p$ and $q$ are replaceable by names of integers, $q \neq 0$.

    **a.** What replacements for $p$ and $q$ would give you the set of even integers? If $p$ were replaced by names of even integers and $q$ were replaced by 1, we would have a set of numbers equivalent to the even integers.

**b.** If $p$ were replaced by names of odd integers and $q$ were replaced by 1, what set of numbers would be obtained? What is the relationship between the sets defined in **a** and **b**?

**c.** If $p$ were replaced by a name of an integer and $q$ replaced by 1, what set of numbers would be obtained? What relationship exists between sets determined in Exercises **a**, **b**, and **c**? Is the set determined in **a** a subset of the set determined in **b**? Are the sets in **a**, **b**, and **c** all *closed* under the operations of addition, subtraction, multiplication, and division? What can be said concerning the union of the sets in **a** and **b**? What can be said concerning the intersection of the sets in **a** and **b**?

**d.** If $p$ were replaced by 1 and $q$ replaced by names of integers, what set of numbers would be obtained?

**e.** If $p$ were replaced by 1 and $q$ replaced by names of even integers, what set of numbers would be obtained? Are the sets **d** and **e** closed under the operations of addition, subtraction, multiplication, and division? Is the set in **e** a subset of the set in **d**?

**3.** Let $U = \{a, e, g, h, i, k, l, r\}$, $A = \{e, h, r\}$, $B = \{g, k, l, r\}$, $C = \{e, l, r\}$.

Determine the following sets:

**a.** $A \cap (B \cup C)$          **c.** $A \cup (B \cap C)$

**b.** $(A \cap B) \cup (A \cap C)$      **d.** $(A \cup B) \cap (A \cup C)$

**4.** Replace $\square$, $\triangle$, and $\bigcirc$ with names of real numbers to make the following sentences true:

**a.** $(-2) \cdot (-3) = \triangle$

**b.** $-6\frac{1}{2} - \square = 9$

**c.** $\bigcirc \div 7 = -19$

**d.** $\dfrac{0}{-2} = \triangle$

**e.** $-6 - \left(-4\frac{1}{2}\right) = \square$

**f.** $5 \cdot (\square + 3) = 5 \cdot 4\frac{1}{4} + 5 \cdot 3$

**g.** $\left(7 + 3\frac{1}{3}\right) + \left(-9\frac{1}{2}\right) = 7 + \left[\triangle + \left(-9\frac{1}{2}\right)\right]$

**h.** $-7 \cdot [6 + (-5)] = [6 + \square] \cdot (-7)$

**i.** $-5 + 3(7 + \square) = -5 + 3(\square + 7)$

**5.** Write simpler number symbols for the following:

**a.** $\frac{2}{3}[(4 - 3 \cdot 7 + 5 \cdot 9) - 10]$

**b.** $\frac{6}{11} \div \frac{5}{3}$

**c.** $\frac{4}{9} + \left(-\frac{7}{4}\right)$

**d.** $\frac{1}{4}\left[\left(\frac{1}{2} \div \frac{3}{4}\right) - \left(\frac{3}{2} \times \frac{9}{5}\right)\right]$

**e.** $\dfrac{\frac{2}{4} - \frac{1}{3}}{\frac{1}{2} + \frac{1}{3}}$

**6.** Classify as true or false:

**a.** $-3 \not< 5$

**b.** $4 \geq -2$

**c.** $3 \leq 7$

**d.** $|-3| \neq |3|$

**e.** $|-7| > 8$

**f.** $\left|\frac{-1}{-3}\right| < \left|\frac{1}{1+2}\right|$

**g.** $|7.6 - 8.2| = |8.2 - 7.6|$

**7.** Is $\frac{4}{11}$ a rational number?

**8.** Determine $\sqrt{7.6}$ to three decimal places.

**9.** Graph each of the following:

**a.** $G = \{(x, y) \mid x, y \in \text{Integers}, -2 \leq x \leq 9\}$
**b.** $H = \{(x, y \mid x, y \in \text{Reals}, x \geq 2y\}$
**c.** $K = \{(r, t) \mid r, t \in \text{Reals}, |t| < r\}$
**d.** $L = \{(x, y) \mid x, y \in \text{Reals}, 3x + y \leq 5 \text{ or } y = 2\}$
**e.** $T = \{(w, v) \mid w, v \in \text{Integers}, |w + 5| < v \text{ and } v < 2\}$

**10.** For each of the following, we have found an equivalent equation in standard form. State the principles involved in moving from one step to another.

**a.** $4y = -5x + 3$

$$4y \overset{(1)}{=} 3 + (-5x)$$
$$4y + 5x \overset{(2)}{=} 3 + (-5x) + 5x$$
$$4y + 5x \overset{(3)}{=} 3 + [5x + (-5x)]$$
$$4y + 5x \overset{(4)}{=} 3 + 0$$
$$4y + 5x \overset{(5)}{=} 3$$
$$5x + 4y \overset{(6)}{=} 3$$

**b.**
$$3(2y - 4x) = -7$$

(1)
$$3 \cdot 2y + 3(-4x) = -7$$

(2)
$$6y - 12x = -7$$

(3)
$$-12x + 6y = -7$$

Solve each problem in Exercises 11–20.

11. What is the area of a parallelogram whose one side is $12\frac{1}{2}$ inches long and the altitude upon this side is $8\frac{1}{2}$ inches long?

12. $ABCD$ is a parallelogram. Its area is 156 square inches. What is the measure of $DC$?

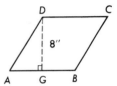

13. How is the area of a parallelogram changed if the length of one set of parallel sides is doubled, and the remaining sides are unchanged?

14. A side of a square is 4 inches long. If the side is increased by 1 inch, what is the change in the perimeter? In the area?

15. A side of a square measures $t$ inches. If the side is increased by $\frac{1}{4}t$ inches, what is the change in the perimeter? In the area?

16. The perimeter of a rectangle is 120 inches. The length of the rectangle is 6 inches more than four times its width. Compute the length and width.

17. You will recall that in a right triangle, the following is true: $a^2 + b^2 = c^2$. In square $ABCD$, compute the measure of $AB$ and $BD$ if the area of the square is 12 square inches.

18. The square $ABCD$ has sides whose measure is 6 inches. Compare the area of the square with the area of the inscribed circle.

19. A circle is circumscribed about square $GRKH$. If the measure of $HK$ is 2 inches and the measure of $KG$ is $2\sqrt{2}$ inches, compare the areas of the square and circle.

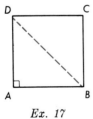

*Ex. 17*

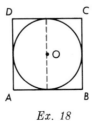

*Ex. 18*

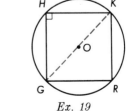

*Ex. 19*

**20.** For each pair of figures below, compare their areas.

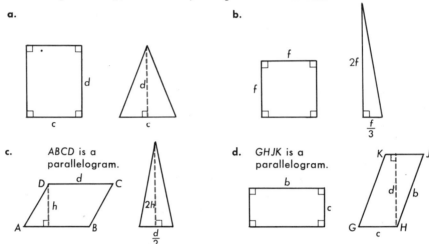

# BIBLIOGRAPHY

Bakst, A., *Mathematics, Its Magic and Mastery*, Van Nostrand, Toronto, 1952, pages 51–78, "Number Giants and Pygmies."

Bakst, A., *Mathematical Puzzles and Pastimes*, Van Nostrand, Toronto, 1954, pages 84–96, "Harnessing Father Time."

Christian, R. R., *Introduction to Logic and Sets*, Ginn and Company, Toronto, 1958.

Dudeney, Henry, *Amusements in Mathematics*, Dover Publications, 1959.

Gamow, and Stern, *Puzzle Math*, Viking Publications, 1958.

School Mathematics Study Group, *Mathematics for High School: First Course in Algebra (Revised Edition)*, SMSG, New Haven, Connecticut, 1960, pages 255–295.

University of Illinois Committee on School Mathematics, *Unit 4, "Ordered Pairs and Graphs,"* UICSM, Urbana, Illinois, 1960.

# Solution Sets of Systems of Equations and Inequalities

## 1 · Solving Systems of Equations by Comparison

You learned that two equations of the form $Ax + By = C$, when graphed, result in two straight lines. If these two lines intersect, they have exactly one common point. The coordinates of this point satisfy each equation. Thus, in this case, there is a pair of numbers satisfying both equations; or, the solution set of the system of equations is an ordered pair of numbers.

We shall learn now to find the pair of numbers satisfying two given equations without having to make graphs. You will see that this non-graphical method has some advantages over the graphical method. Frequently it is difficult to read the coordinates accurately from a graph. The algebraic method that we will now consider gives the exact solutions.

**EXAMPLE**  Solve the following system of two linear equations in two unknowns:

$$x - 4y = -4$$
$$3x + 2y = -5$$

**SOLUTION**  Let us now find two equations in the form $x = My + N$, one equivalent to the first equation, and the other to the second equation.

$$(1) \quad x - 4y = -4$$
$$x = 4y - 4$$
$$x = 4y + (-4)$$

269

$$(2) \quad 3x + 2y = -5$$
$$3x = -2y - 5$$
$$x = \frac{-2y - 5}{3}$$
$$x = -\frac{2}{3}y - \frac{5}{3}$$
$$x = -\frac{2}{3}y + \left(-\frac{5}{3}\right)$$

Now, if each of the equations (1) and (2) is to be satisfied by the same pair of numbers, then the following must be true:

$$-\frac{2}{3}y + \left(-\frac{5}{3}\right) = 4y + (-4)$$

or

$$-\frac{2}{3}y - \frac{5}{3} = 4y - 4$$

or

$$\frac{-2y - 5}{3} = 4y - 4$$

Let us solve the last equation.

$$-2y - 5 = 3(4y - 4)$$
$$-2y - 5 = 12y - 12$$
$$-2y - 12y = -12 + 5$$
$$-14y = -7$$
$$y = \frac{-7}{-14}$$
$$y = \frac{1}{2}$$

We now replace $y$ by $\frac{1}{2}$ in the first of the two original equations:

$$3x + 2 \cdot \frac{1}{2} = -5$$
$$3x + 1 = -5$$
$$3x = -6$$
$$x = -\frac{6}{3}$$
$$x = -2$$

Thus the pair $\left(-2, \frac{1}{2}\right)$ should satisfy both equations.

Let us check. (Note that it is important to check *both* equations.)

$$(1) \quad 3x + 2y = 3 \cdot (-2) + 2 \cdot \frac{1}{2}$$

$$= -6 + 1$$

$$= -5$$

$$(2) \quad x - 4y = -2 - 4 \cdot \frac{1}{2}$$

$$= -2 - 2$$

$$= -4$$

The pair $\left(-2, \frac{1}{2}\right)$ satisfies each equation. The solution set of the given system of equations is the set $\left\{\left(-2, \frac{1}{2}\right)\right\}$.

The method which we just used in determining the roots or the solution set of the system above may be called the *comparison method*. Why is this name a sensible one for this method?

## EXERCISES

Using the comparison method, solve each of the following systems of equations.

**1.** $x + y = 3$
$\quad x - y = -2$

**2.** $3m = \frac{1}{2}n + 3$
$\quad n = 2 - m$

**3.** $2p - 2r = 1$
$\quad p = 7r - 3$

**4.** $\dfrac{u + w}{3} = 2u$
$\quad 2w = 7u + \dfrac{5}{2}$

**5.** $2a + b = 1$
$\quad b = 3 - a$

**6.** $-4s = -3t + 1$
$\quad 3 = s - t$

**7.** $7.5c - 3d = 5$
$\quad 4d = 3c - 6$

**8.** $v + t = 3v - t + 6$ $\left(1, -2\right)$
$\quad 7 - t = 8 + v$

## 2 · Solving Systems of Equations by Substitution

Consider the following system of equations:

$$4x - 3y = 2$$
$$-3x + 7y = -10$$

We shall first find an equation equivalent to the first equation, and which is in the form $x = Ay + B$:

$$4x - 3y = 2$$
$$4x = 3y + 2$$
$$x = \frac{3y + 2}{4}$$

Now we shall replace $x$ in the second equation by $\dfrac{3y + 2}{4}$, and solve:

$$-3x + 7y = -10$$
$$-3 \cdot \frac{3y + 2}{4} + 7y = -10$$
$$\frac{-3(3y + 2)}{4} + \frac{28y}{4} = \frac{-40}{4}$$
$$-3(3y + 2) + 28y = -40 \quad \text{(Why?)}$$
$$-9y - 6 + 28y = -40$$
$$19y = -40 + 6$$
$$19y = -34$$
$$y = -\frac{34}{19}$$

Next, we replace $y$ in one of the original equations by $-\dfrac{34}{19}$, and solve:

$$4x - 3 \cdot \left(-\frac{34}{19}\right) = 2$$
$$4x + \frac{102}{19} = 2$$
$$76x + 102 = 38$$
$$76x = -64$$
$$x = -\frac{64}{76}, \text{ or } -\frac{16}{19}$$

Thus, the pair $\left(-\dfrac{16}{19}, -\dfrac{34}{19}\right)$ should satisfy both equations. Checking,

$$(1) \quad 4x - 3y = 4 \cdot \left(-\dfrac{16}{19}\right) - 3 \cdot \left(-\dfrac{34}{19}\right)$$
$$= -\dfrac{64}{19} + \dfrac{102}{19}$$
$$= \dfrac{38}{19}$$
$$= 2$$

$$(2) \quad -3x + 7y = -3 \cdot \left(-\dfrac{16}{19}\right) + 7 \cdot \left(-\dfrac{34}{19}\right)$$
$$= \dfrac{48}{19} - \dfrac{238}{19}$$
$$= -\dfrac{190}{19}$$
$$= -10$$

Thus, the solution set of the system of equations

$$4x - 3y = 2$$
$$-3x + 7y = -10$$

is the set $\left\{\left(-\dfrac{16}{19}, -\dfrac{34}{19}\right)\right\}$

When we decided to write our equivalent equation in the form $x = Ay + B$, we could just as well have chosen to find an equivalent equation in the form $y = Cx + D$, and substituted for $y$ first. You will note that the method we used here is different from the comparison method. It may be given the name *substitution* method. How would you justify this name?

# EXERCISES

**1-8.** Using the substitution method, solve each of the systems of equations given at the end of the previous section.
Solve, using the substitution method:

**9.** $3x - 2y = 12$  $(4, 0)$
   $4x - 5y = 16$

**10.** $3y - 2 = x$
   $4x - 3 = y$

## 3 · Solving Systems of Equations by Addition

Examine the following arithmetic examples:

$$4 = 3 + 1$$
$$7 = 5 + 2$$
$$4 + 7 = (3 + 1) + (5 + 2)$$
or,   $$11 = 11$$

$$17 = 25 + (-8)$$
$$15\tfrac{1}{2} = 16 + (-\tfrac{1}{2})$$
$$17 + 15\tfrac{1}{2} = [25 + (-8)] + [16 + (-\tfrac{1}{2})]$$

or,   $32\tfrac{1}{2} = 32\tfrac{1}{2}$   [Check the computations for yourself]

The principle illustrated by the two examples above is a result of our basic principles for a field. It may be stated using variables as follows:

For all $a$, $b$, $c$, and $d$, if $a = b$ and $c = d$, then
$$a + c = b + d.$$

To state this principle in the same form as the examples above, we can write

$$a = b$$
$$c = d$$
$$a + c = b + d$$

This addition principle can be used in solving systems of equations. Take, for example, the system

$$2x - y = 3$$
$$x + 5y = 7$$

You know that every equation has many equivalent equations. We shall take the second equation above

$$x + 5y = 7$$

and find an equation which is equivalent to it. But we will choose a particular equivalent equation which turns out to be particularly well suited for our purpose. It will be your job to discover why we chose this particular equation.

The equation is $-2x + (-10y) = -14.$

Do you see that this equation is equivalent to the equation

$$x + 5y = 7?$$

Show how the equation $-2x + (-10y) = -14$ is obtained from $x + 5y = 7.$

You know that two equivalent equations have exactly the same roots. That is, the solution set of $x + 5y = 7$ is also the solution set of $-2x + (-10y) = -14.$

Let us take the first equation in our original system

$$2x - y = 3$$

and the newly obtained equation

$$-2x + (-10y) = -14$$

which is equivalent to the second equation in the original system. You know that whatever pair of numbers satisfies the system

$$2x - y = 3$$
$$-2x + (-10y) = -14$$

also satisfies the original system.

Now we use the addition principle

$$
\begin{aligned}
2x - y &= 3 \\
-2x + (-10y) &= -14 \\
(2x - y) + [-2x + (-10y)] &= 3 + (-14) \\
2x - y + (-2x) + (-10y) &= -11 \\
2x + (-2x) + (-y) + (-10y) &= -11 \\
0 + (-11y) &= -11 \\
-11y &= -11 \\
y &= 1
\end{aligned}
$$

(At this point you should see why we chose the equation $-2x + (-10y) = -14$ rather than some other equation. This choice led us to one equation in one variable which was easy to solve.)

Now we shall replace $y$ by 1 in one of the original equations.

$$
\begin{aligned}
2x - y &= 3 \\
2x - 1 &= 3 \\
2x &= 4 \\
x &= 2
\end{aligned}
$$

Thus, the pair (2, 1) should satisfy the system of two equations we have set out to solve. Checking,

$$(1) \quad 2x - y = 2 \cdot 2 - 1 \quad (2) \quad x + 5y = 2 + 5 \cdot 1$$
$$= 4 - 1 \qquad\qquad\qquad = 2 + 5$$
$$= 3 \qquad\qquad\qquad\quad = 7$$

The solution set of this system of equations is $\{(2, 1)\}$.

The method shown above is frequently called the *Addition Method*.

## EXERCISES

1. Using the addition method, solve each of the systems of equations in Exercises 1–8, page 271. ?

2. Solve each of the systems of equations below by *each* of the three methods you have just studied:

**a.** $m + n = 0$
$m - n = 2$

**b.** $2x - y = 0$
$2x + y = -4$

**c.** $3s = 2 - r$
$-2r = 4s + 2$

**d.** $2v = 4w + 1$
$v = w$

**e.** $7t + \dfrac{5}{2}u = 2$
$-2t = u - \dfrac{17}{2}$

**f.** $5y = 3z$
$2z = 3z + .1$ $\left(-\dfrac{3}{50}, -\dfrac{1}{10}\right).$

**g.** $\dfrac{x + y}{3} = 2$
$\dfrac{x - y}{2} = -1$

**h.** $10h - 6m = 2h + 1$
$2h = 12m + 9$

**i.** $5p + 6q = 2.5p - .28$
$5q = -1.5$

**j.** $\dfrac{2x + 4y}{-3} = -4y - x$
$-x = 4y + 1$

## 4 · Problems Leading to Systems of Equations

To know how to solve systems of equations is helpful in solving many types of problems. Consider, for example, the following problem.

**EXAMPLE** The sum of two numbers is 121. The sum of twice one of the numbers and three times the other number is 17. What are the two numbers?

**SOLUTION** If one number is $a$ and the other $b$, then we have the following two equations:

$$a + b = 121$$
$$2a + 3b = 17$$

We can use any one of the methods we know to solve this system of equations. Let us use the substitution method.

From the first equation

$$a + b = 121$$
$$a = 121 - b$$

Replacing $a$ by $121 - b$ in the second equation,

$$2(121 - b) + 3b = 17$$
$$242 - 2b + 3b = 17$$
$$242 + b = 17$$
$$b = 17 - 242$$
$$b = -225$$

Now replacing $b$ by $-225$ in the first equation (if you wish, you may replace $b$ by $-225$ in the second equation instead),

$$a + (-225) = 121$$
$$a = 121 + 225$$
$$a = 346$$

Thus, the numbers are 346 and $-225$.
Checking,
The sum is 121: $346 + (-225) = 121$
Twice the first number: $2 \times 346 = 692$
Three times the second number: $3 \times (-225) = -675$
The sum of twice the first
  and three times the second: $692 + (-675) = 17$

Thus, we know that the two numbers we are after are 346 and $-225$.

## EXERCISES

Write a system of equations to fit each problem and solve the system. Check the roots of the system in the original problem.

1. The sum of two numbers is 12. Their difference is 14. What are the numbers?

2. *A* and *B* are supplementary angles. *A* is twice as large as $\frac{2}{3}$ of *B*. Compute the measures of *A* and *B*.

3. Sally's father is 3 times as old as Sally is. Five years ago her father was 5 times as old as she was then. How old is Sally and how old is her father?

4. The length of a rectangle is twice its width. Its perimeter is 15 inches. How long is the side of the square whose area is equal to the area of the rectangle?

5. 12 oranges and 9 grapefruit cost $1.02. 20 oranges and 4 grapefruit cost $1.04. What is the price of each?

6. The total number of businesses which failed in 1958 and 1959 was 29,460. If there were 460 more failures in 1958 than 1959, how many businesses failed in each of the two years?

7. The units digit of a certain number is 1 more than twice the tens digit. When the digits are interchanged the resulting number is 2 more than twice the original number. What is the number?

8. A school received a shipment of algebra and geometry books costing $558.75. There were 25 more algebra books than geometry books. How many algebra and how many geometry books did the school purchase, if an algebra book costs $2.55 and a geometry book $2.95.

9. One angle of a triangle is twice as large as another angle. The sum of the degree measures of the two angles is 115. Compute the degree measure of all three angles.

10. In a parallelogram the measure of one angle is $\frac{2}{5}$ of the measure of the adjacent angle. What are the measures of the angles of this parallelogram?

11. The sum of the lengths of two line segments is 7 inches. If the length of the shorter line segment is tripled, the resulting segment is 1 inch shorter than the longer segment.

12. The length of each leg of an isosceles triangle is $2\frac{1}{2}$ times the length of the base. What is the length of each side of the triangle if the perimeter is 38 inches?

13. Mr. Wise invests a sum of money, one part of it earning annual interest at the rate of 4%, and the remainder at 5%. His total interest is $160.50 for one year. How much money did he invest at 4% and how much at 5%, if the total investment sum is $4,450?

## 5 · Inequalities

To solve equations, you needed certain basic principles governing the ways of handling equations. To solve inequalities, you will need some similar fundamental principles. They are already known to you and we will now show how they can be used in finding solution sets of inequalities.

From your work with real numbers, you know that the following is true:

**Inequality Principle.** Given a real number $x$, only one of the following holds:

a. $x$ is positive

b. $x = 0$

c. $-x$ is positive

We agreed that "$x > 0$" will mean "$x$ is positive" and "$x < 0$" will mean "$x$ is negative."

"$x > 0$" is also read "$x$ is greater than zero."

"$x < 0$" is also read "$x$ is less than zero."

"$x \geq 0$" is read "$x$ is greater than or equal to zero."

"$x \leq 0$" is read "$x$ is less than or equal to zero."

Now we shall define the phrase "$x < y$" as follows:

**Inequality Definition.** $x < y$ means $y - x$ is positive, or, $y - x > 0$.

Also, $x < y$ may be written $y > x$.

Using the Inequality Principle and Inequality Definition, we can prove a number of theorems, which you can then use in determining solution sets of inequalities.

*Inequality Theorem 1.* For any two real numbers $x$ and $y$, only one of the following is true:

a. $x < y$

b. $x = y$

c. $x > y$

**Proof:** First observe that $y - x$ is a real number, because the set of real numbers is closed under subtraction. Therefore by the Inequality Principle, only one of the following is true:

a. $y - x$ is positive

b. $y - x = 0$

c. $-(y - x)$ is positive

But $y - x$ is positive means the same as $y - x > 0$ and this means the same as $x < y$.

$y - x = 0$ means the same as $x = y$.

$-(y - x)$ is positive means the same as $-(y - x) > 0$ or $x - y > 0$ which means the same as $x > y$.

*Inequality Theorem 2.* If $x < y$, then $x + z < y + z$, for any real numbers $x$, $y$, and $z$.

> **Proof:** $x < y$ means $y - x > 0$
> but $y - x = (y + z) - (x + z)$
> therefore $(y + z) - (x + z) > 0$
> which means the same as $y + z > x + z$
> or $x + z < y + z$.

*Inequality Theorem 3.* If $x < y$ and $z > 0$, then $xz < yz$.

> **Proof:** $x < y$ means $y - x > 0$.
> Since $z > 0$, we have $(y - x)z > 0$ because the product of two positive numbers is a positive number.
> But $(y - x)z = yz - xz$;
> therefore $yz - xz > 0$,
> which means $yz > xz$
> or $xz < yz$.

## EXERCISES

1. Prove the following theorem:
   If $x < y$ and $z < 0$, then $xz > yz$.
   (Hint: Use the same approach as that used in the proof of Inequality Theorem 3, but remember that the product of a positive and negative number is a negative number.)

2. Prove the following theorem:
   If $x < y$ and $y < z$, then $x < z$.
   (This property is called the "transitive property.")
   [Hint: Use the following fact
   $$(y - x) + (z - y) = z - x]$$

## ★ 6 · Solution Sets of Inequalities

You will find the Inequality Theorems proved above helpful in finding solution sets of inequalities.

**EXAMPLE 1** What is the solution set of the inequality $3x + 5 > 10$?

**SOLUTION** (supply reasons)

$$3x + 5 > 10$$

$$3x + 5 + (-5) > 10 + (-5)$$

$$3x > 5$$

$$3x \cdot \tfrac{1}{3} > 5 \cdot \tfrac{1}{3}$$

$$x > \tfrac{5}{3}$$

The solution set of the inequality $3x + 5 > 10$ is the set of all numbers greater than $\tfrac{5}{3}$. Using set notation, we can describe this set by

$$s = \{x \mid x > \tfrac{5}{3}\}$$

Choose several numbers each greater than $\tfrac{5}{3}$ and check to see whether they satisfy $3x + 5 > 10$.

The graph of this solution set on the number line would be:

$S = \{x \mid x > \tfrac{5}{3}\}$

**EXAMPLE 2** What is the solution set of the inequality

$$-5m - 6 > 17?$$

**SOLUTION**

$$-5m - 6 > 17$$

$$-5m - 6 + 6 > 17 + 6$$

$$-5m > 23$$

$$-5m \cdot (-\tfrac{1}{5}) < 23 \cdot (-\tfrac{1}{5})$$

$$m < -\tfrac{23}{5}$$

The solution set of the inequality $-5m - 6 > 17$ is $T = \{m \mid m < -\tfrac{23}{5}\}$, that is the set consisting of all numbers less than $-\tfrac{23}{5}$.

Make a graph of this solution set.

The sentence $x \leq 5$ means "$x$ is less than *or* equal to 5." The solution set of this sentence, in the universe of real numbers, is the set of numbers consisting of 5 and all numbers less than 5. Thus, the solution set is the union of the solution sets of two sentences: $x < 5$ and $x = 5$.

**EXAMPLE 3**    What is the solution set of the inequality $2 + 2x \leq 5x - 3$?

**SOLUTION**    The solution set is the union of the solution sets of $2 + 2x < 5x - 3$ and $2 + 2x = 5x - 3$. We determine first the solution set of $2 + 2x < 5x - 3$.

$$2 + 2x < 5x - 3$$
$$2 + 2x - 2x < 5x - 3 - 2x$$
$$2 < 3x - 3$$
$$2 + 3 < 3x - 3 + 3$$
$$5 < 3x$$
$$\frac{5}{3} < \frac{3x}{3}$$
$$\frac{5}{3} < x$$
$$\text{or,} \quad x > \frac{5}{3}$$

Thus, $\{x \,|\, 2 + 2x < 5x - 3\} = \left\{x \,\middle|\, x > \dfrac{5}{3}\right\}$

Do you see that $\left\{x \,\middle|\, x = \dfrac{5}{3}\right\}$ is the solution set of the sentence $2 + 2x = 5x - 3$?
Thus, we have

$$\{x \,|\, 2 + 2x \leq 5x - 3\} = \left\{x \,\middle|\, x \geq \frac{5}{3}\right\}$$

# EXERCISES

Using the inequality theorems, determine the solution sets of the following inequalities. (Universe is the set of real numbers.)

1. $3x > -6$
2. $2x + 2 < -1$

**3.** $\frac{1}{2}y + 1 < y - 2$

**4.** $\frac{m}{3} + \frac{1}{2} > m - 1$

**5.** $\frac{n+1}{2} < n - 1$

**6.** $|\,p\,| < 1$   (Hint: $|\,p\,| < 1$ means $p < 1$ and $p > -1$)

**7.** $|\,r + 1\,| > 15$

**8.** $|\,s + 2\,| > 1$

**9.** $|\,5h\,| < 0$

**10.** $\frac{3}{4}t > t - 7$

**11.** $2x \leq 10$

**12.** $3y - 1 \geq 17$

**13.** $2z - 5 \leq z + 3$

**14.** $\frac{5u - 3}{2} \geq 3u + 1$

**15.** $\frac{3w - 1}{3} \leq \frac{2w + 3}{2}$

## ★ 7 · English Sentences and Inequalities

You already learned to make up stories to fit a given equation. Let us now do the same with inequalities.

EXAMPLE 1   Given the inequality $2n - 1 \geq 5$, make up a story which fits the inequality.

SOLUTION   Ed had a certain number of pebbles. If this number is doubled and one pebble is thrown away, he has at least five pebbles left. How many pebbles did Ed have to start with?

Note first that the universe here is the set of natural numbers. Why?

Could Ed have had one pebble? The answer is "no". because $2 \cdot 1 - 1 \geq 5$ is a false sentence.

Do you see that he had at least three pebbles? Here is a proof for this answer.

$2n - 1 \geq 5$ means $2n \geq 6$, which means $n \geq 3$.

The solution set is $\{3, 4, 5, 6, 7, \ldots\}$

**EXAMPLE 2**  The following story will fit the inequality $t + 7 \geq 18$.

On a canoe trip we paddle for one day. If we paddle seven miles the next day, we cover at least 18 miles during the two days. How many miles did we paddle during the first day?

The solution set here is $\{t \mid t \geq 11\}$. Thus, we paddled at least 11 miles during the second day.

**EXAMPLE 3**  For the inequality $y + 7 \leq 18$, the following story can be given.

If Joe puts 7 dollars in the bank, he will have at most 18 dollars. How many dollars did he have to start with? (What is the restriction on the replacement set here?) The answer is: Joe had at most $11.

## EXERCISES

Make up one story for each of the following sentences:

1. $2x + 1 \geq 11$

2. $\dfrac{m}{2} - 1 \leq 100$

3. $3n - 2 > n$

4. $s + 2 < 2s - 1$

Write open sentences which fit the following stories. Determine the solution set of each sentence. State the universal set in each case.

**EXAMPLE**  Five added to a number results in a number that is greater than twice the original number. From what set could have the original number been chosen?

**SOLUTION**  Open sentence:
$$5 + n > 2n$$
$$5 + n - n > 2n - n$$
$$5 > n$$
$$n < 5$$

Letting the universal set be the set of real numbers, the solution set consists of all real numbers less than 5.

5. 5 less than 3 times a certain number is less than the number increased by 2. What numbers satisfy this condition?

**6.** Joe is 7 years younger than Bill. The sum of their ages is less than 49. At most how old is Joe?

**7.** I am thinking of a number, which when added to 7, results in a number less than 11. What numbers satisfy this condition?

**8.** Section $A$ of algebra has 10 more students than section $B$. One half of the number of students in section $A$ added to half the number of students in section $B$ gives at least 30 students. How many students are there in each section?

## VOCABULARY

| | |
|---|---|
| Addition method (276) | Inequality theorems (279) |
| Comparison method (271) | Substitution method (273) |
| Inequality definition (279) | Systems of equations (269) |
| Inequality Principle (279) | Transitive property (280) |

........................................................................

## REVIEW EXERCISES

Solve each system of equations using any method you wish:

**1.** $3x + y = 5$
$x - y = 1$

**2.** $m = -n$
$10m - n = 3.3$

**3.** $\dfrac{p + r}{2} = \dfrac{1}{4}$
$r - 2p = 0$

**4.** $3z = -2w$
$\dfrac{6z + 10w}{3} = 2w$

**5.** $5r = t - 5$
$t + r = -1$

**6.** $3u + w = .25$
$\dfrac{u + w}{5} = -.01$

**7.** $3t + 5v = 110$
$5v - t = 44$

**8.** $x + u = 1$
$50x - u = 100x - 1.49$

Make equations to fit each problem, solve, and check the roots in the given problem:

9. The sum of two numbers is 16. Their difference is 18. What are the two numbers?

10. If one of two numbers is multiplied by 12 a number which is 16 less than the second number is obtained. What are the two numbers?

11. The perimeter of a rectangle is 21.4 inches. Twice the width is .2 inches less than the length. What are the dimensions of the rectangle?

12. A rectangle and square have equal perimeters. If the length of the rectangle is 2 inches more than a side of the square what are the dimensions of each figure, if the length of the rectangle is 4 inches more than its width?

13. A number is $\frac{1}{3}$ of the sum of itself and another number. What are the two numbers, if the first number is one-half of the second number?

14. In a triangle, the sum of the measures of two angles is 51°. If one of these angles is decreased by 11°, it will equal the other angle. What is the measure of each of the three angles of the triangle?

15. The length of an altitude of a triangle whose area is 64 sq. in. is one-half the length of the base. What is the length of the altitude and of the base?

16. A line segment 25 inches long is divided into three parts. Part $A$ is three times as long as Part $B$, and the length of Part $B$ is $\frac{2}{5}$ of the length of Part $C$. How long is each part?

17. Two bicyclists start out from the same point on a circular track with a radius of 60 feet. Bicyclist $A$ rides at a speed of 9 mph and bicyclist $B$ 12 mph. If they started out riding in opposite directions, how long will it take them to meet?

18. The difference between the measures of two complementary angles is 1°. How large is each of the two angles?

19. Mike's age 10 years ago was 7 times Ted's age. 5 years ago Mike's age was twice Ted's age. How old is each now?

20. Mrs. Housewife has two different size measuring spoons. 6 spoonfuls of the large spoon and 2 spoonfuls of the small spoon of flour give 5 lb of flour; 15 spoonfuls of the large spoon and 10 spoonfuls of the small spoon give 14 lb of flour. What is the pound capacity of each spoon?

Determine the solution set of each inequality. (The universe is the set of real numbers.) Graph each solution set on the number line.

★ 21. $x + 2 < -17$

★ 22. $2m + 7 > m$

★ 23. $-\frac{1}{2}y - 2 < 2y + 3$

★ 24. $-.7 + 6n > n - .8$

★ 25. $\frac{2p - 1}{3} > p - 2$

★ 26. $|r| > 1$

★ 27. $|3s - 2| < 2$

★ 28. $|4t + 17| < -1$

★ 29. $\frac{2u + 5}{3u - 2} > 1$

★ 30. $\frac{3 - r}{r - 3} + r > 2r - 1$

# CHAPTER TEST

Solve each problem.

1. The width of a rectangle is 20% less than the length. Compute the width and the length if the perimeter is 342 feet.

2. The sum of two numbers is 21. Three times the smaller number subtracted from the larger number gives 3. What are the two numbers?

3. Tommy is 3 times as old as Nancy. Four years ago he was 11 times as old as Nancy was then. How old is Tommy?

4. 3 is $\frac{5}{2}$ of what number?

5. A grocer mixes a certain number of pounds of 15¢ candy with some 12¢ candy. He obtains 32 pounds of mixed candy which sells for $4.44. How many pounds of each kind of candy did he use?

Determine the solution set for each inequality:

★ 6. $n - 6 > 2$

★ 7. $2x - 2 < 1$

★ 8. $3y + 4 < y - 7$

★ 9. $m > 4m - \frac{1}{2}$

★ 10. $\frac{p - 2}{3} > 6$

★ 11. $\frac{2r - 2}{7} < r + 11$

★ 12. $|w + 2| > 0$

★ 13. $|v - 6| < 0$

Determine the solution set for each system of equations:

14. $m + n = 3$
    $m - n = -4$

15. $p = 3r - 7$
    $r = 3p - 1$

**16.** $3(v + 2u) = 7(3u - 2v)$
$4v - 5(2v - u) = 5v + 4(v - 3u)$

**17.** $1.5x + .4z = 3.6$
$2.5z = 10.5 - .6x$

**18.** $2x - y = \dfrac{1}{2}$

$3x + 2y = -\dfrac{1}{4}$

**19.** $\dfrac{w + z}{3} = \dfrac{w - z}{2}$

$2w + 3z = 6$

# CUMULATIVE REVIEW

In Exercises 1–13 choose the correct answer.

**1.** Which one of the following sets is closed under the operation of subtraction?

   **a.** The set of even natural numbers
   **b.** The set of odd natural numbers
   **c.** The set of all negative integers
   **d.** The set of all directed rational numbers

**2.** Which of the following subsets of real numbers is not an infinite set?

   **a.** Rational numbers
   **b.** Negative integers greater than $-5$ and less than $-1$
   **c.** Irrational numbers
   **d.** Rational numbers less than 11 and greater than 3

**3.** The reciprocal of $-\frac{4}{5}$ is

   **a.** $\frac{4}{5}$
   **b.** $\frac{5}{4}$
   **c.** $0$
   **d.** $-\frac{5}{4}$

**4.** Which of the following pairs of sets are matching sets?

   **a.** $\{2, 3, \frac{22}{7}\}$, $\{\frac{19}{3}, 6, 9\}$
   **b.** $\{\frac{5}{9}, \frac{7}{13}, \frac{6}{7}, \frac{7}{18}\}$, $\{\frac{5}{6}, \frac{7}{13}, \frac{6}{11}\}$
   **c.** $\{a, b, d, e\}$, $\{1, 2, 4\}$
   **d.** $\{A, C, D, F, G\}$, $\{K, L, M, G, R, T\}$

**5.** Which of the following pairs of sets are disjoint sets?

    **a.** $\{1\}, \{1, 2\}$

    **b.** $\{\frac{1}{2}, \frac{1}{3}\}, \{.5\}$

    **c.** $\{\frac{1}{2}, \frac{1}{3}, \frac{1}{4}\}, \{\frac{2}{3}, \frac{3}{4}, \frac{4}{5}\}$

    **d.** $\{\frac{13}{3}, \frac{19}{7}, \frac{3}{2}\}, \{\frac{9}{4}, \frac{5}{2}, \frac{6}{7}, \frac{26}{6}\}$

**6.** Given the sets: $U = \{a, c, f, k, l, r, t, v\}$
$$A = \{a, c, f, k, l\}$$
$$B = \{k, f, r, t, v\}$$

Which of the following is true?

    **a.** $a \in A \cap B$          ★ **d.** $l \in \overline{A}$

    **b.** $l \in A \cap B$           **e.** $a \in \overline{A} \cup B$

    **c.** $r \in A \cap B$         ★ **f.** $\overline{A} \cap \overline{B} = \phi$

**7.** Which of the following is true?

    **a.** $4 \cdot [\frac{3}{4}(\frac{5}{3} + \frac{2}{3}) - \frac{1}{2}] = 5$

    **b.** $\frac{6}{5} + \frac{4}{3} \cdot \frac{3}{5} - \frac{9}{5} = -\frac{1}{5}$

    **c.** $\{[6 + (7 \cdot 8)] \cdot 2\} \cdot \frac{1}{4} = \frac{125}{4}$

    **d.** None of these

**8.** Which of the following statements is *true* for real numbers?

    **a.** Multiplication is distributive with respect to addition.

    **b.** Subtraction is distributive with respect to multiplication.

    **c.** Addition is distributive with respect to multiplication.

    **d.** Multiplication is distributive with respect to division.

**9.** Which of the following is true?

    **a.** $\frac{3}{8} \div \frac{1}{8} = \frac{1}{8} \times \frac{8}{3}$

    **b.** $\frac{3}{8} \times \frac{8}{5} = \frac{8}{5} \div \frac{8}{3}$

    **c.** $3 \div 8 = 6 \div 4$

    **d.** $\frac{8}{3} \times \frac{9}{8} = \frac{3}{8} \div \frac{8}{9}$

**10.** Which of the following is not a rational number?

    **a.** $\frac{7}{3}$

    **b.** $\sqrt{121}$

    **c.** $\frac{-8}{7}$

    **d.** $\sqrt{5}$

    **e.** $3.1416$

11. Which of the following is not a rational number?

    a. $.142857\overset{...}{14}28\overset{...}{57}$

    b. $\dfrac{3\pi}{2\pi}$

    c. $\pi$

    d. $-1.1666$

12. The opposite of $-(-x)$, for every $x$, is

    a. $x$

    b. $-x$

    c. $\dfrac{1}{x}$

    d. None of these

13. Which of the following is true for every replacement of $n$? (The replacement set for $n$ is the set of real numbers.)

    a. $|n| = n$

    b. $\left|\dfrac{n}{n}\right| = -1; (n \neq 0)$

    c. $|n \cdot n| = n^2$

    d. $|n + n| = 2n$

14. Compute the following square roots, carrying the computation to four decimal places and rounding off to three decimal places:

    a. $\sqrt{11.9}$                      b. $\sqrt{108.7}$

15. Replace the frames with number symbols to make the following statements true:

    a. $\tfrac{3}{8} \div \triangle = \tfrac{5}{9}$             e. $0 \div 7 = \bigcirc$

    b. $\square - \tfrac{9}{7} = \tfrac{3}{7}$              f. $3 \div \tfrac{9}{4} = \triangle$

    c. $\tfrac{22}{7} \times \square = \tfrac{3}{8}$             g. $-7 + \square = 8$

    d. $\square + (-\tfrac{9}{13}) = -\tfrac{5}{3}$

16. Replace frames with integer names to obtain (1) a true statement, (2) a false statement.

    a. $\triangle \not< 7$                d. $3\triangle \leq -6$

    b. $3\square \neq -5$            e. $7 \neq 4(\triangle + 2)$

    c. $\dfrac{\square}{6} \geq 7$              f. $5(3 - \square) \geq 7$

**17.** Label each statement as true or false. If $x < 0$,

    **a.** $|x| > x$

    **b.** $-|x| = x$

    **c.** $|x| = -x$

    **d.** $|x| \neq x$

    **e.** $x + x = 2x$

    **f.** $x + x = -2x$

    **g.** $\dfrac{x}{x} = -1$

    **h.** $\dfrac{x}{x} = 1$

**18.** Label as true or false

    **a.** $-6 + (-13) = -7$

    **b.** $9 + (-13) = -4$

    **c.** $-11 - (-15) = -4$

    **d.** $2 + (-7) \neq -5$

    **e.** $19 - 14 \neq +15$

    **f.** $\frac{7}{9} - \frac{8}{9} = -\frac{1}{9}$

Justify progressing from each expression to its equivalent by indicating what principle is involved.

**19.**

$$7[(\tfrac{1}{7} + \tfrac{2}{3}) + \tfrac{5}{7}] \overset{(1)}{=} 7 \cdot [(\tfrac{2}{3} + \tfrac{1}{7}) + \tfrac{5}{7}]$$
$$\overset{(2)}{=} 7 \cdot [\tfrac{2}{3} + (\tfrac{1}{7} + \tfrac{5}{7})]$$
$$\overset{(3)}{=} 7 \cdot (\tfrac{2}{3} + \tfrac{6}{7})$$
$$\overset{(4)}{=} 7 \cdot \left(\frac{7 \cdot 2}{7 \cdot 3} + \frac{3 \cdot 6}{3 \cdot 7}\right)$$
$$\overset{(5)}{=} 7 \cdot \tfrac{32}{21}$$
$$\overset{(6)}{=} \tfrac{7}{21} \cdot 32$$
$$\overset{(7)}{=} \tfrac{1}{3} \cdot 32$$
$$\overset{(8)}{=} \tfrac{32}{3}$$

**20.**

$$3 \cdot (\tfrac{1}{5} + x) + \tfrac{4}{5} \overset{(1)}{=} (\tfrac{3}{5} + 3x) + \tfrac{4}{5}$$
$$\overset{(2)}{=} (3x + \tfrac{3}{5}) + \tfrac{4}{5}$$
$$\overset{(3)}{=} 3x + (\tfrac{3}{5} + \tfrac{4}{5})$$
$$\overset{(4)}{=} 3x + \tfrac{7}{5}$$

**21.**

$$6[(x + 7) + x] \overset{(1)}{=} 6(x + 7) + 6 \cdot x$$
$$\overset{(2)}{=} 6x + 6 \cdot 7 + 6x$$
$$\overset{(3)}{=} 6x + (6x + 6 \cdot 7)$$
$$\overset{(4)}{=} (6x + 6x) + 6 \cdot 7$$
$$\overset{(5)}{=} (6 + 6) \cdot x + 6 \cdot 7$$
$$\overset{(6)}{=} 12x + 42$$

**22.**
$$\tfrac{1}{3} \cdot (\tfrac{1}{5} \cdot \tfrac{2}{3}) \overset{(1)}{=} (\tfrac{1}{5} \cdot \tfrac{2}{3}) \cdot \tfrac{1}{3}$$
$$\overset{(2)}{=} (\tfrac{2}{3} \cdot \tfrac{1}{5}) \cdot \tfrac{1}{3}$$
$$\overset{(3)}{=} \tfrac{2}{3} \cdot (\tfrac{1}{5} \cdot \tfrac{1}{3})$$

**23.**
$$1 \cdot [5 \cdot 9 + 5 \cdot 8] \overset{(1)}{=} 1 \cdot [5(9 + 8)]$$
$$\overset{(2)}{=} [5 \cdot (9 + 8)] \cdot 1$$
$$\overset{(3)}{=} 5(9 + 8)$$

**24.**
$$x \cdot (6 + 0) \overset{(1)}{=} x \cdot 6 + x \cdot 0$$
$$\overset{(2)}{=} x \cdot 6 + 0$$
$$\overset{(3)}{=} x \cdot 6$$
$$\overset{(4)}{=} 6 \cdot x$$

**25.** Solve each of the following equations:

**a.** $-2a = 21$

**b.** $3m + 5 = 2$

**c.** $\tfrac{1}{2} + 4x = x - 1$

**d.** $|c - 3| = \tfrac{1}{2}$

**e.** $(2t - 4) \cdot \tfrac{1}{2} = \tfrac{1}{3}$

**f.** $\dfrac{n + 2}{2n - 1} = -1$

**g.** $u(2u + 7) = 0$

**26.** State the addition and the multiplication principles for equations and give one specific example of the use of each.

**27.** The Principle of One for Multiplication may be stated as:

$$\text{For every } n, \; n \cdot 1 = n$$

As above, state each of the following principles:

**a.** The Principle of Addition of Zero.

**b.** The Principle of Multiplication by Zero.

**c.** The Commutative Principle for Multiplication.

**d.** The Associative Principle for Addition.

**e.** The Distributive Principle.

Solve each of the following problems:

**28.** Adding $-6$ to a number gives the same result as 3 times this number. What is the number?

**29.** Doubling 2 more than a certain number gives 15. What is the certain number?

**30.** A car traveling 45 mph, is traveling how many feet per second?

**31.** What is the area of the interior of a rectangle whose length is 2 feet and whose width is 13 inches?

**32.** What is the cost of an article priced at \$209.98 after 3% tax is added?

**33.** What is the measure of the smaller angle formed by the hands of a clock at 2:15?

**34.** Below there are given six pairs of equations. For each of the four graphs, find one or more pairs of equations represented in the graph.

**a.** $y - 4x = -2$
$x + 4y = 12$

**b.** $x + y = -2$
$x - 2y = 1$

**c.** $y - 3x = 4$
$3x - y = -1$

**d.** $y - x = -2$
$2(x - y) = 4$

**e.** $4x - y = 2$
$x + y = 1$

**f.** $3x - y = 4$
$y - 3x = 2$

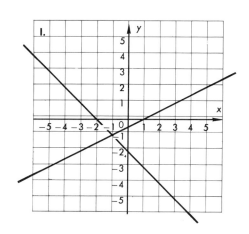

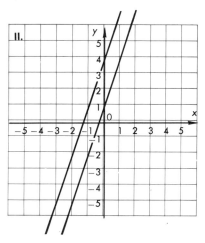

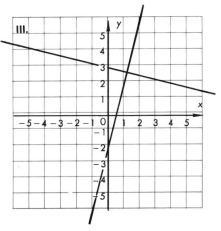

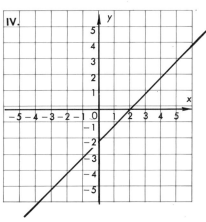

Justify each step by a basic principle.

**35.**
$$(y - x) + (y + x) \overset{(1)}{=} [y + (-x)] + (y + x)$$
$$\overset{(2)}{=} [y + (-x)] + (x + y)$$
$$\overset{(3)}{=} y + [(-x) + x] + y$$
$$\overset{(4)}{=} y + [x + (-x)] + y$$
$$\overset{(5)}{=} (y + 0) + y$$
$$\overset{(6)}{=} y + y$$
$$\overset{(7)}{=} 1 \cdot y + 1 \cdot y$$
$$\overset{(8)}{=} (1 + 1)y$$
$$\overset{(9)}{=} 2y$$

**36.**
$$(-r) \cdot s \overset{(1)}{=} [(-1)(r)]s$$
$$\overset{(2)}{=} (-1)(rs)$$
$$\overset{(3)}{=} -rs$$

**37.**
$$-\frac{(x + y)}{t + v} \overset{(1)}{=} \frac{(-1)[x + y]}{t + v}$$
$$\overset{(2)}{=} \frac{(-1)(x) + (-1)(y)}{t + v}$$
$$\overset{(3)}{=} \frac{(-x) + (-y)}{t + v}$$
$$\overset{(4)}{=} \frac{-x - y}{t + v}$$

**38.** Which of the following are true for all real number replacements of the variables?

**a.** $\dfrac{-s}{t} = \dfrac{s}{-t}, \; t \neq 0$  **b.** $\dfrac{-vx}{t} = \dfrac{v(-x)}{t}, \; t \neq 0$

**c.** $-\dfrac{-(x - y)}{-(t + v)} = \dfrac{-(x - y)}{(t + v)}, \; (t + v) \neq 0$

★ **39.** Graph the following using the real numbers as the universal set of the first and second components:

**a.** $A = \{(x, y) \,|\, x + y = 9 \text{ or } |x| + |y| = 9\}$
**b.** $B = \{(x, y) \,|\, x + y \leq -2 \text{ and } x + 3 = 5\}$
**c.** $C = \{(x, y) \,|\, x - y \neq 3 \text{ or } |y| < 2\}$

In Exercises 40–50, choose the correct answer:

**40.** The single fractional expression equivalent to $\frac{x}{r} + \frac{y}{t}$ $(r \neq 0, t \neq 0)$ is

(a) $\frac{x+y}{rt}$
(b) $\frac{x+y}{r+t}$
(c) $\frac{xr+yt}{rt}$
(d) $\frac{xt+ry}{rt}$

**41.** The solution set of $2 - \frac{4}{r} = \frac{7}{5r}$ $(r \neq 0)$ is

(a) $\left\{\frac{10}{27}\right\}$
(b) $\left\{\frac{-27}{10}\right\}$
(c) $\left\{\frac{27}{10}\right\}$
(d) $\left\{\frac{-10}{27}\right\}$

**42.** The root of the equation $\frac{3}{t-5} = \frac{7}{t} - \frac{5}{t}$ $(t \neq 0, t \neq 5)$ is

(a) 5
(b) −5
(c) 50
(d) −10

**43.** The solution set of $2r + 5 + \frac{3}{2}r = 4r$ is

(a) {1}
(b) $\left\{\frac{1}{10}\right\}$
(c) {100}
(d) {10}

**44.**

The set depicted on the number line is
(a) $\{x \mid x \in$ naturals, $x > -3\}$
(b) $\{x \mid x \in$ integers, $-4 < x < 3\}$
(c) $\{x \mid x \in$ rationals, $-3 \leq x \leq 2\}$
(d) None of these

**45.** Which of the following is *not* a solution set of $2x + y = -4$?
(a) $\{(0, -4)\}$
(b) $\{(-5, 6)\}$
(c) $\{(-2, 0)\}$
(d) $\{(-1, -1)\}$

**46.** Which of the following is a pair of disjoint sets?
(The universe is the set of real numbers.)
(a) $\{x \mid x \leq 0\}$; $\{x \mid x \geq 0\}$
(b) $\{x \mid 3 < x \leq 7\}$; $\{x \mid 7 \leq x < 8\}$
(c) $\{x \mid -3 < x < -2\}$; $\{x \mid -2 < x < 0\}$
(d) $\{x \mid |x| > 0\}$; $\{x \mid |x| < 0\}$

**47.** If Johnny rides his bicycle at the speed of 12 miles per hour what distance in miles does he cover in 9 minutes?

(a) 1
(b) $1\frac{2}{3}$
(c) $1\frac{1}{2}$
(d) $1\frac{4}{5}$

**48.** Which of the following is the empty set? (The universe is the set of integers).

**(a)** $\{n \mid |n + 1| > 150\}$        **(c)** $\{n \mid |n + 1 < 0\}$

**(b)** $\{n \mid |n + 1| < 1\}$        **(d)** $\{n \mid |n + 1 < .006\}$

**49.** Which of the following sets has less than 5 members in it? (The universe is the set of integers).

**(a)** $\{m \mid -6 \leq m \leq -10$        **(c)** $\{m \mid -997 \leq m \leq -1001\}$

**(b)** $\{m \mid -4 \leq m \leq 0\}$        **(d)** $\{m \mid -997 < m \leq -1001\}$

**50.** Which of the following equations is equivalent to $2x - y = \frac{1}{2}$?

**(a)** $y - 2x = \frac{1}{2}$        **(c)** $y - 2x = -\frac{1}{2}$

**(b)** $y - 2x = 2$        **(d)** $y - 2x = -2$

# BIBLIOGRAPHY

Bakst, A., *Mathematics—Its Magic and Mastery*, Van Nostrand, Toronto, 1952, pages 329–358, "How to Have Fun with Lady Luck."

Bakst, A., *Mathematical Puzzles and Pastimes*, Van Nostrand, Toronto, 1954, pages 151–170.

Court, Nathan, *Mathematics in Fun and Earnest*, Dial Press, New York, 1958.

Gamow, G., *One, Two, Three, . . ., Infinity*, Mentor Books, 1947.

School Mathematics Study Group, *Mathematics for High School: First Course in Algebra (Revised Edition)*, SMSG, New Haven, Connecticut, 1960, chapter 9.

# Exponents and Radicals

## 1 · Exponents and Multiplication

We recall the agreement that $3 \times 3$ and $3^2$ [read: "the square of three" or "three squared" or "the second power of three"] name the same number, or, $3 \times 3 = 3^2$. Similarly $(4)(4)(4)$ and $(4)^3$ [read: "the cube of four" or "four cubed" or "the third power of four"] name the same number, or $(4)(4)(4) = (4)^3$. How would you write $2 \times 2 \times 2 \times 2 \times 2$ using the abbreviation above?

In $3^2$, the 2 is called an **exponent** and 3 is called the **base.**

$$3^2 \leftarrow \text{exponent}$$
$$\nearrow$$
$$\text{base}$$

Is there a positive integer whose square is equal to 169? We could write $\triangle^2 = 169$, or $x^2 = 169$, or $r^2 = 169$, and in each case we would find that the number 13 is an answer, because $13^2 = 169$.

We agree that

$$\triangle^2 = \triangle \cdot \triangle, \text{ or } x^2 = x \cdot x, \text{ or } r^2 = r \cdot r$$

and $\qquad \triangle^3 = \triangle \cdot \triangle \cdot \triangle \text{ or } x^3 = x \cdot x \cdot x \text{ or } r^3 = r \cdot r \cdot r$

Is it possible to find a simpler name for $2^3 \times 2^4$? According to our agreement,

$$2^3 \times 2^4 = (2 \times 2 \times 2) \times (2 \times 2 \times 2 \times 2)$$
$$= 2 \times 2 \times 2 \times 2 \times 2 \times 2 \times 2$$
$$= 2^7$$

Thus, $2^3 \times 2^4 = 2^7$.

In a like manner it is reasonable to agree that for all replacements of $x$, $x^2 \cdot x^3 = x \cdot x \cdot x \cdot x \cdot x = x^5$.

Also, for all replacements of $x$, $x^2 \cdot x = x^3$ and $x^5 \cdot x^3 = x^8$.

It follows then that for all $x$ and for all natural number replacements for $m$ and $n$, the following principle is true:

$$x^m \cdot x^n = x^{m+n}$$

According to our previous agreement this means $x^2 \cdot x^2 \cdot x^2 = x^6$. By the same token we observe $(x^3)^3 = x^9$; $(x^3)^2 = x^6$; $(x^4)^2 = x^8$. Each of the following expressions

$$x \cdot x \cdot y \cdot y, \quad x \cdot y \cdot x \cdot y, \quad y \cdot y \cdot x \cdot x, \quad (xy)^2$$

is equivalent to $x^2y^2$ or $y^2x^2$.

How can we simplify $x^2y \cdot xy^3$?

This can be simplified to $x \cdot x \cdot y \cdot x \cdot y \cdot y \cdot y$, which is equivalent to $x^3y^4$.

What would be equivalent to $\left(\dfrac{x}{y}\right)^r$? According to our definition of raising a number to a power

$$\left(\frac{x}{y}\right)^r = \frac{x}{y} \cdot \frac{x}{y} \cdot \ \ldots \ \cdot \frac{x}{y} \quad (r \text{ factors})$$

$$= \frac{x \cdot x \cdot \ \ldots \ \cdot x}{y \cdot y \cdot \ \ldots \ \cdot y} = \frac{x^r}{y^r} \quad \begin{array}{l} (r \text{ factors of } x) \\ (r \text{ factors of } y) \end{array}$$

**EXAMPLE**    Simplify $(x^2y^3)^3$

**SOLUTION**
$$(x^2y^3)^3 = (x^2y^3) \cdot (x^2y^3) \cdot (x^2y^3)$$
$$= x^2 \cdot x^2 \cdot x^2 \cdot y^3 \cdot y^3 \cdot y^3$$
$$= x^6y^9$$

Thus, $(x^2y^3)^3 = x^6y^9$

To summarize : **For all real numbers $a$ and $b$, and for all natural numbers $x$ and $y$, $a^x \cdot a^y = a^{x+y}$ and $(ab)^x = a^x b^x$.**

**Also, for all real numbers $a$ and $b$ ($b \neq 0$), and for any natural number $x$, $\left(\dfrac{a}{b}\right)^x = \dfrac{a^x}{b^x}$**

**For all natural numbers $x$ and $y$ and for any real number $a$, $(a^x)^y = a^{xy}$**

## EXERCISES

**1.** Give number names involving no exponents for each of the following:

**a.** $3^4$

**b.** $(-5)^2$

**c.** $\left(-\dfrac{3}{4}\right)^3$

**d.** $6 \cdot (7)^2$

**e.** $\left(\dfrac{2}{3}\right)^5$

**f.** $(-2)^4$

**g.** $3 \cdot (-2)^4$

**h.** $(6 \cdot 3)^2$

**i.** $4 \cdot (3 \cdot 5)^2$

**j.** $4 \cdot \left(\dfrac{6}{7}\right)^2$

**k.** $(-2)^4(-2)^3$

**l.** $\left(-\dfrac{1}{2}\right)^2\left(-\dfrac{1}{2}\right)^3\left(-\dfrac{1}{2}\right)^5$

**2.** Perform the operations to obtain simpler equivalent expressions:

**a.** $x^4x^5$

**b.** $(r^2)^4$

**c.** $(rs)^6$

**d.** $zz^3z^5$

**e.** $(3r)^2$

**f.** $\left(\dfrac{5d}{3}\right)^3$

**g.** $3xy(5x^2y^3)$

**h.** $(r^6r^2)^4$

**i.** $(w^2v)^5$

**j.** $(-rs^2)^4$

**k.** $yy^5y^7$

**l.** $(r^2s^3)^4$

**m.** $\left(\dfrac{2}{3}\right)^6$

**n.** $2r^3t^2(3r^4t^5)$

**o.** $(-6r^4)^2$

**p.** $\left(\dfrac{c}{3}\right)^4$

**q.** $\left(\dfrac{5}{9}\right)^2$

**r.** $-w^2v^4(3w^3v^5)$

**s.** $(x^2y^3)^5$

**t.** $(wv^3)^2$

**u.** $3rt^2(5r^2t)^2$

**v.** $(2^3 \cdot 2^5)^2$

**w.** $(-3c^2d)^2 \cdot (2cd^2)^3$

**x.** $(4r^2t^3)^5$

**3.** Just by looking at each of the following, tell whether it names a positive or a negative number

**a.** $2^4$

**b.** $(-1)^3$

**c.** $(-1)^{17}$

**d.** $(-1)^6$

**e.** $(-1)^4$

**f.** $(-17)^4$

**g.** $(-17)^{17}$

**h.** $125^4$

**i.** $125^{23}$

**j.** $(-125)^{37}$

**k.** $(-100)^{100}$

**l.** $(-100)^{1001}$

**m.** $(-2)^4(-2)^9$

**n.** $(-17)^4(-17)^{12}$

**o.** $(-100)^{97}(-100)^{98}$

## 2 · Exponents and Division

How can we simplify $3^5 \div 3^2$? This expression is equivalent to $\dfrac{3 \cdot 3 \cdot 3 \cdot 3 \cdot 3}{3 \cdot 3}$, which is equivalent to $3 \cdot 3 \cdot 3$ or $3^3$.

Check the following statements:

(a) $\dfrac{2^6}{2^2} = 2^4$      (b) $\dfrac{5^6}{5^2} = 5^4$      (c) $\dfrac{2^5}{2^2} = 2^3$      (d) $\dfrac{3^4}{3} = 3^3$

Did you find that each of the above statements is true?
It follows then that

$$\frac{x^5}{x^2} = \frac{x \cdot x \cdot x \cdot x \cdot x}{x \cdot x} = x \cdot x \cdot x = x^3, \ (x \neq 0).$$

How can we simplify $\dfrac{x^3 y^4}{xy^2}$?

This expression is equivalent to

$$\frac{x \cdot x \cdot x \cdot y \cdot y \cdot y \cdot y}{x \cdot y \cdot y}, \text{ or } \frac{x \cdot x \cdot y : y}{1} \text{ or } x^2 y^2.$$

Thus, $\dfrac{x^3 y^4}{xy^2} = x^2 y^2, \ (x \neq 0, \ y \neq 0)$.

How can we simplify $\dfrac{x^3 y^2 z^4}{xyz^2}$?

This expression is equivalent to

$$\frac{x \cdot x \cdot x \cdot y \cdot y \cdot z \cdot z \cdot z \cdot z}{xyzz}, \text{ or } \frac{x \cdot x \cdot y \cdot z \cdot z}{1}, \text{ or } x^2 y z^2$$

Thus, $\dfrac{x^3 y^2 z^4}{xyz^2} = x^2 yz^2, \ (x \neq 0, \ y \neq 0, \ z \neq 0)$.

All of the above examples point to the following principle:

$$\frac{x^b}{x^a} = x^{b-a}, \qquad \textbf{a and b positive integers (b > a),}$$
$$\textbf{and}$$
$$\textbf{x is a real number (x} \neq \textbf{0).}$$

What about the following cases?

(a) $\dfrac{2^3}{2^3}$      (b) $3^4 \div 3^4$      (c) $\dfrac{(-3)^2}{(-3)^2}$      (d) $\dfrac{4^6}{4^6}$

Applying our principles to (a) we have the equivalent expressions

$$\frac{2^3}{2^3} = \frac{2 \cdot 2 \cdot 2}{2 \cdot 2 \cdot 2},$$

and this, according to our previous pattern, is equivalent to 1.

Or you may think of each of these examples as a number divided by itself, which, of course, is 1. Thus:

$$\frac{2^3}{2^3} = 1; \quad \frac{3^4}{3^4} = 1; \quad \frac{(-3)^2}{(-3)^2} = 1; \quad \frac{4^6}{4^6} = 1$$

or generally,

$$\frac{x^m}{x^m} = 1 \quad \text{for every real number } x(x \neq 0) \text{ and every positive integer } m.$$

If the principle $\frac{x^b}{x^a} = x^{b-a}$ is to hold for $b = a$, we have

$$\frac{x^m}{x^m} = x^{m-m} = x^0 = 1 \quad (x \neq 0).$$

To look at it another way,

$$x^a \cdot x^b = x^{a+b}$$

Therefore,

$$x^0 \cdot x^1 = x^{0+1} = x^1,$$

and $x^0$ must be 1 if the principle of one for multiplication is to hold.

Thus, for every non-zero real number $x$,

$$x^0 = 1$$

What about the meaning of a negative number exponent? For example, what does $2^{-2}$ mean?

To answer this question, we examine the expression $2^2 \cdot 2^{-2}$. If $x^a \cdot x^b = x^{a+b}$ is to hold, we have

$$2^2 \cdot 2^{-2} = 2^{2+(-2)} = 2^0 = 1.$$

From our study of number fields, we recall that if the product of two numbers is 1, each number is the reciprocal of the other. Thus, since $.2^2 \cdot 2^{-2} = 1$ and $2^2 \cdot \frac{1}{2^2} = 1$,

$$2^{-2} = \frac{1}{2^2}$$

Generally, if $c^x \cdot c^{-x} = c^{x+(-x)} = c^0 = 1 \ (c \neq 0,)$ is to be true, it must hold that $c^{-x}$ is the reciprocal of $c^x$

or, $$c^{-x} = \frac{1}{c^x}$$

Hence, $3^{-4} = \dfrac{1}{3^4}$, $(-2)^{-3} = \dfrac{1}{(-2)^3}$, $5^{-2} = \dfrac{1}{5^2}$, $4^{-3} = \dfrac{1}{4^3}$, and $\left(\dfrac{1}{3}\right)^{-2} = 3^2$

are all true statements.

We now proceed to show that for all real numbers $c \neq 0$, and all integers $x$ and $y$, $\dfrac{c^x}{c^y} = c^{x-y}$.

$$\dfrac{c^x}{c^y} \text{ may be expressed as } c^x \cdot \dfrac{1}{c^y}$$

$$\dfrac{c^x}{c^y} = c^x \cdot \dfrac{1}{c^y} = c^x \cdot c^{-y} = c^{x+(-y)} = c^{x-y}$$

$$\text{Thus, } \dfrac{c^x}{c^y} = c^{x-y}.$$

**EXAMPLE 1**    $\dfrac{4^{-3} \cdot 4^7}{4^2} = \dfrac{4^{-3+7}}{4^2} = \dfrac{4^4}{4^2} = 4^2$

**EXAMPLE 2**    $\dfrac{(-2)^5 \cdot (-2)^{-2}}{(-2)^{-6}}$

$$= \dfrac{(-2)^{5-2}}{(-2)^{-6}} = \dfrac{(-2)^3}{(-2)^{-6}} = (-2)^{3-(-6)} = (-2)^9$$

**EXAMPLE 3**    $\dfrac{r^{-2} \cdot r^7}{r^2} = \dfrac{r^{-2+7}}{r^2} = \dfrac{r^5}{r^2} = r^3$

Fill in the details for yourself.

# EXERCISES

Perform the operations to obtain simpler equivalent expressions.

1. $\dfrac{x^5}{x}$

2. $\dfrac{y^4}{y^{17}}$

3. $\dfrac{c^2 m^3}{cm}$

4. $\dfrac{14y^3}{2y}$

5. $\dfrac{18x^3 y^5}{3xy^2}$

6. $\dfrac{-15r^7 s^5}{-3r^2 s^3}$

7. $\dfrac{-21abc}{3a^3 b^4 c^5}$

8. $\dfrac{c^x b^2 y}{c^x b^y}$

9. $\dfrac{-48r^5 s^1}{-3r^3 s^7}$

10. $\dfrac{m^{-2} n^3}{m^{-7} n^4}$

11. $\dfrac{-3r^3 s^2}{4r^2 s}$

12. $\dfrac{-2k^{-2} m^{-1}}{4k^3}$

## 3 · Rational Number Exponents

You know that $3^2 = 9$. We say then that 3 is a **square root** of 9. Also $(-3)^2 = 9$, therefore $-3$ is a square root of 9. Similarly, $2^3 = 8$, so 2 is a **cube root** of 8. It so happens that no other real number cubed gives 8.

Generally, if $x^n = c$, where $n$ is a positive integer, we say that $x$ is an $n$th root of $c$.

Frequently it is said that 3 is *the* square root of 9. We shall say that the **principal square root** of a number is its positive square root. The **principal root** of a real number is the positive real root in the case of roots of positive numbers; it is the negative real root in the case of odd roots of negative numbers. For example, 3 is the principal square root of 9; 4 is the principal cube root of 64; 5 is the principal fourth root of 625; and 10 is the principal fifth root of 100,000.

The examples above are written in mathematical symbolism as follows:

$$\sqrt{9} = 3; \quad \sqrt[3]{64} = 4; \quad \sqrt[4]{625} = 5; \quad \sqrt[5]{100{,}000} = 10$$

You can easily see that no negative number has a real number as its square root. If it did, there would be a real number which when multiplied by itself would give a negative number for the product. You know that there is no such real number.

We shall accept a principle that every positive real number has exactly one positive square root.

Let $r$ and $n$ be two real numbers. If $r$ is a square root of $n$, then $r^2 = n$. But $(-r)^2 = r^2 = n$ is also true, therefore $-r$ is also a square root of $n$. If $r$ is positive, then $r$ is the principal square root of $c$ and $-r$ is negative.

$\sqrt{c}$ is the positive or principal square root of $c$

$-\sqrt{c}$ then is a negative number

$$(\sqrt{c})^2 = c$$

$$(-\sqrt{c})^2 = c$$

For example, $\sqrt{9}$ is the principal square root of 9; $(\sqrt{9})^2 = 9$. The other square root of 9 is a negative number, namely $-\sqrt{9}$; $(-\sqrt{9})^2 = 9$.

Similarly, there are two square roots of 5. $\sqrt{5}$ is the principal square root of 5, $(\sqrt{5})^2 = 5$. $-\sqrt{5}$ is the other square of 5, $(-\sqrt{5})^2 = 5$.

There are two square roots of 81, 9 and $-9$. $9^2 = 81$. $(-9)^2 = 81$.

$$\text{Thus, } \sqrt{81} = 9, \ -\sqrt{81} = -9$$

You know that $(-9)^2 = 9^2 = 81$. We can say then that

$$\sqrt{(-9)^2} = \sqrt{9^2} = 9$$

It is clear from the last statement that $\sqrt{n^2} = n$ is *not* true for all real numbers $n$, since, for example, $\sqrt{(-9)^2} \neq -9$. But it is true that $\sqrt{(-9)^2} = |-9| = 9$.

A general principle concerning square root is

$$\sqrt{n^2} = |n|$$

Here are some illustrations of this principle:

EXAMPLES
$$\sqrt{(-2)^2} = |-2| = 2$$
$$\sqrt{(-5)^2} = |-5| = 5$$
$$\sqrt{(-\tfrac{1}{2})^2} = |-\tfrac{1}{2}| = \tfrac{1}{2}$$
$$\sqrt{3^2} = |3| = 3$$
$$\sqrt{6^2} = |6| = 6$$
$$\sqrt{(\tfrac{1}{3})^2} = |\tfrac{1}{3}| = \tfrac{1}{3}$$

We call the symbol $\sqrt[r]{c}$ a **radical**. The number $c$ is called the **radicand**. Thus, $\sqrt{9}$ is a radical, and 9 is the radicand.

Since 3 is $\sqrt{9}$, we know that $(\sqrt{9})^2 = 9$. Similarly, since 4 is $\sqrt[3]{64}$, $(\sqrt[3]{64})^3 = 64$. In general,

$$(\sqrt[r]{c})^r = c.$$

We would like to use fractional exponents in a way that will preserve the principles already developed for positive integer exponents.

Consider $c^{\frac{1}{r}}$ where $c$ is a real number and $r$ is a positive integer. According to an earlier principle, $(c^a)^b = c^{ab}$. If we want this to hold for $a$ and $b$ rational numbers, we get

$$\left(c^{\frac{1}{r}}\right)^r = c^{\frac{1}{r} \cdot r} = c^1 = c$$

But we have

$$(\sqrt[r]{c})^r = c$$

$$\text{Therefore, } \sqrt[r]{c} = c^{\frac{1}{r}}$$

According to this principle,

$$\sqrt[3]{8} = 8^{\frac{1}{3}} = 2$$

$$\sqrt[3]{-27} = (-27)^{\frac{1}{3}} = -3$$

$$\sqrt[4]{16} = 16^{\frac{1}{4}} = 2$$

We defined $c^{\frac{1}{r}}$ only when $r$ is a positive integer. Actually, we would like to use fractional powers in such a way that all exponents will follow the principles already developed for positive integral powers.

If these principles are to hold

$$3^{\frac{1}{2}} \cdot 3^{\frac{1}{2}} = \sqrt{3} \cdot \sqrt{3} = 3$$

or

$$\left(3^{\frac{1}{2}}\right)^2 = 3$$

Hence, $3^{\frac{1}{2}}$ must be equivalent to the principal square root of three. Also,

$$2^{\frac{3}{2}} \cdot 2^{\frac{3}{2}} = 2^3 \text{ or } \left(2^{\frac{3}{2}}\right)^2 = 2^3$$

Thus, $2^{\frac{3}{2}}$ should be equivalent to the principal square root of $2^3$.

Accordingly, we define $c^{\frac{v}{r}}$ where $v$ and $r$ are positive integers and $c$ a real number $\neq 0$, to be the principal $r$-th root of $c^v$.

Thus, $c^{\frac{v}{r}} = \sqrt[r]{c^v}$

It also can be readily seen that $c^{\frac{v}{r}} = (\sqrt[r]{c})^v$ also will hold. For example,

$$16^{\frac{3}{4}} = \left(16^{\frac{1}{4}}\right)^3 = \sqrt[4]{16^3} = 8 \text{ and}$$

$$27^{\frac{2}{3}} = \sqrt[3]{(27)^2} = \left(27^{\frac{1}{3}}\right)^2 = 9.$$

$$(\sqrt{3} \cdot \sqrt{5})^2 = \left(3^{\frac{1}{2}} \cdot 5^{\frac{1}{2}}\right)^2 = \left(3^{\frac{1}{2}}\right)^2\left(5^{\frac{1}{2}}\right)^2$$

$$= 3 \times 5 = 15.$$

Thus, by the definition of a square root, $\sqrt{3} \cdot \sqrt{5}$ is a square root of $3 \cdot 5$, or

$$\sqrt{3} \cdot \sqrt{5} = \sqrt{15}$$

In general, $\sqrt[r]{c} \cdot \sqrt[r]{d} = \sqrt[r]{cd}$, where $c$ and $d$ are positive real numbers and $r$ is a positive integer.

In a similar manner we can show $\sqrt[r]{\dfrac{c}{d}} = \dfrac{\sqrt[r]{c}}{\sqrt[r]{d}}$, $(d \neq 0)$.

We give a proof for the theorem $\sqrt{ab} = \sqrt{a} \cdot \sqrt{b}$ $(a \geq 0, b \geq 0)$.

**Proof:** Let $\sqrt{a} = x$

$\qquad\qquad \sqrt{b} = y$

$\qquad$ Then $x^2 = a$ and $y^2 = b$

$\qquad x^2 y^2 = ab$

$\qquad (xy)^2 = ab$

$\qquad xy = \sqrt{ab}$

$\qquad$ but $xy = \sqrt{a} \cdot \sqrt{b}$

$\qquad$ thus $\sqrt{a} \cdot \sqrt{b} = \sqrt{ab}$

Here is a proof of the theorem $\sqrt{\dfrac{a}{b}} = \dfrac{\sqrt{a}}{\sqrt{b}}$

**Proof:** Let $\begin{aligned}\sqrt{a} &= x\\\sqrt{b} &= y\end{aligned}$

$\qquad$ Then $x^2 = a$ and $y^2 = b$

$\qquad \dfrac{x^2}{y^2} = \dfrac{a}{b}$

$\qquad \left(\dfrac{x}{y}\right)^2 = \dfrac{a}{b}$

$\qquad \dfrac{x}{y} = \sqrt{\dfrac{a}{b}}$

$\qquad$ but $\dfrac{x}{y} = \dfrac{\sqrt{a}}{\sqrt{b}}$

$\qquad$ thus $\dfrac{\sqrt{a}}{\sqrt{b}} = \sqrt{\dfrac{a}{b}}$

Study the examples below which illustrate the use of the principles explained above.

**EXAMPLE 1**
$$\begin{aligned}
\sqrt{9x^3} &= \sqrt{9x^2 \cdot x} = \sqrt{9} \cdot \sqrt{x^2} \cdot \sqrt{x}\\
&= 3 \cdot |x| \cdot \sqrt{x}\\
&= 3x\sqrt{x}, \text{ since } x \text{ must be non-negative.}
\end{aligned}$$

**EXAMPLE 2**
$$\sqrt[3]{\dfrac{27}{125x^3}} = \dfrac{\sqrt[3]{27}}{\sqrt[3]{125x^3}} = \dfrac{\sqrt[3]{27}}{\sqrt[3]{125} \cdot \sqrt[3]{x^3}} = \dfrac{3}{5x} \quad (x \neq 0).$$

**EXAMPLE 3**
$$\begin{aligned}
\sqrt{(x-1)^3} &= \sqrt{(x-1)^2 (x-1)}\\
&= \sqrt{(x-1)^2} \cdot \sqrt{x-1}\\
&= |x-1| \cdot \sqrt{x-1}\\
&= (x-1)\sqrt{x-1}, \text{ since } x \geq 1.
\end{aligned}$$

**EXAMPLE 4**
$$\sqrt{(x-y)^4} = \sqrt{(x-y)^2 \cdot (x-y)^2}$$
$$= \sqrt{(x-y)^2} \cdot \sqrt{(x-y)^2}$$
$$= |x-y| \cdot |x-y| = (x-y)(x-y)$$

Why can we say that
$$\forall_{x,y}, \ |x-y| \cdot |x-y| = (x-y)(x-y)?$$

**EXAMPLE 5**  $\sqrt{\sqrt{81}} = \sqrt{9} = 3$

**EXAMPLE 6**  $\sqrt[3]{-8y^3} = \sqrt[3]{-8} \cdot \sqrt[3]{y^3} = -2y$

**EXAMPLE 7**
$$\sqrt{32x^4} = \sqrt{32} \cdot \sqrt{x^4} = \sqrt{16 \cdot 2} \cdot \sqrt{x^4}$$
$$= \sqrt{16} \cdot \sqrt{2} \cdot \sqrt{x^4} = 4 \cdot \sqrt{2} \cdot x^2$$
$$= 4x^2\sqrt{2}$$

## EXERCISES

**1.** Give number names involving no exponents for each of the following:

**a.** $3^{-3}$

**b.** $53^0$

**c.** $4^{-\frac{1}{2}}$

**d.** $3^{-1}$

**e.** $4^{-\frac{3}{2}}$

**f.** $(-3)^{-2}$

**g.** $\dfrac{4^{-2}}{6^0}$

**h.** $3 \cdot 3^{-3}$

**i.** $16 \cdot 8^{-\frac{1}{3}}$

**j.** $\dfrac{6}{4^{-2}}$

**k.** $16^{\frac{1}{2}} \cdot 4^{-\frac{1}{2}}$

**l.** $\dfrac{3}{25^{-\frac{1}{2}}}$

**m.** $25^{-\frac{5}{2}}$

**n.** $\left(\dfrac{3}{4}\right)^{-2}$

**o.** $\left(\dfrac{25}{16}\right)^{-\frac{1}{2}}$

**p.** $32 \cdot 2^{-5}$

**q.** $5^{-1} \cdot 5^{-3} \cdot 5^4$

**r.** $\dfrac{7^{-2}}{7^{-3}}$

**2.** Simplify:

**a.** $x^{\frac{3}{2}} \cdot x^{\frac{1}{2}}$

**b.** $y^{\frac{1}{3}} \cdot y^{\frac{1}{4}}$

**c.** $d^{\frac{4}{3}} \cdot d^{\frac{1}{2}}$

**d.** $r^{\frac{7}{3}} \cdot r^{-\frac{1}{3}}$

**e.** $\dfrac{x^{\frac{2}{3}}}{x^{\frac{1}{3}}}$

**f.** $\dfrac{3y}{y^{\frac{2}{3}}}$

**g.** $\dfrac{8^3}{8^{\frac{1}{3}}}$

**h.** $\dfrac{r^{\frac{5}{6}}}{r^{\frac{1}{3}}}$

**i.** $\dfrac{p^{\frac{1}{3}}}{p^{\frac{1}{2}}}$

3. For each of the following write a name using radical form:
   a. $z^{\frac{1}{3}}$                    d. $2x^{\frac{1}{2}}$
   b. $r^{\frac{2}{3}}$                    e. $3y^{\frac{4}{3}}$
   c. $d^{\frac{4}{3}}$                    f. $r^{\frac{2}{5}}$

4. For each of the following, write a name using fractional exponents:
   a. $\sqrt{3}$                     e. $\sqrt[7]{t^3}$
   b. $\sqrt[3]{11}$                 f. $\sqrt[5]{x^8}$
   c. $\sqrt[5]{x^2}$                g. $\sqrt[3]{(x+y)^2}$
   d. $\sqrt[4]{r^3}$                h. $\sqrt{(r-t)^3}$

5. Perform the indicated operations to yield a simple expression:

   a. $(x^4y^2)^{\frac{3}{2}}$          e. $\dfrac{x^{-2}y^5}{x^5y^{-2}}$          i. $\dfrac{(z^4y^{\frac{3}{4}})^4}{r^{\frac{5}{4}}}$

   b. $\left(\dfrac{125y^4}{216y^{-1}}\right)^{\frac{1}{3}}$          f. $(36x^{-2})^{-\frac{1}{2}}$          j. $(x^{-3})^{-\frac{1}{3}}$

   c. $\left(\dfrac{9x^{-3}}{4z^2}\right)^{\frac{1}{2}}$          g. $(x^{\frac{3}{4}}y^{\frac{4}{3}})^3$          k. $(16r^2t^3)^{\frac{3}{4}}$

   d. $(125y^9)^{\frac{1}{3}}$          h. $(r^{\frac{2}{3}}s^{\frac{1}{3}})^3$          l. $(-1 \cdot a^{-2} \cdot b^{-3})^{-\frac{1}{6}}$

6. Express the following in simplest form using only positive exponents:

   a. $\dfrac{-x^{-2}}{2}$          f. $\dfrac{(x+y)^{-2}}{3}$

   b. $\dfrac{r^{-2}s^{-3}}{t^2}$          g. $\dfrac{5}{(r-t)^{-3}}$

   c. $\dfrac{x^{-\frac{4}{3}}}{x}$          h. $rs^{-3} + r^{-2}s$

   d. $\dfrac{r^{-\frac{3}{4}}}{3}$          i. $3^{-1}cy^{-2}$

   e. $\dfrac{7}{-6s^{-2}}$          j. $2^{-4}dx^{-3}y^{-4}$

## 4 · Multiplication of Radical Expressions

In writing an expression equivalent to $6\sqrt{3} \cdot 2\sqrt{5}$, we proceed as follows:
$$6\sqrt{3} \cdot 2\sqrt{5} = 12\sqrt{15}$$

For $\dfrac{\sqrt{15}}{\sqrt{3}}$, we do the following:

$$\frac{\sqrt{15}}{\sqrt{3}} = \sqrt{\frac{15}{3}} = \sqrt{5}$$

Using the principles $\sqrt[r]{c} \cdot \sqrt[r]{d} = \sqrt[r]{cd}$, and $\sqrt[r]{\dfrac{c}{d}} = \dfrac{\sqrt[r]{c}}{\sqrt[r]{d}}$, we are able to separate the radicand into factors of which as many as possible are perfect $r$-th powers. We determine the $r$-th root of the perfect $r$-th powers and simplify.

**EXAMPLES**
$$\sqrt{45} = \sqrt{9 \times 5} = \sqrt{9} \times \sqrt{5} = 3\sqrt{5}$$
$$\sqrt[3]{8x^4} = \sqrt[3]{(8x^3) \cdot (x)} = \sqrt[3]{8x^3} \cdot \sqrt[3]{x} = 2x\sqrt[3]{x}$$
$$\sqrt[4]{16x^3y^4z^4} = \sqrt[4]{16y^4z^4} \cdot \sqrt[4]{x^3} = 2yz\sqrt[4]{x^3}$$

## EXERCISES

Write a simpler expression for each of the following:

1. $\sqrt{4} \cdot \sqrt{3}$

2. $\sqrt{12} \cdot \sqrt{9}$

3. $\sqrt{48}$

4. $\sqrt{50}$

5. $\sqrt{18}$

6. $3\sqrt{5} \cdot 3\sqrt{32}$

7. $\sqrt[3]{16}$

8. $\sqrt[3]{-16}$

9. $\sqrt{98}$

10. $\sqrt{3} \cdot \sqrt{6}$

11. $\sqrt{r^5}$

12. $4\sqrt{2} \cdot 5\sqrt{3}$

13. $\sqrt{8r^6}$

14. $\sqrt[4]{z^9}$

15. $\sqrt[3]{-27s^7}$

16. $\sqrt{.25t^5}$

17. $\sqrt{5x} \cdot \sqrt{5x^2}$

18. $\sqrt[3]{2x} \cdot \sqrt[3]{4x^2}$

19. $\sqrt[3]{48r^2s^4}$

20. $\sqrt[3]{9x} \cdot \sqrt[3]{9x^3}$

21. $\dfrac{\sqrt{21}}{\sqrt{3}}$

22. $\dfrac{\sqrt{48}}{\sqrt{12}}$

23. $\dfrac{\sqrt[5]{64}}{\sqrt[5]{2}}$

24. $\sqrt[3]{\dfrac{-27}{x^6y^3}}$

25. $\dfrac{\sqrt{98}}{7\sqrt{2}}$

26. $\dfrac{3\sqrt{125}}{3\sqrt{8}}$

27. $\dfrac{\sqrt[3]{54}}{\sqrt[3]{8}}$

28. $\dfrac{\sqrt{64}}{3\sqrt{32}}$

29. $\dfrac{\sqrt{4x^2}}{\sqrt{x^3}}$

30. $\dfrac{\sqrt{84}}{\sqrt[3]{16}}$

## 5 · Radicals and the Distributive Principle

You know that the distributive principle tells you that multiplication is distributive over addition. That is, $5a + 3a = (5 + 3)a$.

Now consider an illustration involving radicals:

**EXAMPLE 1** $\quad 6\sqrt{3} + 8\sqrt{3} = (6 + 8)\sqrt{3} = 14\sqrt{3}$

**EXAMPLE 2** $\quad 3\sqrt{48} + 4\sqrt{18} = 3(\sqrt{16} \cdot \sqrt{3}) + 4(\sqrt{6} \cdot \sqrt{3})$

$$= 3 \cdot 4\sqrt{3} + 4\sqrt{6} \cdot \sqrt{3}$$
$$= 12\sqrt{3} + 4\sqrt{6}\sqrt{3}$$
$$= (12 + 4\sqrt{6})\sqrt{3}$$

**EXAMPLE 3** $\quad (3\sqrt{3} + \sqrt{5}) \cdot (3\sqrt{3} - \sqrt{5})$

$$= (3\sqrt{3} + \sqrt{5}) \cdot 3\sqrt{3} - (3\sqrt{3} + \sqrt{5}) \cdot \sqrt{5}$$
$$= 3\sqrt{3} \cdot 3\sqrt{3} + \sqrt{5} \cdot 3\sqrt{3} - 3\sqrt{3} \cdot \sqrt{5} - \sqrt{5} \cdot \sqrt{5}$$
$$= 9 \cdot 3 + 3\sqrt{15} - 3\sqrt{15} - 5$$
$$= 27 - 5$$
$$= 22$$

## EXERCISES

Simplify each of the following:

1. $5\sqrt{2} + 7\sqrt{2}$

2. $2\sqrt{7} - 16\sqrt{7}$

3. $3\sqrt{8} + 7\sqrt{2}$

4. $\sqrt{48} + \sqrt{96}$

5. $\sqrt[3]{16} + \sqrt[3]{24}$

6. $\sqrt[4]{32} + \sqrt[4]{128}$

7. $(3\sqrt{2} - \sqrt{5})^2$

8. $3\sqrt[3]{5} + 17\sqrt[3]{5}$

9. $\sqrt[4]{32} - \sqrt[4]{2}$

10. $\sqrt[5]{64} - \sqrt[5]{128}$

11. $17\sqrt[3]{3} - 12\sqrt[3]{81}$

12. $(3\sqrt{5} + \sqrt{2})(\sqrt{5} + 3\sqrt{2})$

13. $(\sqrt{2} + \sqrt{3})(\sqrt{2} - \sqrt{3})$

14. $(\sqrt{7} + \sqrt{3})(\sqrt{7} - \sqrt{3})$

15. $(\sqrt{6} + \sqrt{8})(\sqrt{6} - \sqrt{8})$

16. $\left(\frac{1}{2}\sqrt{2} + \frac{1}{3}\sqrt{3}\right)\left(\frac{1}{4}\sqrt{2} + \frac{1}{5}\sqrt{3}\right)$

# VOCABULARY

base (297)

cube root (303)

exponent (297)

principal root (303)

principal square root (303)

radical (304)

radical expression (308)

radicand (304)

square root (303)

....................................................................................................

# REVIEW EXERCISES

**1.** Simplify:

**a.** $2s^{\frac{1}{2}} \cdot s^{\frac{3}{2}}$

**b.** $x^{\frac{5}{3}} \div x^{\frac{1}{3}}$

**c.** $r^{\frac{1}{6}} \cdot r^{\frac{1}{3}}$

**d.** $x^{-3} \cdot x^7$

**e.** $\dfrac{r^{-\frac{2}{3}}}{r^{\frac{1}{3}}}$

**f.** $12y^{-4} \div 3y^{-2}$

**g.** $\dfrac{7x^3}{\dfrac{1}{x^2}}$

**h.** $(36y^6x^2)^{\frac{1}{2}}$

**2.** Give equivalent expressions containing only positive exponents:

**a.** $\dfrac{4x^2}{x^{-5}}$

**b.** $\dfrac{5}{x^{-2}}$

**c.** $\dfrac{x^{-2}}{x^{-4}}$

**d.** $\dfrac{4x^2}{x^{-5}}$

**e.** $\dfrac{a^{-3}b^{-4}}{x^{-2}y^{-3}}$

**3.** Give equivalent expressions containing fractional exponents:

**a.** $\sqrt{r}$

**b.** $\sqrt[5]{s}$

**c.** $\sqrt[3]{x^2}$

**d.** $\sqrt[5]{(x-3)^2}$

**e.** $\sqrt[3]{y^2}$

**f.** $\sqrt[4]{r^3}$

**g.** $\sqrt{x^5}$

**4.** True or False

**a.** $(1.2^3)^2 = (1.2)^5$

**b.** $\forall_r, (r \neq 0), \dfrac{r^2 \cdot r^3}{r^{-5}} = 1$

**c.** $\sqrt[3]{2} = 2$

**d.** $\left(\dfrac{3}{5}\right)^3 = \dfrac{9}{15}$

**e.** $\left(\dfrac{1}{2}\right)^{-1} = 2$

**f.** $\sqrt{\dfrac{3}{5}} = \dfrac{15}{5}$

**g.** $\sqrt[5]{-32} = -2$

**h.** $\sqrt[3]{27} = 4$

**i.** $(16)^{\frac{3}{4}} = 64$

**j.** $\forall_{x,y},\ (16x^4y^2)^{\frac{1}{2}} = 8x^2y$

**k.** $\sqrt{6} \cdot \sqrt{3} = 3\sqrt{2}$

**l.** $\dfrac{\sqrt{56}}{\sqrt{14}} = \dfrac{1}{\sqrt{2}} = \dfrac{\sqrt{2}}{2}$

**m.** $\sqrt{27} = 3\sqrt{3}$

**n.** $(2\sqrt{3} + \sqrt{2})\ (\sqrt{3} - \sqrt{2}) = 4 - \sqrt{6}$

**o.** $4\sqrt{8} + \sqrt{2} = 8\sqrt{2} + \sqrt{2} = 9\sqrt{2}$

**p.** $\sqrt[3]{48} + \sqrt[3]{6} = 2\sqrt[3]{6} + \sqrt[3]{6} = 3\sqrt[3]{6}$

**q.** $(3\sqrt{4})^2 = 36$

**5.** Give equivalent expressions in radical form:

**a.** $r^{\frac{2}{3}}$

**b.** $[(2s)^2]^{\frac{1}{3}}$

**c.** $\left(\dfrac{3t}{2}\right)^{\frac{4}{3}}$

**d.** $(-5x)^{-\frac{1}{3}}$

**6.** Determine the real number replacements for $x$ to obtain true sentences:

**a.** $x^2 = 144$

**b.** $x^3 = -64$

**c.** $x^{-3} = \dfrac{1}{27}$

**d.** $3x^2 = 108$

**e.** $-x^3 = 216$

**f.** $\dfrac{x^3}{x^5} = 64$

## CHAPTER TEST

**1.** Simplify:

**a.** $3\sqrt{11} - 6\sqrt{11}$

**b.** $\sqrt[3]{24} - \sqrt[3]{16}$

**c.** $\sqrt[3]{3x} \cdot \sqrt[3]{9x^2}$

**d.** $\sqrt[4]{81xy^4z^3}$

**e.** $(125x^6)^{\frac{1}{3}}$

**f.** $(16y^{-4})^{-\frac{1}{2}}$

**g.** $\dfrac{r^{\frac{1}{2}}}{r^{\frac{1}{3}}}$

**h.** $(2\sqrt{5} - 2)(\sqrt{5} - 3)$

**2.** Give equivalent expressions containing fractional exponents:

**a.** $\sqrt[4]{x^3}$

**b.** $\sqrt[5]{(xy)^3}$

**c.** $\sqrt[3]{2x^5}$

**d.** $\sqrt[3]{\dfrac{x^2}{y^2}}$

**e.** $\sqrt[7]{\dfrac{a^8}{b^9}}$

**3.** Give equivalent expressions in radical form:

**a.** $x^{\frac{1}{3}}y^{\frac{2}{3}}$

**d.** $\left(\dfrac{x^2}{2}\right)^{\frac{1}{3}}$

**b.** $(3xy)^{\frac{5}{3}}$

**e.** $\left(\dfrac{a^2}{b^2}\right)^{\frac{1}{4}}$

**c.** $r^{\frac{3}{2}}$

**4.** Give equivalent expressions containing only positive exponents:

**a.** $3x^3 \cdot x^{-\frac{2}{3}}$

**d.** $\dfrac{2}{\dfrac{1}{x^{-2}}}$

**b.** $\dfrac{3}{x^{-5}}$

**e.** $\dfrac{3x^3y^{-2}}{x^{-\frac{5}{3}}}$

**c.** $\dfrac{x^{-\frac{2}{3}}}{4}$

**5.** Determine the real number replacements for $x$ to obtain true statements:

**a.** $x^3 = 27$

**d.** $x^{-2} = \dfrac{1}{4}$

**b.** $x^5 = -32$

**e.** $5x^3 = 40$

**c.** $x^4 = 81$

**6.** True or false?

**a.** $\sqrt[3]{-8} = 2$

**b.** $(16)^{\frac{1}{4}} = 2$

**c.** $(2^2)^2 = 8$

**d.** $\left(\dfrac{2}{3}\right)^3 = \dfrac{8}{27}$

**e.** $\forall_x,\ \sqrt[3]{x^2} = x^{\frac{3}{2}}$

**f.** $\sqrt{45} = 3\sqrt{15}$

**g.** $\left(\dfrac{1}{2}\right)^{-2} = 4$

**h.** $\forall_{x,y},\ (4x^2y)^3 = 12x^6y^3$

**i.** $(6\sqrt{3})^2 = 108$

**j.** $\dfrac{\sqrt{39}}{\sqrt{3}} = \sqrt{13}$

**k.** $(3\sqrt{5} - 1)^2 = 46 - 6\sqrt{5}$

**l.** $\sqrt{72} = 6\sqrt{2}$

**m.** $\forall_x,\ \dfrac{2}{x^{-3}} = 2x^3$

**n.** $\forall_s,\ (3s^3)^2 = 9s^4$

**o.** $\forall_{x,y},\ (x \neq 0,\ y \neq 0),\ 16y^3x^5 \div 2yx^2 = 8y^3x^{\frac{5}{2}}$

**p.** $\forall_r,\ r^{\frac{2}{5}} \cdot r^{-\frac{1}{5}} = r^{\frac{3}{5}}$

**q.** $\forall_x,\ (x \neq 0),\ \dfrac{x^{-3}}{x^2} = x^{-5}$

**r.** $\dfrac{2}{\sqrt{2}} = \dfrac{2\sqrt{2}}{2} = \sqrt{2}$

**7.** Simplify:

**a.** $\dfrac{36xy^3z^3}{\frac{1}{3}y^{-2}z^2}$

**d.** $r^{\frac{1}{6}} \cdot r^{\frac{2}{3}}$

**b.** $\dfrac{7x^5}{x^{-3}}$

**e.** $\dfrac{x^{-6}}{\frac{1}{x^2}}$

**c.** $(81x^3y^4)^{\frac{1}{2}}$

**f.** $\dfrac{r^{\frac{7}{3}}}{r^{-2}}$

# CUMULATIVE REVIEW

**1.** $N$ is the set of natural numbers
$I$ is the set of integers
$R$ is the set of real numbers
$R_a$ is the set of rational numbers
State whether the following statements are true or false:

**a.** $0 \in I$

**b.** $-2 \in R_a$

**c.** $-3 \in I$

**d.** $-\frac{2}{3} \in R_a$

**e.** $0 \in N$

**f.** $-3\frac{1}{3} \in R$

**g.** $\frac{5}{9} \in I$

**h.** $7 \in N$

**i.** $R_a \subset R$

**j.** $I \subset R_a$

**k.** $I \subset N$

**l.** $R \supset N$

**2.** State whether the following sets are closed under the operations given:

| Set | Operation |
|---|---|
| **a.** positive integers | subtraction |
| **b.** rational numbers | multiplication |
| **c.** integers | addition |
| **d.** natural numbers | subtraction |
| **e.** real numbers | division |
| **f.** rational numbers | subtraction |

**3.** Write the simplest number symbol for:

**a.** $[(3 + 4) \times 5 - 2] \times \frac{1}{2}$

**b.** $(3 \times 7 + 5 \times 4) \times 6$

**4.** Name the principles illustrated in the following:

   **a.** $3 \times 0 = 0$                  **e.** $(5 \cdot 6) \cdot 7 = 5(6 \cdot 7)$

   **b.** $7 + 0 = 7$                   **f.** $3 \cdot \frac{1}{3} = 1$

   **c.** $2(x + 2) = 2x + 2 \cdot 2$      **g.** $9 \cdot 1 = 9$

   **d.** $x \cdot y = y \cdot x$               **h.** $7 + (-7) = 0$

**5.** Suppose $\odot$ and $\otimes$ are inverse operations. Label the following statement as true or false. Justify your choice.

      If $\frac{1}{3} \odot \frac{1}{4} = \frac{7}{12}$, then $\frac{7}{12} \otimes \frac{1}{4} = \frac{1}{3}$

**6.** Is subtraction in the set of integers associative? Illustrate.

**7.** True or false? For all real numbers $x$ and $y$:

   **a.** $|xy| = |x| \cdot |y|$
   **b.** $|x + y| \le |x| + |y|$
   **c.** If $x < 0$, $y < 0$, $x \cdot y = |x| \cdot |y|$

**8.** Determine $\sqrt{22}$ to two decimal places.

**9.** Using the real numbers, determine the solution sets of the following:

   **a.** $\dfrac{4(7 - 3x)}{3} = 5$         **f.** $\dfrac{6}{y - 3} - \dfrac{7}{3 - y} = 9$

   **b.** $5(3 \cdot |x| - 4) \le 13$

   **c.** $\dfrac{7x + \frac{5}{3}}{\frac{1}{2}} = 8$        **g.** $\dfrac{-4}{x - 3} = \dfrac{2}{3 - x}$

                           **h.** $-4z + 9 \le -13$

   **d.** $\dfrac{3 \cdot |r|}{2} < 4$           **i.** $|3r + 5| \le 16$

   **e.** $\dfrac{4y}{2} - \dfrac{7 + y}{3} = 8$     **j.** $\dfrac{x + 3}{4} > 5$

**10.** True or false?

   **a.** $0.18\dot{1}\dot{8} \cdots$ is a rational number.
   **b.** $-(x + y)$ stands for a negative number provided the replacements for $x$ and $y$ come from the real number set.
   **c.** $|3 + (-8)| = |(-8) + 3|$
   **d.** $\dfrac{6}{-2} = -3$
   **e.** For all $x$ and $y$, $(x \ne 0, y \ne 0,)$
      $\dfrac{1}{x} + \dfrac{1}{y} = \dfrac{x + y}{xy}$

**f.**  $-\dfrac{(x-y)}{(r-s)} = \dfrac{-(y-x)}{(r-s)}$   for all $x$, $y$, $r$, $s$ $[r - s \neq 0]$

**g.**  For all $x$, $y$, $r$, $s$, $s \neq 0$, $y \neq 0$

$$\frac{x}{y} - \frac{r}{s} = \frac{x-r}{ys}$$

**h.**  The opposite of $-\frac{1}{3}$ is 3

**i.**  3.625 is an irrational number

**j.**  The set of rational numbers is a number field

**11.**  Tell whether each of the following is true for all replacements of the variables:

**a.**  $-\dfrac{-t \cdot (-y)}{r} = -\dfrac{t \cdot y}{r}$  $(r \neq 0)$

**b.**  $-[(x-y)+z] = -x + y - z$

**c.**  $\dfrac{-4}{r-t} = \dfrac{4}{t-r}$  $(r \neq t)$

**12.**  For each of the following, write a single fractional expression equivalent to it:

**a.**  $\dfrac{y}{3} \div \dfrac{y^2}{4}$    **b.**  $\dfrac{x}{7} - \dfrac{x}{3}$    **c.**  $\dfrac{3r}{5} \times \dfrac{2r}{3}$

**13.**  Write out in words the description of each set listed below, graph the solution set and describe the graph in words:

**a.**  $G = \{x \mid x \in \text{Real numbers and } 3 > x \geq -1 \text{ or } 5 \leq x < 9\}$

**b.**  $H = \{(x, y) \mid x, y \in \text{Real numbers}, x + 3y = -7\}$

**c.**  $K = \{(x, y) \mid x, y \in \text{Real numbers and } 2x + 3y < 15\}$

**14.**  Graph the solution set of the following system of equations and tell whether the system is simultaneous, dependent, or inconsistent:

$$4x - 2y = 11$$
$$3x - 7y = -5$$

**15.**  Compare the area of triangle $ABE$ with that of the square $ABCD$, if the measure of $AB$ is $k$ units and the measure of $AD$ and $DE$ is the same.

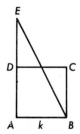

**16.** Express the length of the altitude $h$ of triangle $ABC$ in terms of the length of side $c$ and of the area of the triangle.

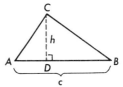

**17.** In electricity we have the formula $I = \dfrac{2E}{R + 2r}$. Given the replacements 2.6 for $I$, 12 for $R$, 8 for $E$, determine the value of $r$.

**18.** Simplify:

**a.** $\dfrac{2x^3 \cdot x^{-1}}{x^4}$

**e.** $(25x^4y^2)^{\frac{1}{2}}$

**b.** $\dfrac{5y^{-3} \cdot y^4}{y^{-2}}$

**f.** $[(5s^2)^3]^{\frac{1}{2}}$

**c.** $\dfrac{3}{x^{-4}x^2}$

**g.** $\dfrac{6x^{-2}y^{-3}}{4xy}$

**d.** $(5x^2y^{-3})^2$

**h.** $(-2m^{-2}n^3)^3$

**19.** True or false?

**a.** $\sqrt[4]{64} = 4$

**e.** $\forall_x,\ (x \neq 0),\ \dfrac{3}{\dfrac{1}{x^3}} = \dfrac{x^3}{3}$

**b.** $\sqrt{75} = 5\sqrt{3}$

**f.** $\dfrac{\sqrt{96}}{\sqrt{8}} = \sqrt{12} = 2\sqrt{3}$

**c.** $16^{\frac{3}{2}} = 36$

**g.** $\dfrac{3}{\sqrt[3]{3}} = \dfrac{3\sqrt[3]{9}}{3} = \sqrt[3]{9}$

**d.** $\left(\dfrac{4}{3}x^2\right)^2 = \dfrac{16}{9}x^4$

**h.** $\left(\dfrac{2}{3}\right)^{-2} = \dfrac{4}{9}$

**20.** The Jones family went on a vacation, spending one-half as much on lodging as on food and $1\frac{1}{2}$ times as much on car expenses as on food. The total expense was $130. How much was spent on each item?

**21.** Mr. Carlson borrowed $4,800 at 6% simple interest. If he paid $480 interest for the privilege of borrowing the money, for what period of time was the loan kept?

## BIBLIOGRAPHY

Bakst, A., *Mathematical Puzzles and Pastimes*, Van Nostrand, Toronto, 1954, pages 171–180, "Some Remarkable Numbers."

Boehm, G. A. W., *New World of Mathematics*, Dial Press, New York, 1959.

Johnson, D. and Glenn, W., *Topology*, Webster, St. Louis, Missouri, 1960.

School Mathematics Study Group, *Mathematics for High School: First Course in Algebra (Revised Edition)*, SMSG, New Haven, Connecticut, 1960.

School Mathematics Study Group, *Mathematics for Junior High School: Applications*, SMSG, New Haven, Connecticut, 1959.

Williams, J. D., *The Compleat Strategyst*, McGraw-Hill, Toronto, 1954.

# INDEX

# INDEX

*The figures in* **bold-faced** *type refer to the pages on which the words and expressions are defined.*